Macmillan Series in Materials Science

Diffraction
Methods
in Materials
Science

Macmillan Series in Materials Science

Editors: MORRIS E. FINE

JOHANNES WEERTMAN

JULIA R. WEERTMAN

Diffraction
Methods
in Materials
Science

J. B. COHEN
PROFESSOR OF MATERIALS SCIENCE
THE TECHNOLOGICAL INSTITUTE
NORTHWESTERN UNIVERSITY

THE MACMILLAN COMPANY, NEW YORK
COLLIER–MACMILLAN LIMITED, LONDON

Second Printing, 1966

Library of Congress catalog card number: 66–11209

THE MACMILLAN COMPANY, NEW YORK
COLLIER–MACMILLAN CANADA, LTD.,
TORONTO, ONTARIO

Printed in the United States of America

Preface

Crystallography and diffractions are vital tools in both the science and the engineering of materials. From residual stresses to vibrational spectra, from phase identification to local atomic arrangements and defects, these tools have provided much of our information, and they will continue to do so. Working knowledge about them is important—and in this age it must be more than a rudimentary brush with the field. This is so because materials are becoming much more complicated. For example, it is not enough to recall the structure of copper and how to analyze its powder pattern; many materials are much more complex. With the physicist no longer as involved as he once was with these areas, the materials scientist or engineer must have a firmer and deeper understanding of the field in order to find what he needs in the extensive literature and to extend the applications for his own purposes. He must know crystallography and be familiar with Fourier methods and reciprocal space; certainly these topics are presented to him in his training in solid-state physics, and such an approach to diffraction may help him to delve more deeply into the solid state as well as into diffraction.

This book is best suited to a one-semester course. Its purpose is to provide a basic textbook for class or self-study and to prepare the student to read more advanced textbooks, of which there are many. I have thus not attempted to include advanced topics in detail but only to provide the starting point and the fundamentals which were really not available in satisfactory form in any one or two books. In a very strong sense, this book is a reorganization of well-established ideas that will initiate the beginner without confusing him with the different notations in the many books he might otherwise have to consult. The approach stems from a "first" course in diffraction I have taught for six years.

The first chapter, on the elements of crystallography, was included to develop the basic concepts of three-dimensional periodicity and to introduce such useful aids as the sterographic projection and vectors for calculations on structures, in case the student has not yet been exposed to them. In the following chapters diffraction is presented as a phenomenon in Fourier space and all of the necessary mathematical tools are presented in the text as they are needed. Electron, neutron, *and* x-ray diffraction are examined, so that the student will be aware of the advantages of each. At the end of each chapter there is a problems section; some of the solutions (or in some cases the beginnings of solutions) are given in Appendix B. Some of the problems are based on actual films. For this purpose the appropriate nets have been superimposed so that the student, even if he does not have any equipment at his disposal, can still learn many of the techniques. In addition, rather than include many tables, I have emphasized the use of the *International Tables of Crystallography*. These are so full of data, references, and tabulations of interest in crystallography and diffraction that a student should be familiar with them. Some will feel that magnetic scattering of neutrons, light scattering, and/or dynamic scattering should have been included; but there is a limit to what can be learned in one semester and I have only mentioned these.

The experimental details have been placed in more or less independent chapters to permit an instructor to use them at a time in the course that is most suitable to him. Rather than give detailed references to the literature, I have referred to the appropriate classics in the field at the end of each chapter. These were my primary sources.

My debts in writing this book are many. Those who have contributed illustrations are acknowledged under their contribution and I appreciate their assistance. Professors J. T. Norton, B. E. Warren, and A. Guinier taught me diffraction, and their friendship and guidance are the source of much of what is good in this book. Professor M. B. Bever, my mentor, inspired me to work in the area of materials, and Professor M. E. Fine has guided me gently over some of the rough spots at the start of my teaching and research career. I deeply appreciate their continued interest.

Finally, let me thank my colleagues at Northwestern and my students. Their questions (and their answers) and their inspiration have helped a great deal by making me think! Particularly, let me acknowledge the stimulating association with my students, Professors Lyle Schwartz, R. H. DeAngelis, and D. E. Mikkola, and Messrs. P. Gehlen, O. Kimball, S. Sass, C. Fairhurst, J. Gragg, and R. Rothman. Mrs. D. Johnson graciously put up with my constant revisions and poor handwriting during the typing of the manuscript. Mr. Joel Meyer prepared the drawings. My wife, as she has always done, put up with my long stays in the "back room" and provided constant encouragement.

                                                                J. B. C.

Glencoe, Illinois

Contents

ix

I   *Principles of Crystallography*

The reader will certainly recall many examples of the relation of atomic arrangement to properties. In fact, ball models of structures have become part of almost every laboratory in the last fifty years. Most of our knowledge of atomic arrangement comes from diffraction—simply because any diffraction grating expresses itself in its diffraction pattern. That is, this pattern can tell us much about the nature of the grating.

Thus we can learn about atomic arrangement (in liquids, gases, or solids) and defects in this arrangement, relative amounts of phases in multiphase structures, phase transformations, size and composition of tiny precipitates, and so on. This information is vital for our understanding of the behavior of materials. Furthermore, in many of these areas, diffraction is the *only* tool for getting this information without gross assumptions. For this reason, it is important that a materials scientist be on intimate terms with the basic concepts of diffraction, regardless of whether or not he intends to use this tool extensively. Only then will he be able to assess the literature to make full use of available information, or to decide if diffraction would be worth using for his problem. The purpose of this book is to provide the basic tools for this understanding; but we shall not attempt to shield the reader from the elegant and, at least initially, difficult concepts that all interested in the field must understand. There are, at the beginning, some simple physical ways of presenting an idea without these concepts, but this way would be a dead end with no path on which to continue. These new concepts will give us the physical understanding and also a roadmap for further trips—we just have to learn how to read the map.

In this chapter we shall examine some of the basic ideas associated with arrangements of atoms in crystals so that we can understand *why* diffraction studies are useful in learning about crystals. Diffraction is by no means useless for noncrystalline materials, but most of its

1

application is with crystalline solids. The material presented in this chapter was, in fact, all available before diffraction was discovered; it is often referred to as classical crystallography. In many cases, however, the *ideas* could not even be tested until diffraction from crystalline solids was discovered. This area is one of the triumphs of scientific prediction. In what follows the reader is advised to draw sketches and build models—using plastic balls, pipe cleaners, or wire, etc.—to aid in understanding what is being said.

The Nature of a Crystal

A ball model immediately reveals the most striking feature of a crystal (Figure 1–1)—the regular periodic nature of the atoms. How

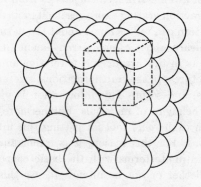

Figure 1–1.   Ball model of a copper crystal.

many ways can atoms arrange themselves periodically? The first answer which seems sound enough, is, "An infinite number of ways." But this is not at all true.

One-Dimensional Crystals

We can see this by starting in one dimension as in Figure 1–2(*a*). A linear periodic array of points is shown. In Figures 1–2(*b*) and 1–2(*c*) we have placed one-dimensional asymmetric molecules at each of these points, in two different ways. Note that these are the *only* two possible ways; we could change the spacing of the points or the size of the molecule, but these changes do not alter the *kind* of arrangement.

As with any field, there is a language to be learned and this is a good place to begin.

The *periodic* array of *points* is purely *imaginary*—it is the molecules that are arranged periodically, and the points merely represent some such position as their center of gravity or a point, say, 1 cm from their tip. This periodic arrangement of imaginary points is referred to as the space lattice in three dimensions, or the net in one or two dimensions. The periodic repetition could also be obtained by *translating* a *unit cell*, outlined in Figure 1–2(a). As this cell contains only one of the lattice points (half at each end) it is called a primitive cell and given the symbol *p*. We could also choose a cell that is not primitive—i.e., one containing

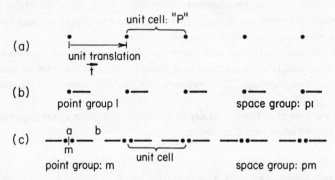

Figure 1–2. Periodic structures in one dimension, (a) lattice; (b), (c) possible arrangements of the molecule. (After *International Tables for X-ray Crystallography*, Vol. I., Kynoch Press, Birmingham, England, 1952.)

two (or more) lattice points—with the understanding that we carry the point within the cell with us when we translate the cell to form the space lattice.

In Figure 1–2(b), our molecule is arranged at the point in a certain way. A 360 degree rotation about the point would reproduce the molecule. In Figure 1–2(c), the molecules are related at a point by reflection, or 180 degree rotation; but if we say we have no freedom in a second direction, only the reflection operation exists. Studying Figure 1–2(b) and (c) several points are obvious:

1. Every lattice point has *identical* surroundings—this must be so to have a *periodic* arrangement.

2. These are the only two *kinds* of arrangements possible.

3. The unit cell in both cases is primitive—even though in Figure

1–2(c) there are two "molecules" in the unit cell, the *repeating* arrangement is represented by a point between them and the lattice is the same as Figure 1–2(a). In Figure 1–2(c) if *a* is a lattice point, *b* is not, because the surroundings do not appear the same at the two locations. Either position is a possible lattice point—but the next one is **t** away from it.

4. The arrangement at a lattice point (referred to as a point group) contains certain symmetries represented by imaginary *symmetry elements*. In Figure 1–2(b) there is only the redundant 360 degree rotation axis. Referring to the rotation as *n*-fold when the rotation is 360 degrees/*n*, the point group can be written simply as "1." In Figure 1–2(c), the point group can be described by a mirror (*m*).

5. Other symmetry elements can arise, such as a rotation axis between two lattice points in Figure 1–2(c), even though we only need a mirror plane and translation to construct the figure.

The entire spatial arrangement—the unit cell (or translation) combined with the symmetries at a point (point group)—define what is called a "space group." The symbols for one dimension are as shown, *p*1 and *pm*.

We see here that there will *not* be an infinite number of arrangements. Only two exist in one dimension.

Two-Dimensional Crystals

We could relax our one dimensional restriction a bit, perhaps by allowing our molecule to be finite in shape and to have freedom in the

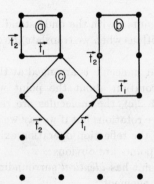

Figure 1–3.   A two-dimensional lattice with three possible unit cells, (*a*) primitive (one lattice point per cell); (*b*), (*c*) double primitive (two lattice points per cell).

second dimension in the page. Rotation around the normal to the page and reflection would not be equivalent, and even if the lattice was a one-dimensional row of points, new space groups would arise. (The reader might try to examine these himself at this point. Such one-dimensional schemes might arise in making long-chain molecules common in biology; polymers may also develop in this manner.) We shall, however, jump directly to two dimensions—again requiring that our configurations be *strictly* two dimensional and that all operations on our molecule be in two dimensions. In Figure 1–3 a two-dimensional lattice is shown and several possible cells are outlined. Any point, or one kind of unit cell, is related to another *just like it* by a set

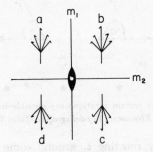

Figure 1–4. Symmetry operations in two dimensions.

of vectors $\mathbf{L} = m\tau_1 + n\tau_2$. A good two-dimensional object to represent the molecules placed at these points would be a "stick hand." (The reader can understand what follows with his own hands!)

Considering operations about a point, Figure 1–4, a and c (or b and d) are related by two reflections through m_1 and then through m_2, by twofold rotation, or by inversion through the central point. A left hand remains a left hand and a and c are "congruent." But a and b are related by reflection only—a left hand is turned into a right hand. The objects are "enantiomorphous."

(*If we relaxed our two-dimensional conditions and allowed rotation out of the paper, could a and b be related by a twofold (180 degree) rotation axis parallel to the vertical line on the paper? Yes! But with your own hands this is not possible, because of the difference between the front and back of your hand! Reflection is really a peculiar, unique operation in nature which cannot be carried out by combining any other operations. Of course, your hands are three dimensional.*)

We see now that we can have reflection, rotation and inversion (or 180° rotation) as well as translation in a two-dimensional periodic structure—furthermore some combinations of operations are equivalent to others.

Our requirement of periodicity—i.e., that each lattice or net point has identical surroundings—places restrictions on the kinds of rotations about each point, if these rotations are to act on the entire lattice. Consider Figure 1–5. In order for the net to remain periodic the

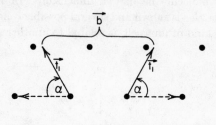

Figure 1–5.   Why only certain rotations are possible in a lattice. (After M. J. Buerger, *Elementary Crystallography*, John Wiley, New York, 1956.)

vector **b** obtained by rotating t_1 around some rotation axis (which must exist at each and every point if it is at one of them) must be an integral multiple of t_1:

$$|\mathbf{b}| = |\mathbf{m}t_1| = |t_1| + 2|t_1| \cos \alpha, \qquad (1\text{–}1a)$$

or

$$\cos \alpha = \frac{m-1}{2} = \frac{M}{2}, \qquad (1\text{–}1b)$$

where M is an integer. Considering the possible values of α, we find that only one-, two-, three-, four-, or six-fold rotations are possible.[1] Combining these with mirror planes, it is easy to show that only 10 *point groups* occur: 1, 2, 3, 4, 6, 1*m*, 2*mm*, 3*m*, 4*mm*, and 6*mm*. (Remember when trying to draw these that, to maintain a two-dimensional figure, the mirrors and the axes are normal to the two-dimensional plane.) The development of two of these is shown in Figure 1–6. Several points are worth noting carefully. First, the type of axis is repre-

[1] A figure such as a five-sided star (i.e., with five-fold rotational symmetry) can be placed at each lattice point, but the *structure* will have only a mirror plane in it.

sented by drawing a simple (filled) geometric figure, which is reproduced after the rotation (an equilateral triangle for a threefold axis, a square for a onefold, a hexagon for a sixfold axis). Second, the combination of symmetry elements may create others. For example, in Figure 1.2(b) m_2 is created, starting only with m_1 and the twofold axis. There is also an inversion center in the figure, represented by the open circle, although we did not need it to construct the figure. The combined operation rotation–reflection is performed by a reflection, then a rotation, reflection, then rotation . . . until we return to our original figure.

If we now return to Eq. (1–1), and calculate $|\mathbf{b}|$ we find the following:

1. For a onefold or twofold axis, there are no restrictions on the lattice. In fact, every net of any shape has one- and two-dimensional symmetry, because points in a lattice have no shape. The unit cell can

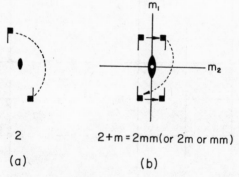

Figure 1–6. The point groups 2, 2mm. Note in (b) that one mirror (m_1) and a two-fold axis create a second mirror (m_2).

be a general parallelogram (P) or a rectangle (R). To see this, draw some two-dimensional lattices.

2. For threefold or sixfold axes, a rhombus is the basic shape, and for a fourfold axis—a square. Again there are other shapes or unit cells that can be used to define each of the nets, but there will *always* be a square cell with a fourfold axis or a rhombus with a sixfold axis.[2] These

---

[2] If we drew a lattice by translating a rhombus in two dimensions (by distances equal to the lengths of its sides and parallel to them), we would find that there is a hexagonal cell possible. However, we cannot create a lattice by translating a hexagon parallel to its edges! Remember the hexagon is filled with atoms in a structure—it is not empty—so that in doing this the hexagonal cells cannot overlap.

cells also have the feature that they clearly exhibit the symmetry of the net they represent.

A net or two-dimensional lattice can then be defined by stating whether the two edges are equal or not and the angle between these edges; there are four such axial *systems* in two dimensions.

All of the unit cells just mentioned are primitive. All *nets* (not the structures) with three-, four-, or six-fold axes in the point groups already contain mirror planes. (Can you understand why? If not, draw a lattice with one of these axes and find the mirrors.) However, for a one- or two-fold axis, one new situation arises when we add point groups with mirror planes to the system. A mirror can be placed in three ways (Figure 1–7). Here, (a) and (b) are identical primitive unit

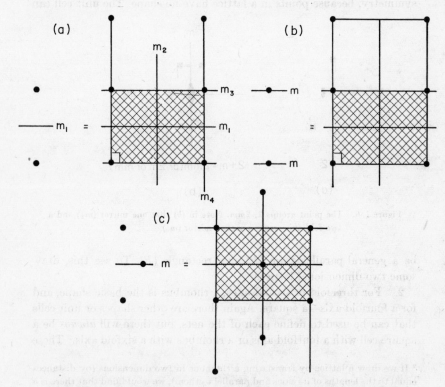

Figure 1–7. Possible positions for a mirror plane in a two-dimensional lattice. (The unit cells are shaded.) Placing one mirror gives rise to others. Note that the axes must be at right angles. (After M. J. Buerger, *Elementary Crystallography*, John Wiley, New York, 1956.)

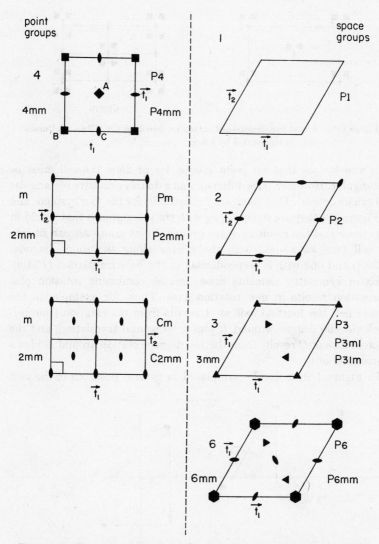

Figure 1–8. The nets, point groups and space groups for two-dimensions. (After M. J. Buerger, *Elementary Crystallography*, John Wiley, New York, 1956.)

(a)   (b)

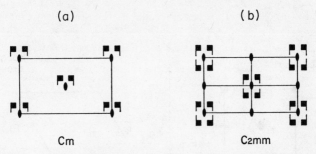

Cm   C2mm

Figure 1-9.   Actual two-dimensional structures based on *Cm*, *C2mm*. A "molecule" is represented by a flag.

cells and we see that for point groups 1*m* or 2*mm* the cell must be rectangular. However, (*c*) is different, and a doubly primitive rectangular cell can be defined. Thus there are *five unit cells* for the four systems, and in Figure 1-8 they are shown along with the point groups that would fit into these and the resulting space groups. Point group 3*m* can fit into its cell two ways—one with the mirror along the short diagonal (*P3m1*) and one with it perpendicular to the base translation (*P31m*).

Extra symmetry elements arise because combining rotation plus translation results in new rotation axes. Thus, for example, in the square net, the fourfold axis at *A* results from the rotation (counterclockwise) 90 degrees around *B* plus a horizontal translation, and the twofold axis at *C* results from the 180 degree rotation around *B* plus a translation of t_1.

In Figure 1-9, molecules are placed in general positions in the unit

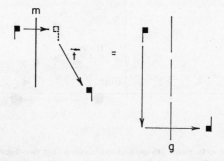

Figure 1-10.   Reflection and translation can lead to an operation called glide. (The glide plane is given the symbol *g* in two-dimensions and is represented by a dashed line.) (After M. J. Buerger, *Elementary Crystallography*, John Wiley, New York, 1956.)

cells of *Cm* and *C2mm*. Note that some of the symmetry elements of the basic net for the *C* cell in Figure 1–8 are *not* present in the space group. Similarly the net based on a fourfold axis has mirror planes in it, but *P4* does not.

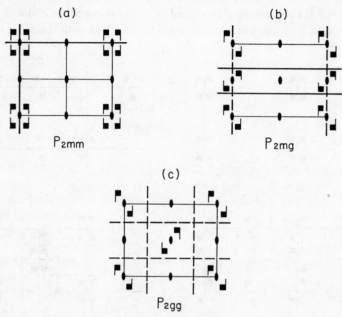

Figure 1–11. How glide planes affect the structure.

For a spatial arrangement we need to consider not only placing the point groups in the various lattices, but also combined operations such as the case of translation and rotation we examined earlier. We saw there that no new space groups occurred, but that extra symmetry elements arose. Now let us consider translation and reflection. This is illustrated in Figure 1–10. The combined operation produces something quite new, and we shall call it a "glide." The combined operation is an equivalent mirror plane *displaced* from the original one (represented by a dashed line) with a translation parallel to it. (It is very important to remember that this "glide" plane is displaced from the original mirror of the point group. The translation must be half the cell edge so that after two operations of a glide, the molecules are returned to the same configuration at the next lattice point.) In Figure 1–11 the space group *P2mm* is examined to see what occurs when the mirror planes are

changed to glide planes. Two new space groups arise. *P2gg* is primitive
not centered, because the molecules in the center of the cells do not
have the same surroundings as the corners—i.e., there is not a lattice
point in the center. In Figure 1–12 glide planes are placed coincident
with the mirrors, and it can be seen that the resulting structure is not
new—it is the same as *P2mm*, and this may occur if the glides are not
displaced from the mirrors. Similar considerations with the other space

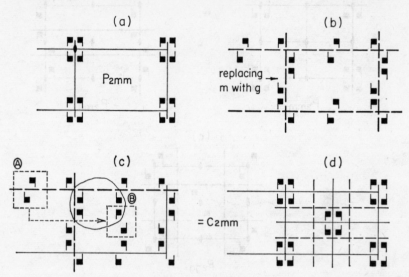

Figure 1–12.   Putting glide planes at the *same positions* as mirror planes does not
create any new configurations.

groups with mirrors will lead to *Pg*, *P4mg*—a total for two dimensions
of seventeen space groups.[3]

We have placed our little flag or "molecule" in a general place in
the space group (it has some undetermined *x*, *y* coordinates). This is
referred to as a "general position." The set of molecules, produced by
the symmetry elements, is called an equipoint and the number of
equivalent positions is referred to as the *rank* of the equipoint. If we
were to place the molecule at certain special positions, say on symmetry
elements, then the rank of the equipoint would change. This is
illustrated in Figure 1–13. [This is a drawing similar to those in the
International Tables for Crystallography, Vol. I (The Kynoch Press,

[3] The reader may easily find these literally all around him—in wall-paper designs,
men's ties, floor tiling, etc.

Birmingham, England), put out by the International Union of Crystallography. There are several volumes and they are excellent references for anyone seriously involved in work in the solid state.] The coordinates of the molecules are given as fractions of the unit translation, $\bar{x} = \overline{X}/a$; the bar over the symbol means minus.

Suppose we could determine the space group and the length of the edges of the cell. Then we can calculate the area A of a unit cell (cm²), and if we could measure the density of our crystal ρ(g/cm²—we are in

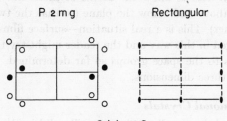

P 2 m g   Rectangular

Origin at 2

Co-ordinates of equivalent positions

Figure 1–13

Rank of equipoint and symmetry at each of its positions		Co-ordinates of equipoints		
4	1	x,y;	$\bar{x},\bar{y}$;	$1/2 + x,\bar{y}$; $1/2 - x,y$
2	m	$1/4,y$;	$3/4,\bar{y}$	
2	2	$0,1/2$;	$1/2,1/2$	
2	2	$0,0$;	$1/2,0$	

(Adapted from *International Tables for X-Ray Crystallography*, Vol. I., Kynoch Press, Birmingham, England, 1952.)

Open circles represent "left handed" figures, closed circles are right handed figures. (In the International Tables, instead of a closed circle a circle with a comma in it is used.)

two dimensions), we could calculate the grams in one cell, ρA. A chemical analysis will then tell us how many grams of each element are in our crystal and from the atomic weights, how many atoms are in the cell. Suppose that for the case in Figure 1–13 it turns out that, within the usual analysis errors of a percent or less, the composition for one cell is A_4B_2 (or two molecules of A_2B). Then the A atom must be in the rank 4 equipoint and B in one of the rank two equipoints. From the atomic radii and the size of the cell it might be that not all of the rank two equipoints are possible without forcing the atoms closer than the sum of the radii—but we shall still most probably be faced with selecting from more than one possibility for the rank two equipoints, and also of course we want to know the actual x, y coordinates. In subsequent chapters we will see how all this information, system, unit cell, cell edges, space group, and coordinates can be determined with diffraction. (In fact all of our *experimental* information on atomic sizes and how they change with structure come from such studies!)

The reader should now assure himself that he understands the terms: lattice (or net), system, unit cell, symmetry elements, point groups, space groups, and equipoints. We could now relax our requirements for two-dimensional nets to allow the atoms or molecules to have slight displacements above and below the plane (so that the two faces of the plane are distinct). This is a real situation—surface films (oxides, etc.) must be arranged in this way and the reader might try to see how this relaxation adds to the space groups so far determined. We shall now continue on to three dimensions.

Three-Dimensional Crystals

All of our work in two dimensions is still valid in three dimensions, because structures, lattices, etc., can be built up by stacking two-dimensional layers. Suppose we take a parallelogram and point group 1. We can stack these in any way because of the low symmetry; in the most general situation a three-dimensional cell (with all edges and angles between the edges unequal) develops. This is called the "triclinic" system. (If we specialize the axes or angles in any way we shall arrive at other unit cells that we are about to consider.) Now suppose we consider a two-dimensional net with twofold axes. In stacking another net with twofold axes over it there are three choices, as shown in Figure 1–14(a), but the second and the third yield the same kind of cell. Note that in all cases the third axis of the cell is perpendicular to the base. The axial system for these two cells is called "monoclinic." All three axes are generally not equal, two of the interedge angles are 90 degrees and one is any angle. If we stack planes of $P4$, the corner of the second plane can be above that of the first, or its corner can be above the center of the net below; there are fourfold axes in these places. In the first case a primitive unit cell arises with all edges at right angles. In the second, if we add a third layer over the center of the second, a body-centered cell arises. The third edge could be equal to the two in the base, giving cubic cells. In this way, fourteen different space lattices can be obtained. These are called the Bravais space lattices (after the French physicist, Bravais, who first showed in 1848 that there were only fourteen). The unit cells for these are shown in Figure 1–14(b) and can be broken into seven axial systems, whose characteristics are given in Table 1–1.

All of the point groups for two dimensions are also valid in three dimensions, but there are now others. First of all, it is possible to have mirror planes perpendicular to axes as well as parallel to them (written, for example, as $4/m$). Combinations of axes are now possible. This is

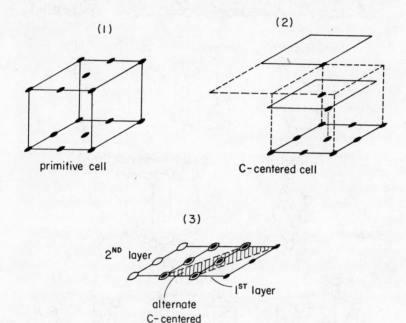

Figure 1–14(a). The stacking of two dimensional nets to make three dimensional lattices. In (3), stacking a second layer so that its corner two-fold axis is over the axis along the centers of the translations of the base creates the same figure as (2). This figure has a lattice point in its center. (After M. J. Buerger, *Elementary Crystallography*, John Wiley, New York, 1956.)

illustrated in Figure 1–15. Rotation around A and B must be equivalent to a rotation around the other axis, C. In a space lattice only a small number of combinations are then possible, and the angles between these axes are also fixed.

We have seen before that reflection is truly a unique operation, especially in three dimensions. Let us look at inversion through a point.

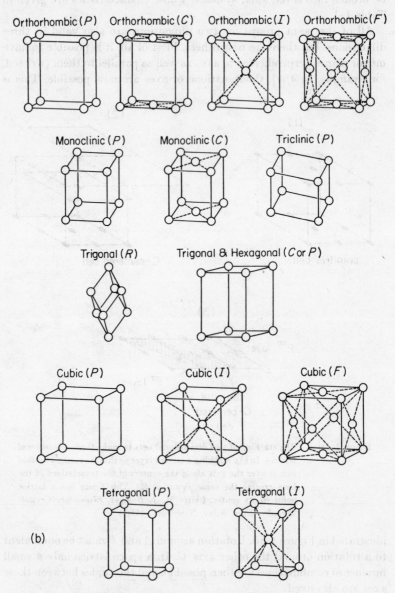

Figure 1–14(b). The fourteen Bravais lattices.

Table 1–1

The Three-Dimensional Systems

	System	Axes	Minimum Symmetry
1.	Triclinic	$a_1 \neq a_2 \neq a_3$ $\alpha \neq \beta \neq \gamma$	None
2.	Monoclinic	$a_1 \neq a_2 \neq a_3$ $\alpha = \gamma \neq \beta = 90°$	One 2-fold axis (along $\mathbf{a}_2$)
3.	Orthorhombic	$a_1 \neq a_2 \neq a_3$ $\alpha = \beta = \gamma = 90°$	Three 2-fold axes (along $\mathbf{a}_1$, $\mathbf{a}_2$, $\mathbf{a}_3$)
4.	Tetragonal	$a_1 = a_2 \neq a_3$ $\alpha = \beta = \gamma = 90°$	One 4-fold axis (along $\mathbf{a}_3$)
5.	Trigonal	$a_1 = a_2 = a_3$ $\alpha = \beta = \gamma \neq 90°$	One 3-fold axis (along $\mathbf{a}_3$)
6.	Hexagonal	$a_1 = a_2 \neq a_3$ $\alpha = \beta = 90°; \gamma = 120°$	One 6-fold axis (along $\mathbf{a}_3$)
7.	Cubic	$a_1 = a_2 = a_3$ $\alpha = \beta = \gamma = 90°$	Four 3-fold axes (along body diagonals of the cube of edge $\mathbf{a}_1$)

Hold your hands parallel to each other, palms inward with the fingers of the left hand up and those of the right down. Your two hands are related by another (imaginary) symmetry element—an inversion center between your hands. However, this relation could be equally well described by a mirror plane between your hands and parallel to the palms followed by a twofold rotation around an axis normal to them (rotation–reflection), so we can choose one description or the other.

Now, if we consider combined operations, such as rotation–reflection ($\tilde{n}$), or rotation–inversion ($\bar{n}$), we find that there are equivalents; in

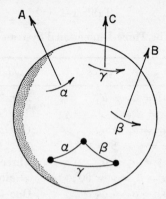

Figure 1–15.   Rotation about *A*, then *B* is equivalent to rotation around *C*. (Adapted from M. J. Buerger, *Elementary Crystallography*, John Wiley, New York, 1956.)

Figure 1–16 we see the operations $\bar{6}$, $\tilde{3}$, or $3/m$. (Open symbols are figures below the plane, closed ones above the plane.) If the operations are continued until the original figure is obtained all three would be found to be the same. (Try this.) All roto–inversion axes are in fact equivalent to roto–reflection axes (not necessarily of the same fold, i.e., $\bar{2} = \tilde{1}$), and the former have been chosen by convention to represent these operations.[4] Note, in Figure 1–17, that a fourfold axis plus

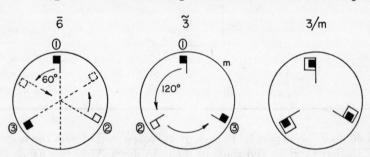

Figure 1–16.   The combined operations of roto-inversion and roto-reflection. Only parts of the operations are shown. The complete figure is obtained by continuing the operation until the original position is obtained.

---

[4] In considering roto-reflection with say, a two-fold-rotation, the reflection *could* be in a plane parallel to the two-fold axis or perpendicular to it. The former case gives $2mm$; only the latter is new!

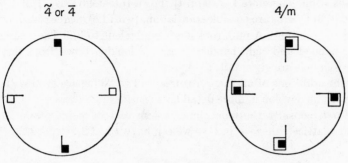

Figure 1-17

inversion center (i) is not equivalent to $4/m$, or $\bar{4}$ (which is the same as $\tilde{4}$). Proceeding in this way we could find 32 independent crystallographic point groups.

If we now add translation to get three-dimensional structures, two important new ideas arise:

1.   Glide planes can be parallel to the a_1a_2, a_2a_3, or a_1a_3 planes of our three-dimensional crystal. The glide translation in any plane can be in either of two directions. There also can be diagonal glide planes, e.g., glides of $(\mathbf{a}_1 + \mathbf{a}_2)/2$ in the a_1a_2 plane or "diamond" glide $(\mathbf{a}_1 + \mathbf{a}_2)/4$.

2.   We examined rotation and translation perpendicular to the rotation axis when two-dimensions were discussed, but now in three-dimensions we can also have rotation combined with translation *parallel* to the axis. This leads to a screwlike motion, as shown in Figure 1-18 for a threefold axis. The fractional translations arise because if we introduce a screw motion and repeat it n times the total translation t must be a multiple m of the cell edge t_1 in the direction of

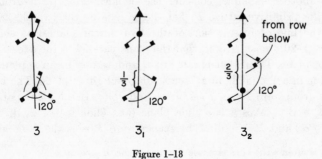

Figure 1-18

translation. Therefore $t = (m/n) \, t_1$. For a threefold axis, $(1/3) \, t_1 = 3_1$ and $(2/3) \, t_1 = 3_2$ are possible translations (with 120 degree rotation after each translation). A pure rotation is equivalent to $3/3$. The figures are left-handed and right-handed "screws," looking down from the top; the symbols are given tails to express this.

The additions of all these features lead to 230 space groups. To see how these develop in more detail let's consider two cases.

First, consider the monoclinic system and its point group 2. The space lattice can be P or C so we can have $P2$, $P2_1$, $C2$, or $C2_1$. (Note

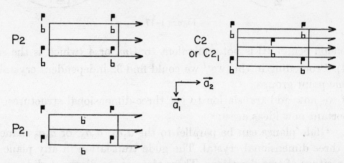

Figure 1–19. Possible space groups based on the monoclinic point group 2. The two-fold axis is parallel to $\mathbf{a}_2$. Screw axes are represented by half arrows. (Adapted from F. C. Phillips, *An Introduction to Crystallography*, 3rd Ed., Longmans, Green and Co., London, 1964.)

the symbols for the symmetry elements.) These are drawn in Figure 1–19. As with rotation axes, the presence of screw axes in $P2_1$ generates other screw axes. The presence of the lattice point in the center of the C cell produces screw axes and therefore $C2$ and $C2_1$ are the same—the only difference is the location of the corner of the cell at the 2 or 2_1 axis.

As another example, consider the orthorhombic point group $2m$[5] and the primitive lattice P. Let the a_3 axis be the twofold axis and also the line of intersection of the two mirror planes, as shown in Figure 1–20. Consider first, that the plane parallel to the axes a_2a_3 is a mirror plane. Then, that parallel to a_1 and a_3 may be an m plane or an a (glide in $\mathbf{a}_1$), c (glide in $\mathbf{a}_3$), or n (diagonal glide) plane. The possible space groups are Pmm, Pma, Pmc, and Pmn. If the plane parallel to the a_2 and a_3 axes is a c glide plane (i.e., glide in the $\mathbf{a}_3$ direction), Pca, Pcc, and Pcn result. The space group Pcm is the same as Pmc,

[5] This is often written as mm; see Figure 1–6 for the reason.

only a change of axial notation is involved (i.e., the a_1 and a_2 axes are interchanged in the two), but the *kind* of arrangement is the same. Remember, it is not the dimensions of the cell that are important but the arrangement. Thus, although the axial lengths are not equal in the orthorhombic cell, this is not important and interchanging the axes does not affect the space group. Also possible are *Pba* and *Pbn*. (*Pbm* is equivalent to *Pma*, *Pbc* is equivalent to *Pca*.) Letting the plane parallel to a_2 and a_3 be a diagonal glide only one new arrangement results, *Pnn*. A total of 10 space groups occur for the point group $2mm$

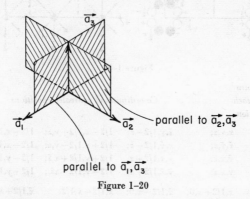

parallel to $\vec{a_2}, \vec{a_3}$

parallel to $\vec{a_1}, \vec{a_3}$

Figure 1–20

in the primitive lattice of the orthorhombic system. (Could we change the axis to a screw axis?)

A more complex space group, with its equipoints is shown in Figure 1–21. Note the symbols for symmetry elements and the equipoints (pp. 28, 49, 50 of Vol. I of the International Tables gives a summary of the symbols).

Proceeding in this way, or in a more sophisticated manner with advanced mathematical tools, it turns out that there are only 230 space groups. This was discovered in the late nineteenth century independently by a Russian mineralogist, Federov, a German mathematician, Schoenflies, and an English businessman, Barlow. At the time, as we shall see more clearly later, there was really no way of verifying this amazing result. Without any consideration as to the types of atomic bonding, the requirements of three-dimensional periodicity indicate that only 230 kinds of arrangements are possible. Of course, which of these is chosen will depend on these bonding forces.

If we now allow an atom with a net electronic spin to, say, have spins pointed in different directions depending on location (symbolically we

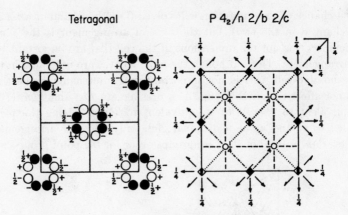

Tetragonal $P\,4_2/n\ 2/b\ 2/c$

Figure 1–21

Rank of Equipoint and symmetry at each equivalent position		Co-ordinates of equivalent positions			
16	1	$x,y,z;$	$\bar{x},y,1/2-z;$	$1/2-x,1/2+y,z;$	$1/2+x,1/2+y,1/2-z;$
		$\bar{x},\bar{y},z;$	$x,\bar{y},1/2-z;$	$1/2+x,1/2-y,z;$	$1/2-x,1/2-y,1/2-z;$
		$\bar{y},x,\bar{z};$	$y,x,1/2+z;$	$1/2+y,1/2+x,\bar{z};$	$1/2-y,1/2+x,1/2+z;$
		$y,\bar{x},z;$	$\bar{y},\bar{x},1/2+z;$	$1/2-y,1/2-x\bar{z},;$	$1/2+y,1/2-x,1/2+z.$
8	2	$x,1/2+x,0,$	$\bar{x},1/2-x,0;$	$x,1/2-x,1/2;$	$\bar{x},1/2+x,1/2;$
		$1/2+x,\bar{x},0;$	$1/2-x,x,0;$	$1/2+x,x,1/2;$	$1/2-x,\bar{x},1/2.$
8	2	$x,0,3/4;$	$\bar{x},0,3/4;$	$1/2+x,1/2,3/4;$	$1/2-x,1/2,3/4;$
		$0,x,1/4;$	$0,\bar{x},1/4;$	$1/2,1/2+x,1/4;$	$1/2,1/2-x,1/4.$
8	2	$x,0,1/4;$	$\bar{x},0,1/4;$	$1/2+x,1/2,1/4;$	$1/2-x,1/2,1/4;$
		$0,x,3/4;$	$0,\bar{x},3/4;$	$1/2,1/2+x,3/4;$	$1/2,1/2-x,3/4.$
8	2	$0,0,z;$	$0,0,\bar{z}$	$0,0,1/2+z;$	$0,0,1/2-z;$
		$1/2,1/2,z;$	$1/2,1/2,\bar{z};$	$1/2,1/2,1/2+z;$	$1/2,1/2,1/2-z.$
8	2	$0,1/2,z;$	$0,1/2,\bar{z};$	$0,1/2,1/2+z;$	$0,1/2,1/2-z;$
		$1/2,0,z;$	$1/2,0,\bar{z};$	$1/2,0,1/2+z;$	$1/2,0,1/2-z.$
8	$\bar{1}$	$1/4,1/4,1/4;$	$3/4,3/4,1/4;$	$1/4,3/4,1/4;$	$3/4,1/4,1/4;$
		$1/4,1/4,3/4;$	$3/4,3/4,3/4;$	$1/4,3/4,3/4;$	$3/4,1/4,3/4.$
4	$\bar{4}$	$0,0,0;$	$1/2,1/2,0;$	$0,0,1/2;$	$1/2,1/2,1/2.$
4	222	$0,1/2,0;$	$1/2,0,0;$	$0,1/2,1/2;$	$1/2,0,1/2.$
4	222	$0,0,1/4;$	$1/2,1/2,1/4;$	$0,0,3/4;$	$1/2,1/2,3/4.$
4	222	$0,1/2,1/4;$	$1/2,0,1/4;$	$0,1/2,3/4;$	$1/2,0,3/4.$

(Adapted from *International Tables for X-Ray Crystallography*, Vol. I., Kynoch Press, Birmingham, England, 1952.)

could think of these as "colored" atoms), then the number of possibilities can increase still further. This area is still being very actively studied.

For further details the reader should consult references 1 and 2 which are excellent treatments involving no more advanced mathematics than that used here; these books were the foundation for our discussion.

Some Real Crystal Structures

In Figure 1–22 the unit cells of several simple structures are given. We should be able to see that a, c, and e have a face-centered cubic cell (f.c.c.), that b is body centered (b.c.c.), and d is simple cubic (s.c.).

In Figure 1–22(a), if we assume the atoms "touch" along a face diagonal, it is a simple matter to get an estimate of the diameter of a copper atom or more correctly the diameter to the outermost orbits. Thus it is just half a face diagonal, or $a/\sqrt{2}$. In this fashion we can proceed to get information on pure elements and then on how the diameters change in compounds due to electron transfer, etc.

The assumption of atoms touching along face diagonals for copper implies quite closely packed planes of atoms. One of these planes is outlined in Figure 1–22(a) and drawn in Figure 1–23(a). What is the point group around any atom, around one of the empty spaces or voids? Why then is there a threefold axis along a cube diagonal? (Note the way such planes are stacked in the unit cell, Figure 1–22(a), for this last point.) The area occupied by one atom is defined by a hexagon. If we call the radius of an atom, r, its area in the plane is πr^2. The hexagon is 12 triangles of area:

$$\frac{r}{\sqrt{3}} \times \frac{1}{2}\,r = \frac{r^2}{2\sqrt{3}}.$$

Therefore the fraction of the total area occupied by atoms is

$$\frac{\pi r^2}{(12r^2)/2\sqrt{3}} = 0.907.$$

For a square array shown in Figure 1–23(b) the fraction is only 0.785. The more efficient close packing is in fact quite logical for such a metal as copper. Because of the lack of directionality of the metallic bond the atoms tend to pack themselves geometrically with as many neighbors as possible. There are six nearest neighbors to any atom in its close packed plane, as well as 3 above and 3 below, or a total of 12. These can easily be seen in Figures 1–23(a) and (c) or Figure 1–22(a) by considering, say, a corner atom and its near neighbors along face diagonals

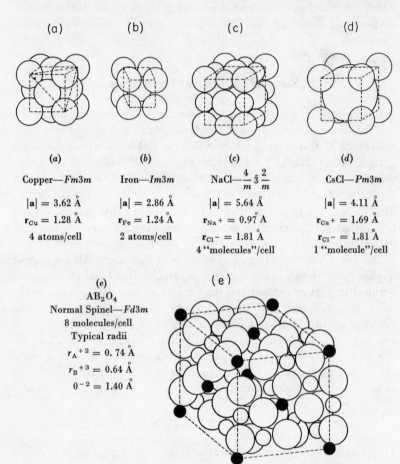

(a)   (b)   (c)   (d)

(a)

Copper—*Fm3m*

$|\mathbf{a}| = 3.62$ Å

$r_{Cu} = 1.28$ Å

4 atoms/cell

(b)

Iron—*Im3m*

$|\mathbf{a}| = 2.86$ Å

$r_{Fe} = 1.24$ Å

2 atoms/cell

(c)

NaCl—$\frac{4}{m}\bar{3}\frac{2}{m}$

$|\mathbf{a}| = 5.64$ Å

$r_{Na^+} = 0.97$ Å

$r_{Cl^-} = 1.81$ Å

4 "molecules"/cell

(d)

CsCl—*Pm3m*

$|\mathbf{a}| = 4.11$ Å

$r_{Cs^+} = 1.69$ Å

$r_{Cl^-} = 1.81$ Å

1 "molecule"/cell

(e)

AB_2O_4

Normal Spinel—*Fd3m*

8 molecules/cell

Typical radii

$r_{A^{+2}} = 0.74$ Å

$r_{B^{+3}} = 0.64$ Å

$0^{-2} = 1.40$ Å

(e)

Figure 1–22 (Adapted from L. V. Azaroff, *Introduction to Solids*, McGraw-Hill, New York, 1960.)

(remember that this is only one unit cell and that there are other cells on all sides of this one).

The volume fraction occupied by copper atoms in its unit cell can easily be found. There are four copper atoms per cell (consider the atoms at one corner and those on 3 faces that are its neighbors—the

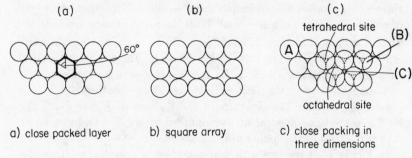

<table>
<tr><td>(a)</td><td>(b)</td><td>(c)</td></tr>
</table>

a) close packed layer   b) square array   c) close packing in
                                               three dimensions

Figure 1–23

other corners and faces "belong" to other unit cells). Thus, the total volume of atoms is $4 \times (4/3)\pi r^3$. The cell edge can be expressed in terms of the atom's radius. Half a cell diagonal, $a/\sqrt{2}$, is $2r$ so that $a = 2\sqrt{2}r$ and $a^3 = 16\sqrt{2}r^3$. The volume fraction of atoms is then

$$\frac{16\pi r^3}{3(16)\sqrt{2}r^3} = 0.74.$$

The rest of the volume is occupied by voids. Notice in Figure 1–23(c) that there are two types of voids. One type has three atoms as neighbors in its plane and one above (a tetrahedral site or void); another is between the planes with three atoms above and three below (an octahedral site or void). In Figure 1–24 the size of the atoms has been reduced to make the voids in the cell more apparent. The void with six neighbors has the shape of an octahedron and this is why it is called an octahedral void or octahedral interstitial site or position. As

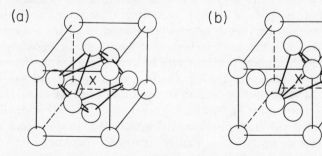

X Octahedral site 1/2, 1/2, 1/2   X Tetrahedral site 3/4, 3/4, 3/4

Figure 1–24

these voids represent some empty space in the cell, another atom (say of radius R) might fit in this void. If all the copper atoms are to touch around such a void then $2R + 2r = a$. But $a = 2\sqrt{2}r$, and therefore $R/r = \sqrt{2} - 1 = 0.414$, and $r/R = 1/0.414$. There are octahedral sites at the centers of all edges. Each edge belongs to four cells, so that including the site in the center, there are four sites per cell or one per atom. Examine the structure of NaCl given in Figure 1–22. The Na^+ ions are in octahedral sites surrounded by six Cl^-, and vice versa. Note the ratios of the ionic radii.

In Figure 1–24 the site with four neighbors is also shown. Its center is a quarter of the way along a body diagonal. The neighbors form a tetrahedron, and so the site is referred to as a tetrahedral site. There are eight of these per unit cell, two per atom. The radius ratio R/r is 0.225. Examine the octahedral and tetragonal holes in Figure 1–22(b); note that the dimensions are different in different directions. Is the structure closely packed?

Note that the f.c.c. cell is bult up of layers of (111) planes, each one in the holes of the previous one, and with the atoms in the fourth layer directly over the atoms in the first—i.e., the stacking of (111) layers is $ABCABC....$ The stacking can be altered so that the third layer is over the first (see Figure 1–23), but so that atoms are still in the holes of the previous layer. The structure is close packed but the stacking is $ABAB....$ Build such a structure and you will see that the holes are the same kind and number as with copper, the density of packing is the same, but the unit cell is hexagonal, with two atoms in the cell.

Many structures are based on just such packing considerations. For example, MgO has a structure just like NaCl; the larger oxygen ions are close packed (f.c.c.) and the Mg ions fit in octahedral interstitial sites. Barium titanium oxide is another interesting oxide shown in Figure 1–25(a). Titanium ions are octahedrally coordinated to the oxygens. In oxides like Al_2O_3 the structure is made of close packed oxygen layers (in essentially hexagonal packing) with Al ions in rows of octahedral sites, as shown in Figure 1–25(b). In these rows every third site is lacking an Al^{+3} ion and, as there is one octahedral site per atom, this leads to the composition Al_2O_3. Spinels are compounds with the formula AB_2O_4 where A and B are metal ions; B must be $+3$ in valence and A, $+2$. The space group is $Fd3m$, and the structure is essentially 8 face-centered (and close packed) unit cells of oxygen. There are 32 atoms of oxygen and 32 octahedral sites (in two equipoints of rank 16) and 64 tetrahedral sites (2 equipoints, one of rank 8 and one of rank 48).

According to the chemical formula, for 32 oxygen atoms in the unit cell there are 16 B atoms and 8 A atoms, and they distribute themselves in different ways over the interstitial positions, depending on the metal ions involved. It is logical to suspect that the A's will be in tetrahedral sites and the B's in octahedral sites, because the B's have more valence and can couple with more oxygen ions. This does occur in $ZnFe_2O_4$, but for $MgFe_2O_4$ and Fe_3O_4 tetrahedral sites are occupied by Fe^{+3} ions and the octahedral sites are shared by the divalent and trivalent ions. (The structures can be written $Fe^{+3}(Mg^{+2}Fe^{+3})O_4$ and $Fe^{+3}(Fe^{+2}Fe^{+3})O_4$.) These are called inverse spinels, and this unusual

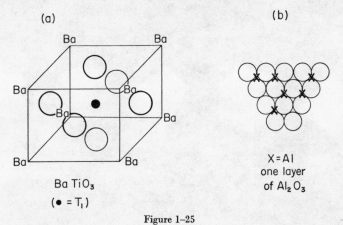

(a)

(b)

Ba TiO$_3$

($\bullet = T_1$)

X = Al
one layer
of Al$_2$O$_3$

Figure 1–25

arrangement leads to some very interesting magnetic properties, so that the spinels are used in computers.

It is worth thinking a bit now about what is meant by the term compound, e.g., NaCl. The larger the crystal the larger the compound! One cannot really see molecules of NaCl in the structure. The whole structure is held together by all the ions.

It is easy to see that much of the behavior of all materials (how the atoms move relative to one another when deformed, or when subjected to an applied field . . .) are associated with their structure. Despite the fact that the kinds of structures are limited, it is not very easy to guess the structure for a given composition. In some cases, now, with the number of structures that have been determined we *can* guess, based on size, considerations of valence and bond type, and the structure of compounds of elements from similar positions in the periodic table. Much remains to be done, however, not only to determine actual atomic coordinates with higher accuracy, but also to answer such questions as why copper is face-centered cubic at all temperatures but iron is body-centered cubic at low temperatures and f.c.c. at high temperatures. In the biological fields, complex structures involving tens of thousands of atoms are revealing vital information concerning the process of life itself.

Although much of the details of possible internal structures was available in the nineteenth century—at least as a mathematical

Figure 1–26

abstraction—all one could do was to look at crystals. Some models of these are shown in Figure 1–26, but they are not always so perfect. It is clear that the most striking feature is the symmetry and the plane faces. The point group is also given and the reader should be sure he can find the symmetry elements (a paper model of the pictures will help). The fact that these could arise by stacking very much smaller building blocks, as shown in Figure 1–27, was recognized quite early. A face of the crystal is repeated by the symmetry elements to produce a set of similar faces called a *form*. Only the symmetry of the point group is observed. The translations associated with glides or screw axes are so small (a few Ångstroms where $1 \text{ Å} = 10^{-8}$ cm) that the difference between the position of a face repeated by a rotation or a screw axis is not detectable. This is illustrated in Figure 1–28.

Figure 1–27. A crystal built up of unit cells. (After R. Hauy (*Phil. mag.* **1** (1798), 35, 46, 287, 376, and F. C. Phillips, *An Introduction to Crystallography*, 3rd Ed., Longmans, Green and Co., London, 1964.)

If there is no center of symmetry, we can sometimes detect this from the shape of etch pits on opposite faces, or by seeing if the crystal is piezoelectric. It cannot develop a voltage across opposite faces when a stress is applied if there is such a center. Screw axes can be detected if a crystal is transparent. The screwlike arrangement influences the phase relationships in the scattered light. We can see why in Figure

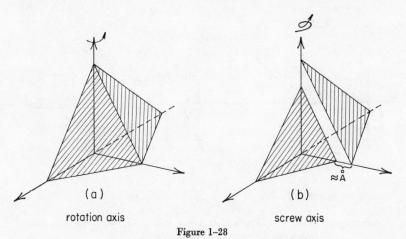

Figure 1–28

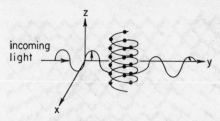

Figure 1-29.   How a screw axis changes the polarization of light. (After R. P.
Feynman, R. B. Leighton and M. Sands, *The Feynman Lectures
on Physics*, Vol. I., Addison-Wesley Co., Reading, Mass., 1963.)

1-29. Polarized light with its electric field in the y,z-plane will move
atoms up and down. If there is a screw axis present the atoms will be
forced to move in the x-direction, forward on one side and backward on
the other. The field in the x-direction is not zero because the incoming
field has a different value at both points. The interference of this field
with the incoming field causes the polarized light to be rotated an
amount depending on the thickness of the crystal. The sense of the
screw can also be ascertained.

Naming Planes, Points and Directions

Rational planes on the surface of a crystal (Figure 1-27) arise from
the presence of planes of lattice points. For simplicity, let us look at two
dimensions, Figure 1-30. Solid lines have been drawn that could occur

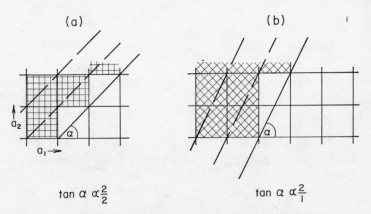

Figure 1-30.   (After F. C. Phillips, *An Introduction to Crystallography*, 3rd Ed.,
Longmans, Green and Co., London, 1964.)

if the unshaded unit cells were not present. We can also think of imaginary planes of lattice points or atoms *within* the crystal, drawn as dotted lines. If we express the tangent of α in terms of the ratio of unit translations we see that this ratio is one of small integers. This idea, recognized in the eighteenth century, has led to a very simple shorthand for "naming" various planes, so that we do not need to have a drawing or lengthy discussion to indicate what plane we are talking about. Three axes not on the same plane are chosen, such as simple directions on a macroscopic crystal.

A "parametric" plane is picked, such as one of the faces or a plane imagined inside the crystal; this plane should cut all three axes, and where it cuts the axes, defines their unit length—i.e., the lengths of the axes a_1, a_2, and a_3. The intercepts of any plane on these axes are set equal to a_1/h', a_2/k', and a_3/l' (i.e., $a_1/2 = a_1'/h'$). Thus h', k', l' are obtained and common factors are removed to obtain hkl. Some examples are given in Figure 1–31. As illustrated by Figure 1–31(a) and (b) it is quite important to state the kind of unit cell or the lengths of the edges. The same plane is shown in both cases, but the a_1 edge is twice as long in Figure 1–31(b). The indices are enclosed in parentheses, and the numbers represent a whole "family" of planes—i.e., all parallel planes in the crystal. Some other planes in a family are shown in Figure 1–31(e) with dashed lines.[6] (Referring to Figure 1–22, what are the indices of a closed packed plane in a face-centered cubic crystal? In a body-centered cubic crystal?) These "Miller" indices can be negative, and such a case is illustrated in Figure 1–31(c). The bar over a number means minus h, k, or l just as it did for the coordinates of equipoints.

Because of symmetry elements any one plane is often repeated. The collection of planes generated in this way is called a form and is represented by $\{hkl\}$. For example, in a cubic crystal $\{100\}$ implies the planes (100), (010), (001), ($\bar{1}$00), (0$\bar{1}$0), and (00$\bar{1}$). If the structure was, say, tetragonal $a_1 = a_2 \neq a_3$. Then $\{100\}$ would mean (100), (010), ($\bar{1}$00), and (0$\bar{1}$0) but *not* (001) or (00$\bar{1}$); the last two are a separate form because these planes do not have the same spacing as the $\{100\}$. The number of planes in a form is called its *multiplicity*.

In Figure 1–26 it was shown that in a cube or regular octahedron the symmetry elements are the same. The reason for this is that they represent the same symmetry. The only difference in the two crystals is the relative development of different *forms*; this is illustrated in

[6] The indices are read one-one-one, not one hundred and eleven.

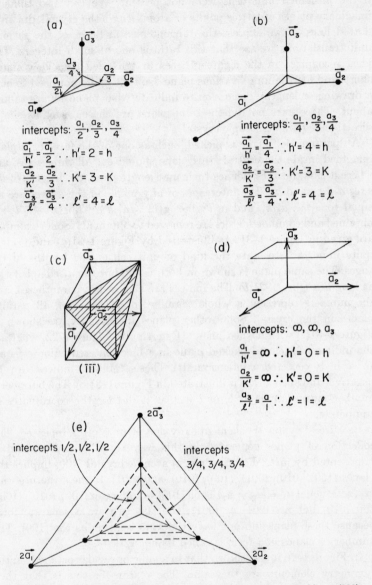

Figure 1–31.   Examples of Miller indices. All the planes shown in (e) are (111), and the intercepts are given as fractions of a_i.

Figure 1–26(d) and (e) and it may be seen that a variety of shapes can arise based on the same system and point group. This relative development of forms is called *habit* and it was, and is, quite an annoying feature in examining the external features of a crystal. It soon became obvious, however, that it really was not important in defining the crystal in terms of its symmetries; what is important is the type of plane, its form, and its relation to others in the crystal—i.e., its angles with respect to other planes. In considering internal symmetry and structure we are not interested in the size of the plane at all—whether we look at it on a crystal or draw it in the lattice; what we are interested in is the *kind* of plane. Thus, by removing the common factor, as in Figure 1–31(e), we describe the kind of plane, not its size. In all cases in Figure 1–31(e) the indices are (111).

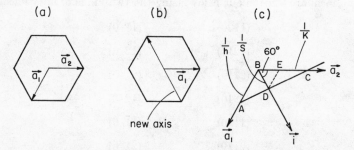

Figure 1–32.   How the fourth axis arises in the hexagonal system.

We have already seen how to write points in the structure or coordinates of an atom, x, y, z. The set of symmetry equivalent points can also be written x, y, z. Remember that these coordinates are expressed as fractions of the lengths of the chosen axes. Directions—such as edges of a crystal where faces intersect, or rows of lattice points—are written by picking a point on the direction, writing its indices, clearing fractions, and common factors. A single family of directions is written $[uvw]$. A form of directions is written $\langle uvw \rangle$.

These rules for indices are conventions used throughout the world and it is well to learn them carefully. One interesting point occurs in the hexagonal system. As shown in Figure 1–32, rotation of 120 degrees around the threefold or sixfold axis, produces a new axis. The indices can be written ($hkil$) where i is the index on this new axis. In Figure 1–32(c) the trace of a plane is shown; a parallel (DE) to the a_1 axis, from the plane's intercept on this new axis, has been drawn to

a_2. Because triangles ABC and DEC are similar, and BED is an equilateral triangle;

$$\frac{1/h}{1/k} = \frac{1/s}{1/k - 1/s},$$

$$\frac{1}{h} = \frac{1/ks}{1/k - 1/s} = \frac{1/ks}{(s-k)/ks} = \frac{1}{s-k},$$

or

$$h + k = s = \bar{\imath}.$$

Because of this relationship, the index along this third axis is not really necessary. Note that $(12\bar{3}0)$ can also be written $(12\cdot0)$, where the dot implies the intercept on the other axis. There is a definite advantage in using all the indices, though. Consider the form $\{11\bar{2}0\}$. All of the planes in the form are written out below using the two kinds of notations.

$(11\bar{2}0)$	$(11\cdot0)$
$(1\bar{2}10)$	$(12\cdot0)$
$(2\bar{1}\bar{1}0)$	$(2\bar{1}\cdot0)$
$(\bar{1}2\bar{1}0)$	$(12\cdot0)$
$(\bar{1}\bar{1}20)$	$(\bar{1}\bar{1}\cdot0)$
$(\bar{2}110)$	$(\bar{2}1\cdot0)$

The three-index notation does not clearly indicate that all the planes are in one form.

With this four-index "Miller–Bravais" notation, it is especially important to be careful and it is recommended that initially the student draw a grid as in Figure 1–33 to help indexing. Ruled graph paper can be obtained. For directions in a hexagonal crystal the three-axis scheme $\langle uvw \rangle$ should be used: the indices of a direction based on four axes $\langle UVTW \rangle$ are quite different. (Draw the $[11\bar{2}1]$. What are the indices with only three axes?) The reader can prove that $U = 1/3\,(2u - v)$, $V = 1/3\,(2v - u)$, $T = -(U + V)$, $W = w$.

We now have a scheme for naming planes, directions, and points. The next step is to seek methods for examining relations between planes graphically or dealing with them analytically. Would there be many uses for such methods? If we see a line on a face of a crystal what planes could it be? What are the angles between planes, etc.? The graphical representation that should be most useful is one which

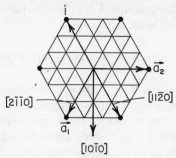

Figure 1–33. A ruled net like this is often helpful in indexing in the hexagonal system.

emphasizes the angular relationships and de-emphasizes the size or shape of the planes. For higher accuracy and for dealing with general relations, the analytical approach might be helpful. We shall consider the latter approach first.

Analytical and Graphical Calculations in Crystallography

As we have already seen, the position of any point in a lattice, or more generally, any atom (**A**) can be expressed as a vector involving

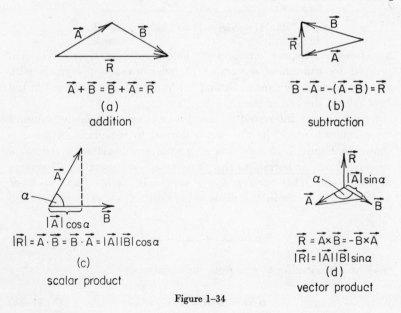

$$\vec{A} + \vec{B} = \vec{B} + \vec{A} = \vec{R}$$

(a)

addition

$$\vec{B} - \vec{A} = -(\vec{A} - \vec{B}) = \vec{R}$$

(b)

subtraction

$$|\vec{R}| = \vec{A} \cdot \vec{B} = \vec{B} \cdot \vec{A} = |A||B|\cos\alpha$$

(c)

scalar product

$$\vec{R} = \vec{A} \times \vec{B} = -\vec{B} \times \vec{A}$$
$$|\vec{R}| = |\vec{A}||\vec{B}|\sin\alpha$$

(d)

vector product

Figure 1–34

the basic lattice translations for a lattice point and, in addition, fractions of these to the atomic positions:

$$\mathbf{A} = m_1\mathbf{a}_1 + m_2\mathbf{a}_2 + m_3\mathbf{a}_3 + x\mathbf{a}_1 + y\mathbf{a}_2 + z\mathbf{a}_3, \qquad (1\text{–}2)$$

m_1, m_2, m_3 are integers; x, y, z are not. It certainly seems logical to look at vector algebra to see if it can provide the necessary analytical representations. In Figure 1–34 the basic operations of the addition and scalar and cross products of vectors are reviewed. (The reader might briefly review the fundamentals of vector algebra at this point; we will

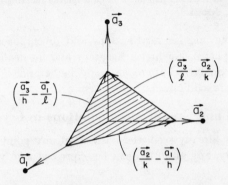

Figure 1–35. Three vectors in the (shaded) plane *hkl*.

not, however, require much more than these operations.) We shall proceed by examining a number of questions about crystals with vectors. Some more exercises using this approach can be found in the Problems at the end of the chapter.

As we are not interested in the size or shape of a plane, a useful representation would be the vector normal to the plane. A plane is shown in Figure 1–35, and the intercepts are described in terms of vectors. A vector normal to the plane would be normal to all vectors in the plane. The vectors $\mathbf{a}_2/k - \mathbf{a}_1/h = \mathbf{D}$, $(\mathbf{a}_1/h - \mathbf{a}_2/k) = \mathbf{B}$ or $\mathbf{a}_3/l - \mathbf{a}_2/k = \mathbf{C}$ are in the plane. Therefore, if we write the normal $\mathbf{n}$ as

$$\mathbf{n} = u\mathbf{a}_1 + v\mathbf{a}_2 + w\mathbf{a}_3,$$

then we can solve for u, v, w from the equations:

$$\mathbf{n}\cdot\mathbf{D} = \mathbf{n}\cdot\mathbf{B} = \mathbf{n}\cdot\mathbf{C} = 0. \qquad (1\text{–}3a)$$

It would be useful to expand one of these equations at this point. Let $\cos(a_1, a_2)$ be the cosine of the angle between vectors $\mathbf{a}_1$ and $\mathbf{a}_2$:

$$\mathbf{n} \cdot \mathbf{D} = 0 = u\left[\frac{1}{k}\,|\mathbf{a}_1|\,|\mathbf{a}_2|\,\cos(a_1, a_2) - \frac{|\mathbf{a}_1|^2}{h}\right]$$
$$+ v\left[\frac{|\mathbf{a}_2|^2}{k} - \frac{|\mathbf{a}_1|\,|\mathbf{a}_2|}{h}\,\cos(a_1, a_2)\right]$$
$$+ w\left[\frac{|\mathbf{a}_3|\,|\mathbf{a}_2|}{k}\,\cos(a_3, a_2) - \frac{|\mathbf{a}_3|\,|\mathbf{a}_1|}{h}\,\cos(a_3, a_1)\right]. \quad (1\text{-}3b)$$

It is important to remember that the angles between the vectors are *not necessarily* right angles; our coordinate system is not always orthogonal.

There are three such equations, and therefore we can solve for the normal $[uvw]$ to a plane (hkl) if we know the lengths of the axes and the angles between them. Actually, though, we only need the ratios u/v, v/w, u/w, for a direction $[111]$ is the same as $[222]$! Therefore, only two of the equations are really required.

There is a set of vectors, called reciprocal lattice vectors, that makes many of the calculations very simple. They are also very useful for diffraction and studies in solid-state physics. These vectors are defined as:

$$\mathbf{b}_1 = \frac{\mathbf{a}_2 \times \mathbf{a}_3}{\mathbf{a}_1 \cdot \mathbf{a}_2 \times \mathbf{a}_3} \qquad (1\text{-}4a)$$

$$\mathbf{b}_2 = \frac{\mathbf{a}_3 \times \mathbf{a}_1}{\mathbf{a}_1 \cdot \mathbf{a}_2 \times \mathbf{a}_3} \qquad (1\text{-}4b)$$

$$\mathbf{b}_3 = \frac{\mathbf{a}_1 \times \mathbf{a}_2}{\mathbf{a}_1 \cdot \mathbf{a}_2 \times \mathbf{a}_3} \qquad (1\text{-}4c)$$

The denominator of these expressions is merely a scalar quantity. $\mathbf{a}_2 \times \mathbf{a}_3$ is the vector whose magnitude is the area of a parallelogram with sides a_2 and a_3. It is normal to this plane of $\mathbf{a}_2$ and $\mathbf{a}_3$ and therefore $\mathbf{a}_1 \cdot \mathbf{a}_2 \times \mathbf{a}_3$ is the volume of the cell defined by $\mathbf{a}_1$, $\mathbf{a}_2$, and $\mathbf{a}_3$, V_a.

In Figure 1-36 the axes $\mathbf{a}_i$ and $\mathbf{b}_i$ are shown superimposed. The $\mathbf{b}_i$ are located merely by using the definitions of $\mathbf{b}_i$ and the meaning of the cross product. Note that the angles between the $\mathbf{b}_i$ are the supplements of the corresponding angles between the $\mathbf{a}_i$.

These reciprocal lattice vectors have one interesting property, which makes them so useful:

$$\begin{aligned}\mathbf{a}_i \cdot \mathbf{b}_j &= 0,\ i \neq j,\\ \mathbf{a}_i \cdot \mathbf{b}_j &= 1,\ i = j.\end{aligned} \qquad (1\text{-}5)$$

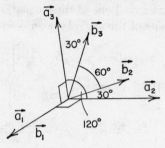

Figure 1–36.   Vectors in real space (a_i) and reciprocal space (b_i).

Consider the reciprocal vector $\mathbf{r}^*_{hkl} = h\mathbf{b}_1 + k\mathbf{b}_2 + l\mathbf{b}_3$. If we take the dot product of this with vectors in the plane (hkl), keeping in mind Eq. (1–5),

$$\left(\frac{\mathbf{a}_2}{k} - \frac{\mathbf{a}_1}{h}\right) \cdot \mathbf{r}^*_{hkl} = 0,$$

$$\left(\frac{\mathbf{a}_3}{l} - \frac{\mathbf{a}_1}{h}\right) \cdot \mathbf{r}^*_{hkl} = 0.$$

As $\mathbf{r}^*_{hkl}$ is normal to two vectors in a plane it is normal to the plane; we can write the equation for the normal to any plane (hkl) in terms of $\mathbf{b}_i$ immediately. The magnitude of $\mathbf{r}^*_{hkl}$ is also interesting. If $\mathbf{N}$ is a unit normal to the plane (hkl),

$$\mathbf{N} \cdot \frac{\mathbf{a}_1}{h} = d, \qquad (1\text{–}6)$$

where d is the spacing between planes in a family. A unit normal could be written as $\mathbf{r}^*_{hkl}/|\mathbf{r}^*_{hkl}|$. Thus,

$$\frac{\mathbf{r}^*_{hkl}}{|\mathbf{r}^*_{hkl}|} \cdot \frac{\mathbf{a}_1}{h} = d = \frac{1}{|\mathbf{r}^*|}.$$

The magnitude of $\mathbf{r}^*$ is inversely proportional to the interplanar spacing.

The volume defined by the $\mathbf{b}_i$ is $\mathbf{b}_1 \cdot \mathbf{b}_2 \times \mathbf{b}_3$.

$$\mathbf{b}_2 \times \mathbf{b}_3 = \frac{\mathbf{a}_3 \times \mathbf{a}_1}{\mathbf{a}_1 \cdot \mathbf{a}_2 \times \mathbf{a}_3} \times \frac{\mathbf{a}_1 \times \mathbf{a}_2}{\mathbf{a}_1 \cdot \mathbf{a}_2 \times \mathbf{a}_3}.$$

Let

$$\mathbf{a}_1 = \mathbf{b}, \qquad \mathbf{a}_2 = \mathbf{c}, \qquad \mathbf{a}_3 \times \mathbf{a}_1 = \mathbf{a}.$$

As

$$\mathbf{a} \times (\mathbf{b} \times \mathbf{c}) = \mathbf{b}(\mathbf{a} \cdot \mathbf{c}) - \mathbf{c}(\mathbf{a} \cdot \mathbf{b}),$$

$\mathbf{b}_2 \times \mathbf{b}_3$ can be written:

$$\frac{1}{V_a^2} \{\mathbf{a}_1[\mathbf{a}_2 \cdot (\mathbf{a}_3 \times \mathbf{a}_1)] - \mathbf{a}_2[\mathbf{a}_1 \cdot (\mathbf{a}_3 \times \mathbf{a}_1)]\}.$$

The first term in parentheses is V_a and the second is zero. Therefore,

$$\mathbf{b}_2 \times \mathbf{b}_3 = \frac{\mathbf{a}_1}{V_a},$$

$$V_b = \mathbf{b}_1 \cdot \mathbf{b}_2 \times \mathbf{b}_3 = \frac{\mathbf{b}_1 \cdot \mathbf{a}_1}{V_a} = \frac{1}{V_a}. \tag{1-7}$$

The volumes defined by the two sets of vectors are reciprocal.

Let us examine some problems to see how useful these vectors can be. A group of planes that have parallel intersections is called a *zone*, and the direction of the lines of intersection is called a zone axis. If we know the planes, what is the zone axis? As an extension of this, we can ask the question, what is the trace or vector we can expect when we look at one plane $(h_1k_1l_1)$, from some other plane $(h_2k_2l_2)$? Conversely, if we see such a trace, what plane is it from?

Let the zone axis be $\mathbf{r} = u\mathbf{a}_1 + v\mathbf{a}_2 + w\mathbf{a}_3$. This vector must be normal to the normals of the planes in the zone, i.e., for any plane in the zone:

$$\mathbf{r} \cdot \mathbf{r}_{hkl}^* = 0 = hu + kv + hw. \tag{1-8a}$$

If we have a (100) plane, its zone axis can be [0vw]—i.e., [001], [012], etc. Only u must be zero. For a (110):

$$u + v = 0.$$

That is, [1$\bar{1}$0], [1$\bar{1}$3], etc., are possible zone axes for this plane.

Now, if we have two planes $(h_1k_1l_1)$, $(h_2k_2l_2)$ their zone axis, or the trace of one in the other, can be found:

$$\begin{cases} h_1u + k_1v + l_1w = 0, & (1-8b) \\ h_2u + k_2v + l_2w = 0. & (1-8c) \end{cases}$$

Again, although there are only two equations for three unknowns, we only need the ratios u/v, u/w, v/w. Dividing Eq. (1-8b) by l_1w and

Eq. (1–8c) by $l_2 w$ and multiplying the former by h_2/l_2 and the latter by h_1/l_1:

$$\frac{h_2 h_1 u}{l_2 l_1 w} + \frac{k_1 v h_2}{l_2 l_1 w} = \frac{-h_2}{l_2}, \tag{1–8d}$$

$$\frac{h_1 h_2 u}{l_1 l_2 w} + \frac{h_1 k_2 v}{l_1 l_2 w} = \frac{-h_1}{l_1}. \tag{1–8e}$$

Subtracting Eq. (1–8e) from (1–8d):

$$\frac{v}{w}\left(\frac{k_1 h_2}{l_1 l_2} - \frac{k_2 h_1}{l_1 l_2}\right) = \frac{h_1}{l_1} - \frac{h_2}{l_2},$$

or

$$\frac{v}{w} = \frac{h_1 l_2 - h_2 l_1}{k_1 h_2 - k_2 h_1}.$$

Similar relations can be written immediately for u/w, v/w. It is then a simple matter to calculate the direction of a trace of a plane on another plane. Note how useful were the reciprocal vectors in setting up the initial equations.

As a second practical example, suppose we wish to change from one unit cell to another. Reindexing the planes could be a tedious job, involving laborious work with models, but our vector algebra can help us. Consider a new set of axes $\mathbf{A}_i$ in terms of the old set $\mathbf{a}_i$

$$\begin{aligned}
\mathbf{A}_1 &= u_1 \mathbf{a}_1 + v_1 \mathbf{a}_2 + w_1 \mathbf{a}_3 \\
\mathbf{A}_2 &= u_2 \mathbf{a}_1 + v_2 \mathbf{a}_2 + w_2 \mathbf{a}_3 \\
\mathbf{A}_3 &= u_3 \mathbf{a}_1 + v_3 \mathbf{a}_2 + w_3 \mathbf{a}_3
\end{aligned} \tag{1–9a}$$

Now a distance is the same regardless of the coordinate system; hence in reciprocal space,

$$H\mathbf{B}_1 + K\mathbf{B}_2 + L\mathbf{B}_3 = h\mathbf{b}_1 + k\mathbf{b}_2 + l\mathbf{b}_3. \tag{1–9b}$$

Taking the dot product of both sides of Eq. (1–9b) with $\mathbf{A}_1$,

$$H = hu_1 + kv_1 + lw_1, \tag{1–9c}$$

and using A_2:

$$K = hu_2 + kv_2 + lw_2, \tag{1–9d}$$

or

$$L = hu_3 + kv_3 + lw_3, \tag{1–9e}$$

or

	h	k	l
H	u_1	v_1	w_1
K	u_2	v_2	w_2
L	u_3	v_3	w_3

$$\tag{1–9f}$$

Thus, knowing u, v, and w it is possible to calculate (HKL) from (hkl). Or, if we know three (HKL)'s and their corresponding (hkl)'s we can solve for u, v, and w.

In such a transformation the volume of the unit cell changes to $\mathbf{A_1 \cdot A_2 \times A_3}$.

$$\mathbf{A_2 \times A_3} = u_2 v_3 (\mathbf{a_1 \times a_2}) + u_2 w_3 (\mathbf{a_1 \times a_3})$$
$$+ v_2 u_3 (\mathbf{a_2 \times a_1}) + v_2 w_3 (\mathbf{a_2 \times a_3})$$
$$+ w_2 u_3 (\mathbf{a_3 \times a_1}) + w_2 v_3 (\mathbf{a_3 \times a_2})$$
$$= (u_2 v_3 - v_2 u_3) \mathbf{a_1 \times a_2}$$
$$+ (w_2 u_3 - u_2 w_3) \mathbf{a_3 \times a_1}$$
$$+ (v_2 w_3 - w_2 v_3) \mathbf{a_2 \times a_3}.$$

Recalling the definitions of $\mathbf{b}_i$ [Eq. (1–4)]:

$$\mathbf{A_2 \times A_3} = V_a [(u_2 v_3 - v_2 u_3) \mathbf{b_3} + (w_2 u_3 - u_2 w_3) \mathbf{b_2}$$
$$+ (v_2 w_3 - w_2 v_3) \mathbf{b_1}].$$

Thus,

$$V_A = \mathbf{A_1 \cdot A_2 \times A_3} = V_a \begin{vmatrix} u_1 & v_1 & w_1 \\ u_2 & v_2 & w_2 \\ u_3 & v_3 & w_3 \end{vmatrix}. \qquad (1\text{–}10)$$

Let us move now to graphical techniques. We have seen that a particularly simple way of representing a plane, disregarding habit, is by using its normal (which we can readily write in terms of $\mathbf{r}^*_{hkl}$). The angle between two normals is simply the supplement of the angle between the planes, as shown in Figure 1–37. Imagine a very small crystal with its normals at the center of a large sphere, as in Figure 1–38. We can concentrate on the interrelation of the normals by

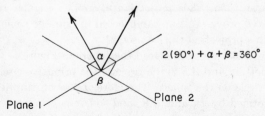

Figure 1–37. The angle between normals (α) is the supplement of the angle between the planes (β).

considering the intersection of these with the sphere. We cannot carry such a sphere around though, so the results must be projected on to two dimensions. One of the most popular ways of doing this is the stereographic projection. The intersections of the normals with the sphere are called poles and are projected back to point P_1; the intersection of the projection with a great circle (called the primitive circle) is used to represent the pole. The index of the plane represented by the pole is not placed inside any kind of bracket.

It is clear from the figure that if P_1, $00\bar{1}$, is used as the projecting point, poles below the primitive circle will project out of this circle.

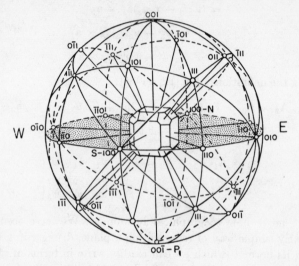

Figure 1–38.   Stereographic projection of normals to a crystal's planes (onto the shaded circle).

We can correct this by switching to projection point P_2, 001, for such poles, using open circles for these points and filled circles for the others, to distinguish them. This projection maintains angular relationships; once we have proven this we can proceed to examine some of the ways in which this projection can be used.

In Figure 1–39, we have placed the sphere in Figure 1–38 so that P_1 is on the bottom and AB is the trace of the primitive circle. Thus LM is a small circle on the sphere. Therefore, LN is an elliptical section of the cone formed by P_1 and LM, and so QN is also a circular section, if $\alpha_1 = \alpha_2$. MR is drawn parallel to the primitive circle and the angles RMP_1, and P_1LM are equal because they cut equal arcs. Angles

P_1LM and P_1NQ are equal; therefore angles RMP_1 and P_1NQ are equal. The circular cross section QN is thus parallel to the projection plane AB and projects as a circle, CDE. Angular relationships are maintained. *However*, the center of the actual circle is *not* the center of the projected circle—i.e., CD is not equal to DE.

As a start in examining the manner of using this projection, let us try to locate the poles of the faces of the small cubic crystal in Figure 1–38. It is a good idea to label North, South, East, and West on the projection plane so that as we twist and turn it we shall not lose track of where we started. All planes perpendicular to the primitive plane will have poles that lie on the perimeter of the primitive circle. The (001)

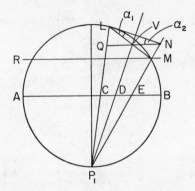

Figure 1–39.   A stereographic projection of a small circle. (Adapted from F. C. Phillips, *An Introduction to Crystallography*, 3rd Ed., Longmans, Green and Co., London, 1964.)

face has its pole at the center of the projection, the 100 pole is the "South pole" and 010 is the "East pole" for this cubic crystal, as shown in Figure 1–40(a). Faces such as the (110), ($1\bar{1}0$), ($\bar{1}10$), and ($\bar{1}\bar{1}0$) have poles which also lie on the primitive circle and are readily located as in Figure 1–40(b). The normal to a plane such as the (011) is 45 degrees between the 001 and 010 poles. This can be located along the East–West axis, by imagining the sphere rotated around this axis so that the projection plane is now a line, Figure 1–40(c). The pole of the (011) is now located 45 degrees from the (001) and projected back onto the projection plane, as shown in Figure 1–40(c). Note that the *distance* on the projection from the center is $s = R \tan \alpha/2$ where R is the radius of the primitive circle. It is only necessary now, to locate such poles, to place points in (b) a distance s from the center, as shown in Figure

1–40(d). The poles of {111} planes make an angle of approximately 56 degrees with the {011} planes and in fact form a zone with these planes and the {110}, as can be seen in Figure 1–38.[7] The great circle that contains the normals to both planes is 45 degrees from the East–West axis, and the poles of the {111} must lie along the trace of this plane (AB), as shown in Figure 1–40(e). We can then readily locate the {111} poles with a new projection point P_2, obtained by rotating the

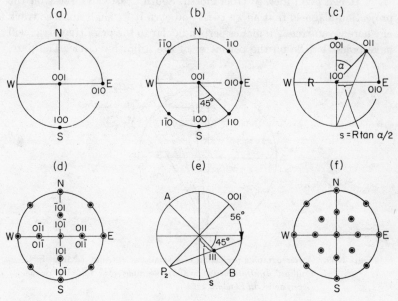

Figure 1–40. The location of poles of planes shown in Figure 1–38. In (c), $\alpha = 45°$.

001 around AB, out to the edge of the primitive circle, and the plane of projection AB is as shown in Figure 1–40(e); s is also shown. All of the poles are shown in Figure 1–40(f). Note the symmetry elements in the final drawing; they correspond to those in point group $m3m$.

In Figure 1–41 it can be seen that a great circle in projection appears very much as a longitude line in a map. This is what the plane containing all the normals to crystal planes in any one zone looks like in

[7] The angles between planes can be calculated in any system from $\mathbf{r}_{hkl} \cdot \mathbf{r}_{h'k'l'}$. In all systems but the cubic these are of course sensitive to the axial ratios. A table of interplanar angles for the cubic system can be found in the International Tables, Vol. II, p. 120. Occasionally, one can find such a table for some other material in the literature.

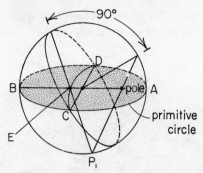

Figure 1–41. Finding the normal to a plane in stereographic projection.

projection; they form a great circle. If we have a pole in a projection
(the zone axis) we can always find the trace of its plane (CD) (i.e., the
plane containing the poles in its zone) by drawing a diameter back
through the pole and a line from the projection point. Then a point is
located 90 degrees from the pole, and with this point and the points C
and D on a line perpendicular to AB, the great circle in projection can
be drawn. It will, as we shall see, be very helpful in a projection if we
place markings of such traces of great circles (longitude "lines") every
few degrees. This could easily be done by displacing the pole a few
degrees at a time and determining the trace of each great circle. Then
we could place small circles or latitude lines as shown in Figure 1–42.

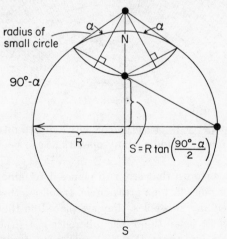

Figure 1–42. Drawing a small circle around the North pole in a stereographic
projection.

Such a net, known as a Wulff net, is shown in Figure 1–43. Note that the equal degree markings are closer at the center than near the primitive circle. Why?

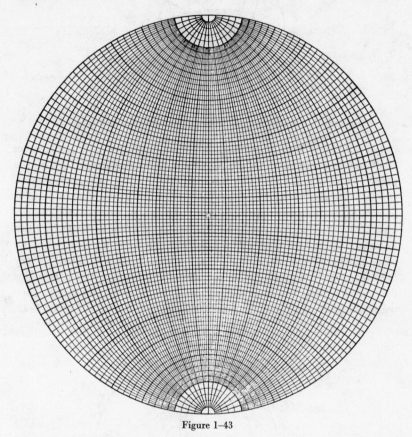

Figure 1–43

A tracing paper with the primitive circle drawn on it is placed over this with a pin in the middle. Many operations can be carried out quite simply.

1. We have shown that any two planes determine a zone axis and therefore their poles lie on a great circle. It follows that to measure the angles between any two poles, they are placed on the same longitude, and their angular separation is the difference in latitude.

2. Any rotation about the N–S axis moves poles along latitude lines.

3. Rotation around the E–W axis is accomplished by placing the E–W axis on the tracing paper coincident with N–S on the Wulff net and following 2. After the rotation the tracing paper is returned to its original position.

4. Rotation about a direction normal to the projection is accomplished by rotation around the center pin.

5. Rotation around *any* pole can be accomplished by rotating the pole into the center or N–S positions. After the rotation the pole is

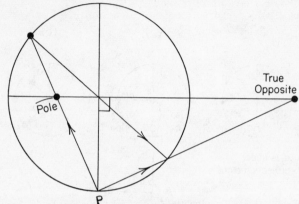

Figure 1–44. Finding the true opposite of a pole in stereographic projection. (After F. C. Phillips, *An Introduction to Crystallography*, 3rd Ed., Longmans, Green and Co., London, 1964.)

returned to its original position. In these operations, *all* poles in the projection *must* be moved in the same manner.

6. The pole of any great circle is 90 degrees along a diameter from the point where the diameter bisects the longitude line.

7. The opposite of a pole, if the projection point is reversed, is located on a diameter through the pole, an equal number of degrees on the opposite side of the center of the projection. The true opposite however, must be constructed, as shown in Figure 1–44. This operation can be useful in trying to draw the circle on which two poles lie; a third point can be obtained from the opposite of one.

8. A small circle around any pole—i.e., the locus of all poles a certain number of degrees from the given pole—can be drawn in the following way. The pole on the tracing paper is projected to the circumference of the projection (by "imagining" the sphere tilted around the perpendicular to the great circle connecting the point and the

point P). The degrees are marked off on either side; these end points are projected back on the primitive circle and the distance between them is bisected to find the circle's construction center.

We now turn to exploring some of the ways of using this stereographic projection in actual situations.

We have so far dealt with a cubic crystal, to simplify presenting the fundamentals of a stereographic projection. Let us look now at a more complex situation, say, a triclinic crystal. How can we plot the axes and poles?

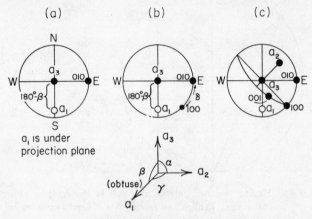

Figure 1–45.   Stereographic projection of a triclinic crystal. (After F. C. Phillips, *An Introduction to Crystallography*, 3rd Ed., Longmans, Green and Co., London, 1964.)

To start we shall assume that β is obtuse and that the N–S direction in our projection is parallel to the $\mathbf{a}_1 - \mathbf{a}_3$ plane with $\mathbf{a}_3$ normal to the projection. We know immediately that the 010 pole, because (010) is parallel to the $\mathbf{a}_1$ and $\mathbf{a}_2$ axes, is on the primitive circle as shown in Figure 1–45(a). The 100 pole is also on the primitive circle, as (100) is parallel to $\mathbf{a}_3$ and $\mathbf{a}_2$ (*not* normal to the $\mathbf{a}_1$ axis)! By calculating or measuring the angle between the (100) and (010) and calling the supplement δ, the 100 pole is located as in Figure 1–45(b). The 001 pole is at the intersection of two circles around 100 and 010 of radii equal to the supplements of the angle between (100) and (001), (010) and (001). The $\mathbf{a}_2$ axis is the pole of the zone containing 001 and 100 poles, as shown in Figure 1–45(c).

Finally, we may have to index the poles of other planes which we can locate on the projection by measuring angles between it and other planes such as (001) and (010). Recall that, if $\mathbf{N}$ is a unit normal to a plane, $\mathbf{N} \cdot \mathbf{a}_1/h = |N| \, |\mathbf{a}_1/h| \cos [N, a_1] = d$. We can write three such equations for all three a_i. Thus:

$$|\mathbf{N}| \left| \frac{\mathbf{a}_1}{h} \right| \cos (N, a_1) = d = |\mathbf{N}| \, \frac{|\mathbf{a}_2|}{k} \cos (N, a_2),$$

$$\frac{h}{k} = \frac{a_1}{a_2} \frac{\cos (N, a_1)}{\cos (N, a_2)}.$$

and similarly for h/l, k/l. The required angles from the pole to the axes can be measured on the projection. If we define a parametric plane (the (111)), the angles between its pole and the 100 and 010 poles give the axial ratios, a_1/a_2. Examining the poles around an unknown pole often helps indexing; also from Eq. (1–8), the pole at the intersection of two great circles must be the zone axis of the two planes represented by these great circles.

We can measure the angles between faces by shining a well-collimated light beam on the crystal and measuring the tilt that is required to get a bright reflection on turning the crystal from one face to another. Measurements can be made quickly if a zone axis of a group of planes is aligned vertically, so that it is only necessary to rotate the crystal around this axis. A simple device for holding a crystal and tilting it in a variety of different ways is the goniostat shown in Figure 1–46. The crystal can be translated, or rotated, about two different axes that meet at a common point (hence the name goniostat) so that the crystal is not displaced from this point during tilting. A variety of forms of this device are in use, depending on whether the crystal is big or small, whether it is to be cut along certain planes, etc.

Another useful application of the stereographic projection concerns learning something about markings on the surface of a crystal. These might be traces of planes of shear (slip lines) due to deformation, transformation markings, etc. In Figure 1–47(a) we show such a marking on a face of a crystal. It would be informative to know what is the plane of this marking. This could tell us what the slip plane is or what is the interface between the matrix and transformation product of the markings (the composition plane).

We take the face of the marking as the projection plane, and as we can see in Figure 1–47(b), we *cannot* tell what the plane is; it could be any one of a number of planes. This, of course, is fairly obvious. From the trace we cannot tell how the plane slants back into the crystal.

What we can be sure of is the line AB—the locus of the poles of all possible planes. This is simply another statement of the fact that in a zone there are many planes [see Eq. (1-8)]. The trace on one face represents only the zone axis of the plane and the face. If there are several markings on the surface (and they all appear similar), then we

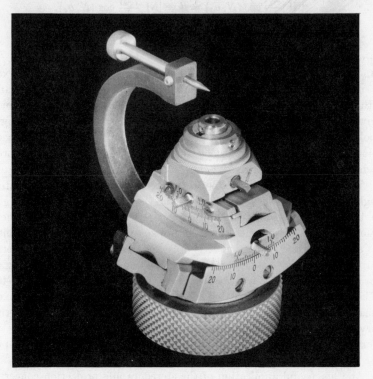

Figure 1-46.   A two-circle goniostat. The needle points to the intersections of the centers of the two axes. (*Courtesy of Electronics and Alloys, Inc., Ridgefield, N.J.*)

can proceed further. In the first place the number of different directions is helpful; these cannot exceed the multiplicity of the plane. For example, there cannot be more than three directions for traces from {100} in a cubic system. Second, with several traces, we shall have several lines like $A-B$. We can superimpose on this projection a projection of many poles as they appear with this face as a projection (if we know the indices of the face). That form of poles that all fall on the lines like AB identifies the traces. If we do not know the face we are dealing with, projections of various low index poles can be superimposed, and rotations (of all poles equal amounts) can be tried to see if one set can be found that also falls on the diameter lines after such a

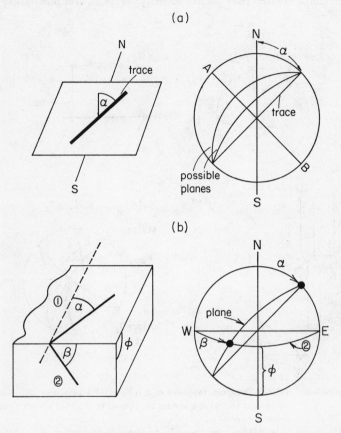

Figure 1–47. Analysis of traces: (a) on one surface, (b) on two surfaces. (After B. D. Cullity, *Elements of X-ray Diffraction*, Addison-Wesley, Reading, Mass., 1956.)

rotation. This will identify the orientation as well as the traces, but there is little chance of success in such a trial-and-error process and it should be used only as a last resort. (If the indices of the traces are known but not the orientation, a similar procedure can be used to find the orientation. For example, if we know the indices of slip markings in some crystal, their traces on a face can be used to index the face.)

From Eq. (1–8) it is clear that what we need to find $\{hkl\}$ is its traces on two faces (i.e., analytically two sets of $[uvw]$). This situation is illustrated in Figure 1–47(b). If the orientation of the crystal is known (which simply means that we can identify the faces and put indices on

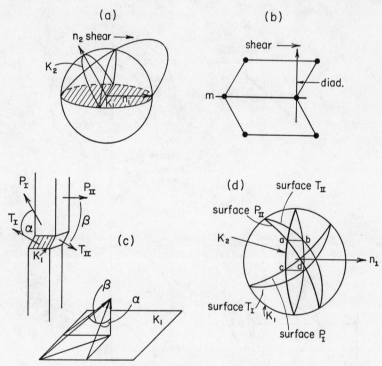

Figure 1–48.   (a), (b) Twinning. (a) shear of a sphere; (b) a twin in a lattice is equivalent to rotation around the normal to the twin plane (m) or reflection across m.

(c), (d) Determination of twin elements. (c) Surface tilts and (d) plotting these tilts to get the twin elements.

the directions to solve Eq. (1–8)) the pole of the unknown plane can be indexed. If it is now known we can again try the trial-and-error techniques just mentioned. Conversely if the (hkl) of the trace is known we can find the crystal's orientation by these procedures.

By the methods described above we can find the composition plane (where the matrix and precipitate or transformation product meet) as well as identifying the plane of slip markings. But we can learn even more.

Suppose the crystal is sheared (in a direction n_1) as illustrated in Figure 1-48(a). There are two undistorted planes K_1 and K_2. Now if the shear is a certain value the crystal structure will not change. There are two possibilities for this. First, the shear could be a lattice distance—one unit translation. This is "slip." Another possibility exists. The shear could be such that the *lattice*[8] is a mirror image across some plane—a "twin." This mirror plane could be either K_1 or the one perpendicular to K_1 and n_1. A twinned lattice is shown in Figure 1-48(b). It is clear that as far as the lattice is concerned mirror reflection across K_1 could also be described by a twofold axis. This axis would be the normal to K_1 for reflection across K_1, or n_1 for reflection in the plane normal to K_1 and n_1. If the crystal is mounted on a goniostat, with some shear marking we think is a twin, in a horizontal position, then with a finely collimated light source (say a light at the end of a long tube), the crystal can be tilted to measure the angles between the faces of the crystal and the marking, as in Figure 1-48(c). If the traces of these faces are plotted in a stereographic projection on to K_1 as in Figure 1-48(d), we can find a pole common to both faces—i.e., their zone axis—before the shear and after. Their connection is the shear direction, n_1. The second undistorted plane is located by finding some plane such that distances ab and cd are equal. The angle of shear can thus be measured right on the projection. Now, we have six poles before and after the shear. These are the poles of the planes K_1, K_2, P_I, P_{II}, and n_1, n_2. If the shear produced a twin, or if it was just slip, then the angles between the poles will still be possible angles for the same crystallographic system (not necessarily poles of the same indices, though). If they do not, then a new phase has been created. There is a 2 to 3 degree error in these plotting procedures. It is not always possible to measure the tilts— e.g., if the twin is small—and we shall have more tools for this problem very shortly.

In our projection on K_1, during the shear, all poles move along diameters, because their traces on K_1 are not altered; only their traces on other faces are tilted. (Study Figure 1-48(a) to see this.)

Finally, the trace a plane (1) will make on another plane (2) is the pole at the intersection of their great circles (which we can index as described above).

We have gathered some information about the basic structure of materials, and learned how to deal with it quantitatively. Now we turn

---

[8] We emphasize the word Lattice because the actual *structures* may be related by rotation or reflection.

our attention to the problem of how we can learn about the details of this internal structure experimentally. Real crystals are not perfectly periodic. The atoms are vibrating. There are imperfections, such as missing atoms (vacancies), interstitial atoms, missing portions of planes (dislocations), etc. The crystal is generally "broken up" into regions (subgrains or mosaic structures) tilted slightly with respect to each other. Although these play a key role in the properties, they are low in concentration compared to the atomic density. At first, we shall ignore these things and concentrate on learning about the arrangement of atoms.

ADDITIONAL REFERENCES

1. F. C. Phillips, *An Introduction to Crystallography* (3rd Ed.) (Longmans, Green and Co., Ltd., London, 1964).
2. M. J. Buerger, *Elementary Crystallography* (John Wiley, New York, 1956).
3. A. Holden and P. Singer, *Crystals and Crystal Growing* (Doubleday and Co., Garden City, New York, 1960).
4. E. A. Wood, *Crystals and Light* (D. Van Nostrand Co., Princeton, New Jersey, 1964).
5. G. G. Koerber, *Properties of Solids* (Prentice-Hall, New Jersey, 1962).
6. J. F. Nye, *Physical Properties of Crystals* (Clarendon Press, Oxford, 1957).
7. J. D. Dana, *Manual of Mineralogy* (revised by C. S. Hurlbut, Jr.) (John Wiley, New York, 1952).
8. W. B. Pearson, *A Handbook of Lattice Spacings and Structures of Metals and Alloys* (Pergamon Press, New York, 1958).

For Wulff Nets write to: Polycrystal Book Service Box 11567, Pittsburgh, Pennsylvania 15238.

SUGGESTIONS FOR EXPERIMENTS

At least three laboratory sessions would be helpful in establishing the ideas presented in this chapter. In the first two laboratories, emphasis on symmetry can be developed by examining ball models of crystals and making drawings of point groups. Actual crystals can be readily obtained following the recipes in reference [3] and these could be examined. An excellent and easily built group of objects representing point group symmetries can be found in an Appendix to reference [3]. Rochelle salt crystals can be used to set up a demonstration of the piezoelectric effect (again reference 3). Sodium nitrate is a good crystal to demonstrate birefringence, and sodium chlorate is good for demonstrating the action of a screw axis. With these two and alum, Problem 8 can be made much more realistic. Small crystals can be made to grow quite easily under a microscope by saturating a water solution of CdI_2 at 85°C and then putting a drop on a slide. This shows quite clearly how faces develop, and a great deal more about crystal growth (J. B. Newkirk (1955), *Acta Met.*, **3**, 121; A. J. Forty (1951), *Phil. Mag.*, **42**, 670; (1952), **43**, 72, 377).

The second lab might be assigned after the student has some experience with the stereographic projection. In this session some of the difficulties that arise can be gone over and also one or two of the more complicated projections (say of a trigonal crystal).

There is some excellent programmed teaching material, on Bravais lattices, close-packing and Miller indices, available from Appleton-Century-Crofts, 440 Park Ave. South, New York, New York 10016.

PROBLEMS

1. What symmetry elements can you find in your own external appearance, i.e., in the human body?

2. Give the equipoints and their rank for the two-dimensional space group *Pm*.

3. Show what happens to a 4_1 axis, if (*a*) a center of symmetry is added, and (*b*) a mirror is added parallel to the axis.

4. Consider a growing two-dimensional crystal. The path of growth in the four *x*-directions at 90 degrees to each other is 6/5 that of the *y*-directions which are 45 degrees to the *x* directions. Draw the crystal at various stages of growth. Start with a seed with edges perpendicular to *x* and *y* all of equal length. What conclusions can you reach?

5. Draw several different planes in a two-dimensional lattice. Which have the highest density of points? Which have the greatest interplanar spacing? How might this affect the habit?

6. Show that changing mirror planes to glide planes introduces nothing new for the two-dimensional space groups $P31m$, $P3m1$, $P6m$.

7. Consider $P2mm$ of the two-dimensional groups. Allow for atomic motion above and below the plane and show some of the new space groups.

8. Draw a stereographic projection for point groups 23 and $m3$. Indicate what differences you might expect in the appearances of crystals of each point group.

9. Add a center of symmetry to those three-dimensional point groups which do not have one. Group those that are now indistinguishable.

10. With the aid of sketches, show that a primitive tetragonal lattice could not be centered on the faces of the unit cell parallel to the fourfold axis to produce a true space lattice.

11. What point groups in the tetragonal system can have their rotation axes replaced by screw axes, when placed in a lattice?

12. Show, in a series of drawings, how the space group $Pnma$ develops.

13. Given three-dimensional point group 4.

   (a) Draw a stereographic projection representing this point group.

   (b) What should be a likely form for crystals with this point group?

   (c) What unit cells are consistent with this point group?

   (d) Indicate any new symmetry elements.

   (e) What space groups are consistent with the cells?

   (f) Add an inversion center and mirror planes to the point group 4. What point group results?

   (g) List a few of the space groups possible for this new point group.

14. What is the point group of the interatomic forces on a carbon atom in diamond? What is the nearest neighbor distance in terms of the cell edge? How many near neighbors?

15. Certain intermetallic compounds have the fluorite structure—a cubic structure with four CaF_2 molecules per cell, where the cation has eightfold coordination and the anion fourfold coordination. Others have the antifluorite structure with the cations and anions reversed. Sketch the structure. Give coordinates of the atoms. Indicate the radius ratios possible.

16. The radius ratio for twelvefold coordination (i.e., twelve nearest neighbors) is unity. What prevents a simple ionic AB compound, having ions of equal size, from adopting a crystal structure in which each atom is coordinated by 12 ions? (*Hint:* What materials do you know that have twelvefold coordination?)

17. In a hexagonal close-packed structure, if all the atoms touch and are spherical, what is c/a?

18.* (a) GeSe is orthorhombic crystal; its space group is *Pbnm*. Find this in the International Tables. (*Hint:* You may have to change the axial system. Look at pp. 546–547 in the International Tables, Vol. I.)

   (b) Its density is 5.52 gm/cm³. How many molecules are there in the unit cell? $a_1 = 440$ Å, $a_2 = 10.82$ Å, $a_3 = 3.85$ Å.

   (c) What are the possible distributions among the equipoints?

19. Sketch the following planes and directions in each of the seven systems.

$$(\bar{1}00), \quad (2\bar{3}4), \quad [121].$$

20. Calculate the multiplicity of $\{h00\}$, $\{hk0\}$, and $\{hhh\}$ in the tetragonal and orthorhombic systems.

21. Using vectors find the angles between (111) and (100) planes in a cube.

22. Write an equation for a normal to a plane.

23. Find the indices of a normal to a plane in terms of the actual crystal axes (i.e., not in terms of reciprocal vectors).

24. Show in which of the seven crystal systems the normal to a plane *always* has the same indices as the plane. Are there any special cases?

25. What plane is at the intersection of the zones for (111) ($\bar{1}$11) and (100) ($\bar{1}$00)?

26. The Weiss zone rule says that all poles of possible faces lying in a zone between two given faces (hkl) and $(h_1k_1l_1)$ have indices of the type

$$mh + nh^1, \quad mk + nk^1, \quad ml + nl^1$$

where m, n are integers. Prove this, using vectors.

27. Find a primitive unit cell for the f.c.c. unit cell and write out the equations to transform the Miller indices.

* These problems will be expanded in future chapters and should be worked out now.

28. Derive an equation for $1/d^2$ for a lattice based on a hexagonal unit cell.

29. Using the stereographic projection without the Wulff net:

(a) Find the opposite end of a pole.

(b) Find a pole 30 degrees from another pole.

(c) Draw a great circle through three poles within the primitive circle.

(d) Find the zone axis of a great circle.

30. (a) Sketch in a stereographic projection the positions of all poles of the {111} for a cubic system. Let the center of the projection be a pole normal to one of the cube axes. Index each of the poles.

(b) If the crystal suddenly expands normal to the plane of projection, sketch on the projection what happens to these {111} poles.

31. Draw a standard (100) projection for a cubic crystal. Rotate it to a (111) projection.

32. Draw a (100) standard projection for the tetragonal form of tin.

33. How many poles are needed to fix the orientation of a crystal?

34. Optical examination of a crystal gives the following measurements of interfacial angles along four zones. The faces have been lettered:

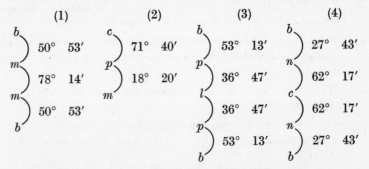

	(1)		(2)		(3)		(4)
b–m	50° 53′	c–p	71° 40′	b–p	53° 13′	b–n	27° 43′
m–m	78° 14′	p–m	18° 20′	p–l	36° 47′	n–c	62° 17′
m–b	50° 53′			l–p	36° 47′	c–n	62° 17′
				p–b	53° 13′	n–b	27° 43′

(a) Draw a stereographic projection of the crystal and give its system. (The same letter repeated represents faces which appear similar on the crystal—not necessarily the same face.)

(b) Index the faces and find the axial ratios.

(c) If a (111) plane made traces on the (100) and (001) faces, sketch the angles you would observe.

35. (a) Consider a substitutional solution of Fe^{+2} in MgO. Can the Fe^{+2} ion be expected to fit in place of Mg^{+2}? Suppose Fe^{+2} is oxidized to Fe^{+3}. Will it fit in any other positions?

     (b) The spinel $MgFe_2O_4$ precipitates from the solid solution $(Fe_xMg_{1-x})O$. Look up the phase diagram. Examine the crystal structures and the dimensions of the unit cell and matrix. Are there any planes that are similar? What do you expect then that the precipitates will look like in the microscope?

36.* You are looking down on a $(\bar{1}10)$ plane of a cubic material with [001] running North and South.

     (a) With the aid of a stereographic projection sketch give the indices of trace of $(11\bar{1})$, (001), 100, $(\bar{1}11)$ planes.

     (b) Project the face diagonals of the (100) on this $(\bar{1}10)$ surface. What are the indices of these projections.

     (c) Indicate how you would also solve a and b analytically.

37. It sometimes happens that one part of a crystal is rotated about some axis of the rest of the crystal—in a twin, e.g., or in a deformation band. Suppose you wish to know what is the rotation axis and the amount of rotation. The situation is represented schematically below. The subscript I represents the major portion of the crystal and F represents the rotated region. You know the location of several poles of both regions, such as P, P'.

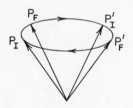

Problem 1–37

     (a) Where is $\mathbf{P}_I + \mathbf{P}_F$? How could you locate it on a stereogram? (The vectors are to the poles, i.e., normal to planes.)

     (b) Where is $\mathbf{P}_I - \mathbf{P}_F$ and how could you locate it?

     (c) How could you determine the axis of rotation?

     (d) How could you determine the amount of rotation?

* These problems will be expanded in future chapters and should be worked out now.

38.* F.C.C. crystals often twin on {111} in ⟨112⟩.

(a) Pick a plane normal to a (111) and containing a ⟨112⟩ direction and sketch the atomic arrangement. Include atoms above and below the plane, using different symbols for each level.

(b) Shear part of the crystal along (111) to obtain a twin. What is the index of the direction of shear you have chosen?

(c) On a stereogram place poles of the parent and twin. (*Hint:* Remember, reflection is equivalent to twofold rotation in the lattice.) Are there any new rotation axes or mirror planes? Why?

(d) Replace the face atoms with copper and the corners with gold. (Cu_3Au). What is the unit cell? After twinning what is the unit cell? Can you generalize this as to the effect of a twinning shear on atoms not at lattice points?

(e) For Cu_3Au indicate the motions required to restore the structure in the twin to that of the matrix.

* These problems will be expanded in future chapters and should be worked out now.

2 *The Nature of Diffraction*

Suppose we shine monochromatic light from a distant source in the direction of a grating, *A*, in Figure 2–1. The spacing of the slits or elements (Figure 2–1) is "*a*." We place a screen at a (large) distance *R* from the grating and parallel to it. At a point *X* (and at other points) we shall obtain an intense line if the waves scattered from the openings 1, 2, 3 differ in their path length by multiples of the wavelength λ. That is, if the path difference to *X* between rays from 1 and 2 is 1 × λ (or 2, 3 or 4 × λ), that between 1 and 3, 2 × λ, and so on, then the light waves will be in phase and "reinforce" or add. Assume that

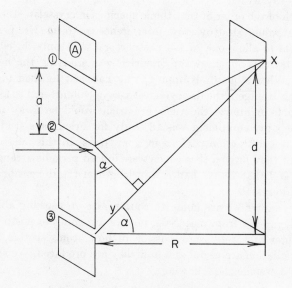

Figure 2–1. Diffraction from a grating.

the rays all arrive at the screen, in phase:

$$a \sin \alpha = y = m\lambda,$$

$$d = R \tan \alpha,$$

and therefore,

$$\lambda = \frac{ad}{mR} \cos \alpha.$$

We see from these equations, that if the diffraction pattern is to be seen, d/R cannot be too small and λ must be of the same magnitude as "a." In addition, "a" cannot be smaller than λ.

In 1912 there was a young German physics professor in Munich, M. von Laue, who was inspired by a discussion with one of Sommerfeld's doctoral candidates, Ewald. Ewald was studying refraction in periodic structures, for, as we have seen, many solids were thought to be made up of atoms or groups of atoms in periodic arrangements. Laue's primary interest was in optics, and he had just finished a chapter for a book on diffraction from gratings. He wondered what would happen if radiation propagating in a periodic structure had a wavelength about that of the spacing of the atoms . . . a diffraction pattern *should* occur. His colleagues discouraged him; even if this were a possible situation—say with x-rays (which were thought at the time to have a wavelength of the order of the atomic spacings in crystals)—the atomic vibrations would destroy any interference pattern. He persuaded Sommerfeld to allow one of his postdoctoral assistants, Friedrich, to help him try this out anyway; Friedrich was studying the nature of x-rays. Another student, Knipping, who had just finished his Ph.D. degree with Röntgen, the discoverer of x-rays, volunteered to assist the other two to minimize the time Friedrich would be away from his work. The x-ray equipment was all ready for Friedrich's studies, and they found a diffraction pattern in a few days! In this one beautiful experiment they proved that solids were indeed periodic arrangements of atoms and that x-rays had a wavelength of the dimensions of the spacings in crystals.

In this chapter we are going to concentrate on learning about this diffraction process from materials, but we are going to postpone to a later chapter any detailed discussion of how atoms scatter or what types of radiation are useful and how they are produced. We shall also continue to assume the following:

1. Waves from the source travel like light or ripples on water.
2. The path difference is a linear function of the spacing of the

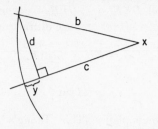

$$d^2 = b^2 - c^2 = (b-c)(b+c) \cong y(2b)$$

$$y = \frac{d^2}{2b}$$

Figure 2–2.   The difference in path (y) if the measurement of the scattering from x is close to the grating, compared to the grating spacing. (After R. P. Feynman, R. B. Leighton and McSands, *The Feynman Lectures on Physics*, vol. I., Addison-Wesley, Reading, Mass., 1964.)

scattering elements, as in Figure 2–1. If the measuring position is very close to the grating compared to the spacing of the scattering elements, then the path difference is proportional to the square of the spacing, as shown in Figure 2–2.

3.   There is conservation of energy in the scattering process. That is, there is no change in energy (and hence wavelength) of the scattered radiation, compared to the incident radiation.

4.   A once-scattered beam inside a material does not rescatter.

We shall examine all of these assumptions soon, but shall put off these complications until we get to the fundamentals.

Consider a series of planes of atoms, with an incident beam of some wavelength of the order of the planar spacing d, as shown in Figure 2–3. The atoms scatter the rays in some fashion. If the path difference

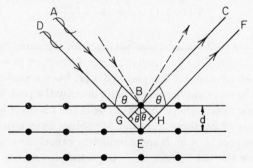

Figure 2–3.   Scattering from planes of atoms.

between rays ABC and DEF—i.e., GEH—is a multiple (n) of λ, the scattered rays will reinforce and produce diffraction.

$$GE = EH = d \sin \theta$$

Therefore

$$n\lambda = 2d \sin \theta \qquad (2\text{–}1)$$

for diffraction from atomic planes. (This "Bragg's law" was derived by Sir W. L. Bragg in 1912 just after he had completed his graduate training.) If $2d$ is greater than λ we can observe different orders in different directions. If the path difference for the rays discussed above is $1 \times \lambda$, the second order for a difference of 2λ would be observed as shown by the dotted rays. If we plot

$$\frac{n}{d} = \frac{2 \sin \theta}{\lambda} \text{ vs. amplitude } A,$$

we should expect the pattern shown in Figure 2–4.

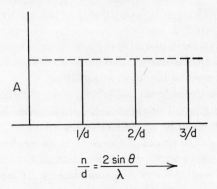

Figure 2–4.   Amplitude vs. $\dfrac{2 \sin \theta}{\lambda}$.

Suppose now that we interpose planes with the same type of atoms at $d/4$, as in Figure 2–5. For the first order diffraction ($n = 1$) from the planes d apart (A and B), the planes $d/4$ (a) have a path difference of one-fourth of a wavelength and partially destroy the peak in amplitude. For the second order, where the waves from the planes A and B have a path difference of 2λ, those from the "a" planes have a path difference of $\lambda/2$ with respect to A or B and completely cancel the scattering from A and B. For the third order there is partial destructive interference again, but at the fourth order all planes add amplitudes. The resultant

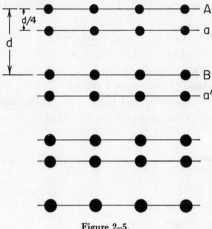

Figure 2–5.

pattern is given in Figure 2–6. Suppose that the atoms on the planes at $d/4$ are different from those on A, B, etc. Then the amplitude will not completely vanish in the second order; there will be a small peak for which the amplitude depends on the difference in the scattering of the different types of atoms.

In Figure 2–7 the structure due to a rotation axis and a screw axis are shown schematically. The twofold screw axis reduces the spacing of planes normal to it to half the value without it, but does not affect planes at an angle to it. A similar thing is true for glide planes. Thus

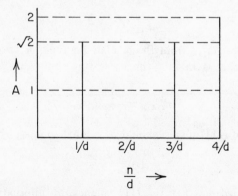

Figure 2–6. Amplitude vs. $\dfrac{2 \sin \theta}{\lambda}$ for the planes in Figure 2–5 (compare to Figure 2–4).

with x-rays we can expect to detect these symmetry elements that were so hard to find with other methods!

Let us now apply this to a real structure in a way analogous to the method used by the Braggs, father and son, in their pioneering studies of crystal structures. Sodium chloride crystals are known to be cubic from optical studies. (They have 4 threefold axes.) We shall measure the intensity of x-rays scattered from (100), (110), and (111) faces, as shown in Figure 2–8, using a counter to "explore" around the crystal.

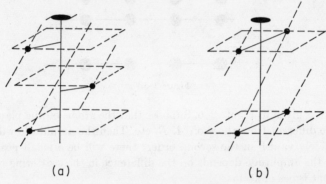

(a)   (b)

Figure 2–7. A screw axis (a) reduces the interplanar spacing only for planes perpendicular to the axis. Compare to (b) which is a rotation axis.

Such a device is known as a *diffractometer*. At the time there were no accurate values for λ, but if the crystal was cubic,

$$\frac{d_{(100)}}{d_{(110)}} = \sqrt{2}.$$

Calculating $d_{(100)}/d_{(110)}$ from Bragg's law for the first two experiments we see that this is in fact the case. But combining the measured $d_{(111)}$ and $d_{(100)}$,

$$d_{(111)} \simeq \frac{2}{\sqrt{3}} d_{(100)}.$$

The spacing of (111) planes should be related to $d_{(100)}$ by

$$d_{(111)} = \frac{d_{(100)}}{\sqrt{3}}.$$

Let us then assume that the (111) planes are alternating planes of sodium and chlorine ions: consider (111) planes x, y, and z. If planes x and z scatter with a path difference of λ, then the y plane will have a path difference of $\lambda/2$ and partially cancel the scattering from x. (The first peak in pattern (c) should be weaker than the others because of the difference in scattering by Na^+ and Cl^-; this is true and in fact

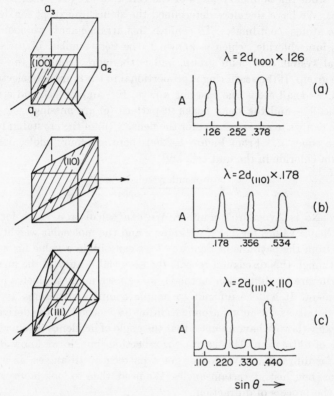

Figure 2–8.   Diffraction from different faces of an NaCl crystal. (After W. H. Bragg, *Proc. Roy. Soc.*, London, A*89*, 246, 1913.)

suggests this arrangement.) We can then write, for the x, y planes,

$$\frac{1}{2}\lambda = 2d_{(111)}\sin\theta,$$

or

$$\lambda = 2(2d_{(111)})\sin\theta$$

This is why twice the spacing was measured! Considering this structure (Figure 1–22(c)) we see that all the {110} and {100} planes are identical in composition. All the peaks from these planes should be equal in amplitude, as they are in the patterns, but in the unit cell there are {100} and {110} planes at half the usual spacing so that the first peaks in patterns (a) and also in (b) must be second order peaks. The first order from the boundary faces of the cell is destroyed by these midplanes. We have therefore determined the structure except for details of the atoms' coordinates. To confirm this arrangement, we could try potassium chloride, which is known to be very similar, of the same crystal system and point group, and is therefore probably the same space group. If the scattering is proportional to the number of electrons, which we shall see is the case for x-rays, K^+ and Cl^- should scatter identically—and the small peaks in pattern (c) are missing!

We can write an expression for the density (ρ) of the crystal in terms of the edge "a." From Figure 1–22(c) there are four "molecules" of sodium chloride in the unit cell, and

$$\rho = \frac{\text{molecular weight} \times 4}{a^3} \frac{}{\text{No}}$$

where No is Avogadro's number. We can calculate a value for "a" (and hence values for d's) if we know ρ and the molecular weight, and then from the patterns in Figure 2–7 we can obtain a value for λ.

Although this discussion reveals the essential beauty of the analysis of structure by diffraction methods, we can see many problems in our treatment. It will be difficult to handle complex structures and get such details as the actual atomic coordinates. Second, in the derivation of Bragg's law we have *assumed* that the angle of incidence (θ) equals the angle of diffraction. This is true for reflection, but do we know if it is true for diffraction? We do not get a pattern at all angles, as with a mirror, but just at certain angles. We need then to look more deeply into the process of diffraction.

The Interference of Scattered Waves

Consider a plane wave traveling at velocity V and imagine that you are observing this wave go by you from a point X' (see Figure 2–9). (By a plane wave, we mean one that has a given amplitude at some instant, say its maximum, in all points in a plane perpendicular to its direction of travel—perpendicular to Figure 2–9.) After a time, t,

$$\mathbf{A} = \mathbf{A}_0 \cos \frac{2\pi}{\lambda} (x - Vt).$$

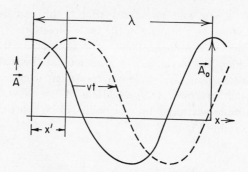

Figure 2–9. A traveling cosine wave.

(The vector notation indicates the direction of "vibration," i.e., the direction of the amplitude in Figure 2–9. This is up and down in this case; the wave is a transverse wave with oscillation perpendicular to its direction of propagation. This is the kind of wave we will mainly be concerned with.)

As $V = v\lambda$, where v is the frequency,

$$\mathbf{A} = \mathbf{A}_0 \cos \left(2\pi v t - \frac{2\pi x}{\lambda} \right).$$

$2\pi x/\lambda$ is often called a phase angle. It is 2π when $x = \lambda$.

We can represent the motion of this wave on a circle with radius $|\mathbf{A}_0|$ sweeping counterclockwise at an angular velocity $2\pi v$, as shown in Figure 2–10. The instantaneous value, $\mathbf{A}$, is merely the resolved components of $\mathbf{A}_0$ on the horizontal diameter. If we wish to add two waves

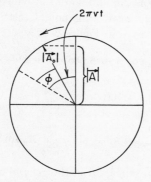

Figure 2–10. Representing a traveling cosine wave with a circle.

of different A_0's, φ's, and v's at any time t, this can be done as in Figure 2–11 for waves vibrating in the same direction.

Now consider a one-dimensional collection of scattering points separated by identical distances; we shall look at the scattering at an angle α at one instant, and follow a treatment suggested by M. J. Buerger, *Crystal Structure Analysis* (John Wiley, New York, 1960). Let the amplitude scattered by one point (n) be represented by the vector A_n. Examine Figure 2–12.

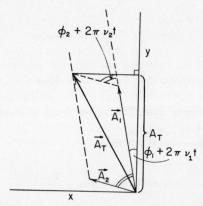

Figure 2–11.   Adding cosine waves of different amplitudes, frequencies and phase angles but the same vibration direction.

The phase angles in the cosine terms from the various points are proportional to the distance of the wave front from our reference plane. If the difference in phase between points 1 and 2 is β, then between 1 and 3 this phase difference is 2β, and so on, provided that the measuring position is far from the scattering points relative to their spacing. Adding the scattered waves in Figure 2–12:

$$A_T = \sum A_n = A_1 \cos \varphi + A_2 \cos (\varphi + \beta) + A_3 \cos (\varphi + 2\beta)$$

$$= \sum_{n=0}^{N-1} A_n \cos (\varphi + n\beta)$$

$$= \cos \varphi \sum_{n=0}^{N-1} A_n \cos n\beta - \sin \varphi \sum_{n=0}^{N-1} A_n \sin n\beta.$$

We leave the A's in the sums, for in the general case all points are not identical. The total phase angle is $\varphi + n\beta$ because, as the incoming wave reaches all the points at the same time, the wave scattered from the nth point is *behind* the point at $(n - 1)$. From now on, consider waves of only one vibrational direction.

Let

$$\sum_n \mathbf{A}_n \cos n\beta = X,$$

$$\sum_n \mathbf{A}_n \sin n\beta = Y.$$

Then we can write

$$\mathbf{A}_T = X \cos \varphi - Y \sin \varphi$$

$$= \sqrt{X^2 + Y^2} \left(\frac{X}{\sqrt{X^2 + Y^2}} \cos \varphi \, \frac{-Y}{\sqrt{X^2 + Y^2}} \sin \varphi \right)$$

$$= \sqrt{X^2 + Y^2} \, (\mathbf{B} \cos \alpha \sin \varphi - \mathbf{B} \sin \alpha \sin \varphi),$$

where $\tan \alpha = Y/X$ and $\mathbf{B}$ is a unit vector in representing the vibrational direction. Thus,

$$\mathbf{A}_T = \sqrt{\left(\sum \mathbf{A}_n \cos n\beta \right)^2 + \left(\sum \mathbf{A}_n \sin n\beta \right)^2} \cos (\varphi + \alpha).$$

$$(2\text{--}2)$$

With ripples on a liquid we could measure the resultant amplitude, but with x-rays and the other forms of radiation we will find useful we can only measure energy—the blackening on a film, e.g.—not the amplitude. In fact we can only measure *average intensity* (average

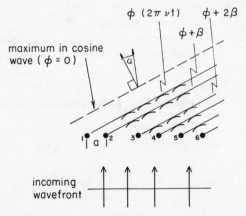

Figure 2–12. Scattering from a row of atoms. (After M. J. Buerger, *Crystal Structure Analysis*, John Wiley, New York, 1960.)

energy per unit time per unit area) because it takes a finite time for us to make a measurement. We know that fields, such as electric fields, cause atomic motion and that therefore the energy of the resultant field will be proportional to its square. We do not have to be concerned about the proportionality constant, because the incident field determines the scattering of each element; hence an expression for intensity will include, on the right-hand side, the intensity of the incident wave. The constant on both sides of the equation will then cancel. That is $\mathbf{A}_n$ depends on the incident field and $\mathbf{A}_T$ on the resultant field, and the intensities of each are related to the square of these fields by the same constant. If we are interested in intensity we need concern ourselves only with the term under the square root in Eq. (2–2) (averaged overtime and the area irradiated if the intensity varies with these). We can obtain the same result for this term if we write the waves in exponential form, which we shall find to be generally easier to handle.

$$\mathbf{A}_T = \sum_n \mathbf{A}_n e^{i(n\beta + \varphi)} = e^{i\varphi} \sum_{n=0}^{N-1} \mathbf{A}_n e^{in\beta} \tag{2–3}$$

$$\mathbf{A}_T = e^{i\varphi}\left(\sum_n \mathbf{A}_n \cos n\beta + i \sum_n \mathbf{A}_n \sin n\beta\right).$$

Multiplying $\mathbf{A}$ by $\mathbf{A}_T^*$, the complex conjugate (i replaced by $-i$), and recalling that $i^2 = -1$,

$$\mathbf{A}_T\mathbf{A}_T^* = |\mathbf{A}|^2 = \left(\sum_n \mathbf{A}_n \cos n\beta\right)^2 + \left(\sum_n \mathbf{A}_n \sin n\beta\right)^2. \tag{2–4}$$

Equation (2–4) is exactly the term we seek. From here on we shall consider waves in this exponential form.

We can carry out the sum indicated in Eq. (2–3) graphically on a complex plane. Assume all the A_n's are identical and equal to f.

Consider in Figure 2–13 the circle of radius r which encloses the partial polygon formed by these vectors. The term $e^{i\varphi}$ can be ignored; it merely represents the position of the first vector relative to the axes, and we can put this in later.

$$\sin \beta/2 = \frac{f/2}{r}; \qquad r = \frac{f/2}{\sin \beta/2},$$

$$\sin \frac{N\beta}{2} = \frac{1/2(P)}{r}; \qquad r = \frac{1/2(P)}{\sin N\beta/2}.$$

$$|\mathbf{P}| = f \frac{\sin N\beta/2}{\sin \beta/2}.$$

Now P has a phase which is equal to that of the middle vector when N is odd or the average of the two middle vectors when N is even. This phase can then be written:

$$e^{i(N-1)\beta/2}.$$

Thus,

$$\mathbf{A}_T = f \frac{\sin (N\beta)/2}{\sin \beta/2} \, e^{i(N-1)\beta/2} = \mathbf{P} \qquad (2\text{--}5)$$

$$\mathbf{A}_T \mathbf{A}_T^* = f^2 \frac{\sin^2 (N\beta)/2}{\sin^2 \beta/2} = |\mathbf{A}_T|^2. \qquad (2\text{--}6)$$

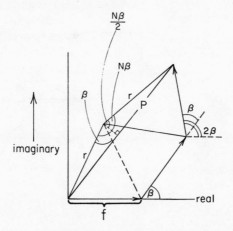

Figure 2–13. Addition of many waves of amplitude f.

Ignoring f, the rest of Eq. (2–5) is often referred to as the interference function. Its maximum value is N. In Figure 2–14, the numerator, denominator, and quotient are plotted for $N = 8$.

From these drawings we can make the following statements about the resulting amplitude and intensity:

1. The maximum value of the amplitude N occurs for $\beta = m2\pi$. The maximum value of the intensity is N^2. The second maximum in *intensity* (the first minimum in amplitude) occurs at about $(N\beta)/2 = 3\pi/2 + Nm(\pi)$, because for large N, the numerator is varying much more rapidly than the denominator and we can locate the maxima from the maxima of the numerator. Putting this value in Eq. (2–6) the intensity of this second maximum is only about 5 per cent of the first peak.

2. Zero values of amplitude and intensity occur whenever $N\beta/2 = Nm\pi + \pi$ or for $\beta = 2m\pi + 2\pi/N$. Thus the width of the peak, in β, is of the order of $2(2\pi/N)$.

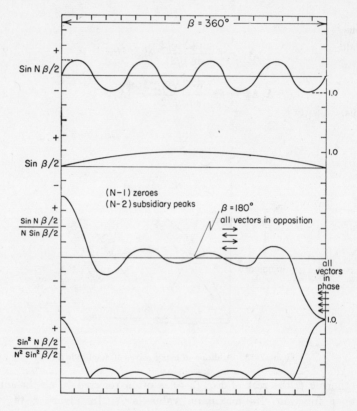

Figure 2–14. Schematic of the interference function. (After M. J. Buerger, *Crystal Structure Analysis*, John Wiley, New York, 1960.)

3. For $\beta = 360$ degrees, when N is even the phase is such that the amplitude is negative; when N is odd the phase is such that the amplitude is positive. However, if we can only measure average intensity, equal to $A_T A_T^*$, we can never tell the difference!

4. Considering our wave addition as a polygon of vectors, as in Figure 2–13, which is close to a circle for large N; (a) the circle's radius gets smaller and then bigger as β increases with a fixed N (β varies with the spacing of the scatterers and the position of observation around

them). The resultant $\mathbf{A}_T$ is from the origin to the end of the circle. (b) For fixed β, as N increases the circle has a fixed radius but closes and opens.

5. As N increases, the large peaks sharpen up. (See (2) above.) This is due to the fact that when N is large we have a great many vectors which in general add up to zero unless they are all parallel. Our resultant pattern then looks like Figure 2–15. These maxima

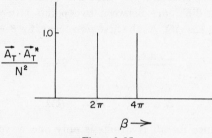

Figure 2–15.

occur around the row of atoms. We can find the directions by searching for the angle where the path difference is an integral multiple of λ. If the incident beam is normal to the row, Figure 2–16(a),

$$\cos \nu = \frac{m\lambda}{a}; \qquad (2\text{--}7a)$$

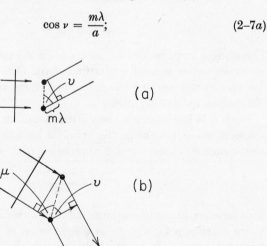

Figure 2–16. Location of diffraction peaks for (a) normal incidence and (b) inclined incidence.

more generally, if the beam is incident at an angle u, Figure 2–16(b),

$$\cos \nu - \cos \mu = \frac{m\lambda}{a}. \qquad (2\text{–}7b)$$

Note that the directions of the maxima depend only on "a" for a given λ. The intensity will depend on f^2, on the "scattering ability" of each point, and on N^2—the number of scattering elements.

6. We can see physically why the zeros occur. Referring to Figure 2–16(a) the path difference between two points is $a \cos \nu$; the phase difference is $(2\pi a \cos \nu)/\lambda$. As the first zero occurs for $\beta = 2\pi/N + 2m\pi$,

$$\frac{2\pi a \cos \nu}{\lambda} = \frac{2\pi}{N} + 2m\pi,$$

or

$$N a \cos \nu = (Nm + 1)\lambda.$$

The path difference for all N atoms is only one wavelength. All the intermediate points destructively interfere. Vectors of the whole range of orientations are present and they cancel.

The first maximum occurs for $\beta = 2\pi m$. Thus,

$$2\pi m = \frac{2\pi a \cos \nu}{\lambda},$$

$$m\lambda = a \cos \nu.$$

Therefore, a large maximum occurs when the path difference between successive points is λ (or a multiple of it). That is, it occurs when all the vectors representing the scattering atoms are parallel—i.e., have 360 degrees for a phase angle.

7. If a is less than λ no repeating maximum can occur, as we can see from the equations in the previous paragraph. As a gets smaller and approaches zero, $\sin^2 \beta/2$ approaches $\beta^2/2$, and

$$P^2 = \frac{2 \sin^2 N\beta/2}{\beta^2}.$$

This function has only one large maximum, for $N\beta/2 = 0$. Thus, there is one maximum for $a \leq \lambda$—in the direction of the incoming beam or back into it—i.e., $\cos \nu$ must be unity in Eq. (2–7a). The beam is "traveling" right through the material or is reflected back in the direction of the incoming beam. This second case is nothing more than reflection!

8. Actually Eq. (2–7) describes cones of radiation whose axis is the row. To see this more clearly, we can write Eq. (2–7a, b) in vector notation. Let S_0 be a unit vector in the direction of the incident beam and S a unit vector in the direction of the diffracted beam. Then,

$$(S - S_0) \cdot a = h\lambda, \tag{2–8}$$

or if n is a unit vector in the direction of a,

$$\frac{S - S_0}{\lambda} \cdot n = \frac{h}{|a|}. \tag{2–9}$$

In Figure 2–17 we have sketched the meaning of the equation. A series of planes with spacing $1/a$ perpendicular to the row of scattering

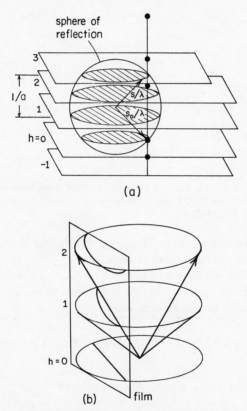

Figure 2–17. (a) After P. P. Ewald, *Fifty Years of X-Ray Diffraction*, N. V. A. Oosthoek's Uitgeversmaatschaapij, Utrecht, The Netherlands, 1962. (b) Diffraction from a row of scattering points.

points is shown as well as the incident and diffracted beams. Equation (2–9) tells us that the component of the difference in the two vectors representing the incoming and diffracted beams on the direction normal to the planes must be an integral multiple of $1/|\mathbf{a}|$. This condition is represented by the intersection of a sphere (the "sphere of reflection"), of radius $1/\lambda$, with the plane h. The diffracted beam can be anywhere around a cone centered on the direction of the row. In Figure 2–17(b) we see the type of pattern we would expect on a film placed next to the row.

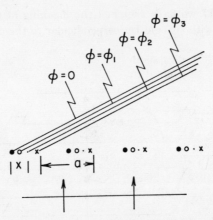

Figure 2–18.   Scattering from a periodic group of (different) scattering elements. (After M. J. Buerger, *Crystal Structure Analysis*, John Wiley, New York, 1960.)

Now let us consider a *set* of points of *different* scattering power, where the set or "molecule" is repeated at equal intervals, as in Figure 2–18. We can consider each type of point as a row spaced equal values of a apart, each row having a different phase φ relative to the origin. Therefore, we can at once write,

$$\mathbf{A}_m = A_1 e^{i\varphi_1} \sum_0^{N-1} e^{in\beta} + A_2 e^{i\varphi_2} \sum_0^{N-1} e^{in\beta} + A_3 e^{i\varphi_3} \sum_0^{N-1} e^{in\beta}$$

$$= (A_1 e^{i\varphi_1} + A_2 e^{i\varphi_2} + A_3 e^{i\varphi_3}) \sum_{n=0}^{N-1} e^{in\beta} \qquad (2\text{–}10)$$

$$= \mathbf{A}_T \sum_{n=0}^{N-1} e^{in\beta}.$$

The terms in parentheses represent the combination of wavelets from points within *one* group. The same sums ($\sum_n^{N-1} e^{in\beta}$) appear as with our simple row of similar scattering elements. Therefore, diffraction peaks will appear in the same place or angle around the row; their position is clearly dependent on only the spacing. The *intensity* at any peak depends on the basic collection of points being repeated at each lattice point.

For the hth order diffraction, identical points are $h2\pi$ out of phase. However, consider the relation between *different* points in Figure 2–16:

$$\frac{\varphi_i}{X} = \frac{h(2\pi)}{a}$$

or

$$\varphi = \frac{hX}{a} 2\pi.$$

Therefore,

$$A_T = A_1 e^{(ihx_1/a)2\pi} + A_2 e^{(ihx_2/a)2\pi} + A_3 e^{(ihx_3/a)2\pi};$$

and if u represents the fractional coordinate X/a along the a axis,

$$A_T = A_1 e^{ihu_1 2\pi} + A_2 e^{ihu_2 2\pi} + A_3 e^{ihu_3 2\pi};$$

or

$$A_T = \sum_n A_n e^{ihu_n 2\pi}. \tag{2-11}$$

The term A_T can be complex. It will in general have a magnitude and phase. We can see this by simply representing the terms in Eq. (2–11) on a vector diagram in the complex plane as we did for the simple row, and this is shown in Figure 2–19. If we can only measure intensity,

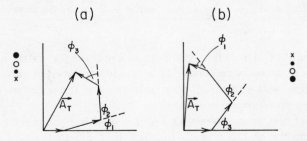

Figure 2–19. $|\mathbf{A}_T|$ is the same for the two arrangements.

we lose the phase and can determine only $|A_T|^2$. As shown in Figure 2–19 we lose information about the atomic arrangement that we could have if the amplitude could be measured.

As the reader will see, we have really learned at this point all of the major features about diffraction from periodic structures. Our study of two or three dimensions will complicate the treatment just as we found many new details by going from one to three dimensions in studying the structures themselves!

Fourier Methods

It is natural to look for mathematical methods that may be of use to us; this is how we found the complex notation helful. As we are dealing with waves there is another branch of mathematics that will prove quite fruitful—Fourier methods. In this section we shall concern our-selves with the principles of this topic, and in the next we shall return to the problem of diffraction to see how this area of mathematics can be helpful.

If a function $f(x)$ is periodic with period (a) and has no more than a finite number of discontinuities and

$$\int_{-a/2}^{+a/2} |f(x)|\ dx$$

is finite—all of which are true for essentially all functions encountered in physical problems—then $f(x)$ can be decomposed into a Fourier series of sine and cosine terms with the argument $2\pi nx/a$ (n being positive). That is,

$$f(x) = A_0 + 2 \sum_{n=1}^{\infty} A_n \cos 2\pi nx/a + 2 \sum_{n=1}^{\infty} B_n \sin 2\pi nx/a.$$
$$(2\text{–}12)$$

If the function is even (i.e., symmetrical about the $f(x)$ axis), then only the cosine series is necessary. If it is odd, or inverted through the origin (i.e., antisymmetric), then only the sine terms are needed. In general both terms are necessary.

One of the most interesting features of this Fourier series is the orthogonality of the waves—the fact that different waves do not interact. We can see this from the following integrals.

$$\int_{-a/2}^{+a/2} \cos 2\pi nx/a \, \cos 2\pi mx/a \, dx = \begin{array}{ll} 0 & \text{if } n \neq m \\ a/2 & \text{if } n = m \end{array} \qquad (2\text{–}13a)$$

$$\int_{-a/2}^{+a/2} \cos 2\pi nx/a \, \sin 2\pi nx/a \, dx = 0 \qquad (2\text{–}13b)$$

$$\int_{-a/2}^{+a/2} \sin 2\pi nx/a \, \sin 2\pi mx/a \, dx = \begin{array}{ll} 0 & \text{if } n \neq m \\ a/2 & \text{if } n = m \end{array} \qquad (2\text{–}13c)$$

Therefore, to obtain the coefficients, if we know the function $f(x)$,

$$\int_{-a/2}^{+a/2} f(x) \cos 2\pi mx/a \, dx = A_m a \qquad (2\text{–}14a)$$

$$\int_{-a/2}^{+a/2} f(x) \sin 2\pi mx/a \, dx = B_m a \qquad (2\text{–}14b)$$

$$\int_{-a/2}^{+a/2} f(x) \, dx = A_0 a \qquad (2\text{–}14c)$$

The last relation tells us that the area of the function is the first coefficient A_0.

We can write our Fourier series in a slightly different way, if we say that $A_{(-n)} = A_n$, $B_{(-n)} = -B_n$. Then,

$$f(x) = \sum_{-\infty}^{+\infty} A_n \cos 2\pi nx/a + \sum_{-\infty}^{+\infty} B_n \sin 2\pi nx/a. \qquad (2\text{–}15)$$

Our two series Eqs. (2–12), (2–15) are equivalent: If the function is even, $f(-x) = f(x)$ and the B's are all zero; when $f(-x) = -f(x)$, the A's are zero. The restrictions we have placed on the coefficients maintain a general series for $f(x)$. For example, if, when $n = -4$, the sine term is negative, then if B_n did not change sign in Eq. (2–15), this sine term would cancel the term for $n = +4$; only the cosine series would remain.

We can write the series in still a more compact way. Suppose we define a complex coefficient:

$$C_n = A_n - iB_n, \qquad (2\text{–}16)$$

and write

$$f(x) = \sum_{-\infty}^{+\infty} C_n e^{(2\pi inx/a)}. \qquad (2\text{–}17)$$

Negative values of n merely correspond to clockwise rotations on the complex plane, whereas positive values are counterclockwise rotations.

Replacing C_n by Eq. (2–16) and recalling that $e^{i\theta} = \cos\theta + i\sin\theta$,

$$f(x) = \sum_{-\infty}^{+\infty} (A_n \cos 2\pi nx/a + B_n \sin 2\pi nx/a)$$

$$+ i\sum_{-\infty}^{+\infty} (A_n \sin 2\pi nx/a - B_n \cos 2\pi nx/a).$$

The second sum must be zero to correspond to Eq. (2–15), which is for a real function. Therefore,

$$A_n = A_{(-n)},$$

and

$$B_{(-n)} = -B_{(n)}, \tag{2–18}$$

or

$$C_{(-n)} = C^*_{(n)}.$$

we can find the coefficients from

$$aC_m = \int_{-a/2}^{+a/2} f(x)e^{(-2\pi imx/a)}\,dx, \tag{2–19}$$

or we can find the sine or cosine coefficients by replacing the exponent by $\sin 2\pi mx/a$ or $\cos 2\pi mx/a$. (The reader should prove this to himself, by substituting Eq. (2–15) or (2–17) for $f(x)$ in (2–19).)

If two functions are multiplied together and averaged over the period a,

$$\frac{1}{a}\int_{-a/2}^{+a/2} f_1(x)f_2(x)\,dx = \frac{1}{a}\int_{-a/2}^{+a/2}\left\{\sum_{n=-\infty}^{+\infty} (C_1)_n e^{(2\pi inx/a)}\right\}f_2(x)\,dx$$

$$= \frac{1}{a}\sum_{n=-\infty}^{+\infty} (C_1)_n \int_{-a/2}^{+a/2} f_2(x)e^{(2\pi inx/a)}\,dx$$

$$= \sum_{n=-\infty}^{+\infty} (C_1)_n(C_2)_{-n}. \tag{2–20}$$

The average value of the product is the sum of the products of the coefficients. Suppose the two functions are identical. Then we are taking the average value of $[f(x)]^2$ over the period (which for our diffracted waves might be the intensity averaged over the unit cell). Recalling that $C_{-n} = C_n^*$,

$$C_nC_{-n} = C_nC_n^* = |C_n|^2$$

and

$$\frac{1}{a}\int_{-a/2}^{+a/2} (f(x))^2\,dx = \sum_{n=-\infty}^{+\infty} |C_n|^2 = \sum_{n=-\infty}^{+\infty} (A_n^2 + B_n^2). \tag{2–21}$$

According to Eq. (2–21), which is known as Parseval's theorem, the sum of the squares of the coefficients will give us the average "intensity" of the function. Look at Eq. (2–15), and consider the average value of the square of one term. This sum of the squares of the coefficients is merely the sum of the average "intensity" in the unit cell of each wave in the series, and this is the total average intensity because the waves do not interact.

We can plot the coefficients A_n and B_n as a function of n/a and such a plot will consist of a series of discrete lines spaced $1/a$ apart. As the period a becomes larger these lines move closer together until in the limit as a goes to infinity a continuous curve develops. This is the limiting case of the Fourier series.

Rewriting the series, Eq. (2–12), using the definitions of the coefficients,

$$f(x) = \frac{1}{a} \int_{-a/2}^{+a/2} f(\lambda)\,d\lambda + 2 \sum_{n=1}^{\infty} \frac{1}{a} \cos \frac{2\pi n x}{a} \int_{-a/2}^{+a/2} f(\lambda) \cos \frac{2\pi n \lambda}{a}\,d\lambda$$

$$+ 2 \sum_{n=1}^{\infty} \frac{1}{a} \sin \frac{2\pi n x}{a} \int_{-a/2}^{+a/2} f(\lambda) \sin \frac{2\pi n \lambda}{a}\,d\lambda$$

$$= \frac{1}{a} \int_{-a/2}^{+a/2} f(\lambda)\,d\lambda + \frac{2}{a} \sum_{n=1}^{\infty} \int_{-a/2}^{+a/2} f(\lambda) \cos 2\pi n \frac{(x-\lambda)}{a}\,d\lambda,$$

where λ is a dummy variable.

Let a go to infinity—i.e., the function is now no longer periodic. The first term goes to zero; if the function still satisfies the conditions for a Fourier series, the integral is finite.

If we further state that when $1/a$ goes to zero and n goes to infinity, n/a goes to zero, then n/a is a continuous variable, which we shall call s. Thus, with these conditions,

$$f(x) = 2 \int_{0}^{\infty} ds \int_{-\infty}^{+\infty} f(\lambda) \cos 2\pi s (x - \lambda)\,d\lambda.$$

This is known as Fourier's integral theorem. Expanding the cosine:

$$f(x) = 2 \int_{0}^{\infty} ds \int_{-\infty}^{\infty} f(\lambda)\{\cos 2\pi s\lambda \cos 2\pi s x + \sin 2\pi s\lambda \sin 2\pi s x\}\,d\lambda$$

$$= 2 \int_{0}^{\infty} \cos 2\pi s x\,ds \int_{-\infty}^{\infty} f(\lambda) \cos 2\pi s\lambda\,d\lambda$$

$$+ 2 \int_{0}^{\infty} \sin 2\pi s x\,ds \int_{-\infty}^{\infty} f(\lambda) \sin 2\pi s\lambda\,d\lambda$$

or

$$f(x) = 2 \int_0^\infty \{a_s \cos 2\pi s x + b_s \sin 2\pi s x\} \, ds$$

$$= 2 \int_0^\infty \sqrt{(a_s)^2 + (b_s)^2} \left\{ \frac{a_s}{\sqrt{(a_s)^2 + (b_s)^2}} \cos 2\pi s x \right.$$

$$\left. + \frac{b_s}{\sqrt{a_s^2 + b_s^2}} \sin 2\pi s x \right\} \, ds.$$

Letting $R_s = \sqrt{a_s^2 + b_s^2}$ and $\tan \varphi_s = (-b_s/a_s)$,

$$f(x) = 2 \int_0^\infty R_s \cos \{2\pi s x + \varphi_s\} \, ds$$

$$= \int_0^\infty R_s [e^{i(2\pi s x + \varphi_s)} + e^{-i(2\pi s x + \varphi_s)}] \, ds.$$

From the definitions,

$$a(-s) = a(s) \qquad \varphi_{-s} = -\varphi_s.$$

$$b(-s) = -b(s)$$

Therefore, we can rewrite the integral for $f(x)$ in two parts:

$$f(x) = \int_0^\infty R_s e^{2\pi i s x} e^{i\varphi_s} \, ds + \int_0^\infty R_s e^{2\pi i s x} e^{i\varphi_s} \, d(-s).$$

Therefore,

$$f(x) = \int_0^\infty R_s e^{2\pi i s x} e^{i\varphi_s} \, ds + \int_{-\infty}^0 R_s e^{2\pi i s x} e^{i\varphi_s} \, ds,$$

$$= \int_{-\infty}^\infty R_s e^{2\pi i s x} e^{i\varphi_s} \, ds.$$

Letting $F(s) = R_s e^{i\varphi_s}$,

$$\boxed{f(x) = \int_{-\infty}^\infty F(s) e^{2\pi i s x} \, ds.} \tag{2-22a}$$

$$F(s) = \sqrt{a_s^2 + b_s^2} \, e^{i\varphi_s} = \sqrt{a_s^2 + b_s^2} \{\cos \varphi_s + i \sin \varphi_s\}$$

$$= \sqrt{a_s^2 + b_s^2} \left\{ \frac{a_s}{\sqrt{a_s^2 + b_s^2}} + \frac{b_s}{\sqrt{a_s^2 + b_s^2}} \right\} \tag{2-22b}$$

$$= a_s - i b_s, \tag{2-22c}$$

or substituting our definitions of a_s, b_s

$$a_s = \int_{-\infty}^{+\infty} f(x) \cos 2\pi sx \, dx$$

and

$$b_s = \int_{-\infty}^{+\infty} f(x) \sin 2\pi sx \, dx$$

in Eq. (2–22b):

$$F(s) = \int_{-\infty}^{+\infty} f(x) \cos 2\pi sx \, dx - i \int_{-\infty}^{+\infty} f(x) \sin 2\pi sx \, dx,$$

$$\boxed{F(s) = \int_{-\infty}^{+\infty} f(x) e^{-2\pi isx} \, dx.} \qquad (2\text{–}23)$$

Here, $F(s)$ is known as the Fourier transform of $f(x)$. If $f(x)$ is real, substituting Eq. (2–22c) in (2–22a) and rewriting the exponents as sines and cosines,

$$f(x) = \int_{-\infty}^{+\infty} a_s \cos 2\pi sx \, ds + \int_{-\infty}^{+\infty} b_s \sin 2\pi sx \, ds.$$

Thus, if $f(x)$ is real and even, b_s is zero because the second integral is of an odd function and vanishes in the integration, and if $f(x)$ is odd and real a_s is zero.

We can think of the Eqs. (2–22) and (2–23) in terms of two spaces—a Fourier transform space s for $F(s)$ and a "real" space x where our function $f(x)$ is plotted. There is a great similarity in the equations for the coefficient of a Fourier series of a function and the transform of the function. From the nature of the Fourier transform, we can see certain basic properties:

$$F(0) = \int_{-\infty}^{+\infty} f(x) \, dx, \qquad \text{or} \qquad f(0) = \int_{-\infty}^{+\infty} F(s) \, ds. \qquad (2\text{–}24)$$

The integral of a function equals its transform at the origin of s-space.

Other important properties to note, which the reader can prove to himself, are

$$\text{Transform of } cf(x) = cF(s). \qquad (2\text{–}25a)$$

$$\text{Transform } \sum_i c_i f_i(x) = \sum_i c_i F_i(s). \qquad (2\text{–}25b)$$

$$\text{Transform of } f(cx) = \frac{1}{|c|} F\left(\frac{s}{c}\right). \qquad (2\text{–}25c)$$

For example, if $c = -1$,

$$\text{Transform of } f(-x) = F^*(s).$$

Shifting the origin of $f(x)$ to x_0, the transform of $f(x - x_0)$ is

$$\int_{-\infty}^{+\infty} f(x - x_0)e^{-2\pi isx}\,dx = \int_{-\infty}^{+\infty} f(x_1)e^{-2\pi is(x_1 + x_0)}\,dx_1$$

$$= e^{-2\pi ix_0 s}\int_{-\infty}^{+\infty} f(x_1)e^{-2\pi isx_1}\,dx_1$$

$$= e^{-2\pi ix_0 s}F(s). \qquad (2\text{--}26)$$

Combining this with Eq. (2–25b), the transform of

$$\sum_{n=-\infty}^{+\infty} f(x - nx_0) = \sum_{n=-\infty}^{+\infty} F(s)e^{-2\pi insx_0}.$$

It is also easy to find Parseval's theorem for transforms.

$$\frac{1}{a}\int_{-\infty}^{+\infty} f_1(x)f_2(x)\,dx = \int_{-\infty}^{+\infty} F_1(s)F_2^*(s)\,ds. \qquad (2\text{--}27)$$

$$\frac{1}{a}\int_{-\infty}^{+\infty} f(x)^2\,dx = \int_{-\infty}^{+\infty} F(s)F^*(s)\,ds = \int_{-\infty}^{+\infty} |F(s)|^2\,ds. \qquad (2\text{--}28)$$

As an example of a transform consider the function:

$$f(x) = 1 \quad \text{for } |x| < 1/2,$$

$$= 0 \quad \text{for } |x| > 1/2.$$

Its transform is then

$$\int_{-\infty}^{+\infty} f(x)e^{-2\pi isx}\,dx = \int_{-1/2}^{+1/2} e^{-2\pi isx}\,dx$$

$$= \frac{e^{\pi is} - e^{-\pi is}}{2\pi is}$$

$$= \frac{\sin \pi s}{\pi s}$$

and

$$F(0) = \int_{-1/2}^{+1/2} f(x)\,dx = 1.$$

The function and its transform are plotted in Figure 2–20. We shall obviously be able to use this function when we return to our diffraction problem, as it is very close to our form for the sum of scattering from periodic elements. The result for this function allows us to handle similar functions. For example, if $F(s)$ is

$$\frac{\sin as}{s},$$

then:

$$f(0) = \int_{-\infty}^{+\infty} \frac{\sin as}{s}\, ds = \pi \int_{-\infty}^{+\infty} \frac{\sin \pi s_1}{\pi s_1}\, ds_1,$$

$$= \pi \int_{-\infty}^{+\infty} \frac{\sin \pi s_1}{\pi s_1}\, ds_1 = \pi.$$

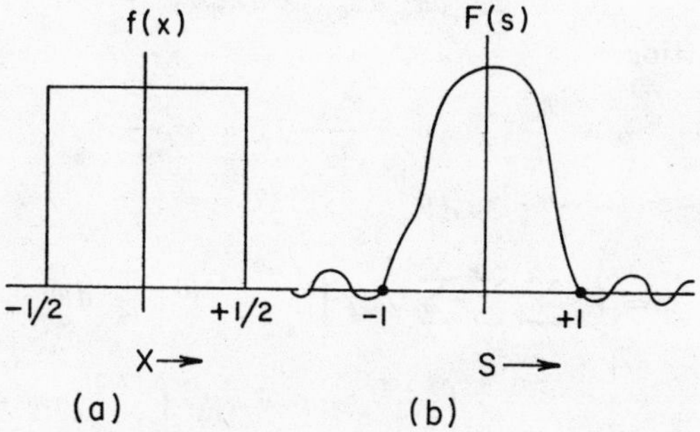

Figure 2–20. A square (*a*) and its transform (*b*).

Take the origin of a line at its center:

$$-t/2 \ \underline{\hspace{2cm} t \hspace{2cm}} \ + t/2.$$

Its transform is $\sin \pi\, ts/\pi s$. Now if t is large the transform is sharp, and if t is small the transform is broad. Thus the transform has a reciprocal nature; this is also true of the Fourier coefficients of a function; they fall off with n more rapidly as the function is broad.

So far we have been dealing with one-dimensional functions; let us now turn to three-dimensional functions. Consider a function of three variables, x_{a_1}, x_{a_2}, x_{a_3}, which are the coordinates along three axes, $\mathbf{a}_1$, $\mathbf{a}_2$, $\mathbf{a}_3$; i.e., our function has values at the tip of a general three-dimensional vector $\mathbf{r}$. $f(x_{a_1}, x_{a_2}, x_{a_3})$ can then be written as $f(\mathbf{r})$. Let

$f(\mathbf{r})$ be a function that is triply periodic, such as a lattice whose edges are defined by $\mathbf{a}_1$, $\mathbf{a}_2$, $\mathbf{a}_3$.

$$f(\mathbf{r}) = \sum_h \sum_{\substack{k \\ -\infty}}^{+\infty} \sum_l C_{hkl} e^{2\pi i \left(\frac{hx_{a_1}}{a_1} + \frac{kx_{a_2}}{a_2} + \frac{lx_{a_3}}{a_3} \right)}. \qquad (2\text{--}29)$$

In order to obtain the coefficients of this series, we can operate in the same way as for the one-dimensional series we considered before. Consider the integral:

$$\int_{V_c} f(\mathbf{r}) e^{-2\pi i \left(\frac{h'x_{a_1}}{a_1} + \frac{k'X_{a_2}}{a_2} + \frac{l'x_{a_3}}{a_3} \right)} dV_{\mathbf{r}} \qquad (2\text{--}30)$$

over the volume V_c of the unit cell. Even if the cell edges are not perpendicular:

$$\frac{dV_{\mathbf{r}}}{dx_{a_1} dx_{a_2} dx_{a_3}} = \frac{V_c}{a_1 a_2 a_3}.$$

Therefore, letting

$$u = \frac{x_{a_1}}{a_1}, \qquad v = \frac{x_{a_2}}{a_2}, \qquad w = \frac{x_{a_3}}{a_3},$$

$$\int_{V_c} f(\mathbf{r}) e^{-2\pi i (h'u + k'v + l'w)} \, dV_{\mathbf{r}}$$
$$= V_c \sum_h \sum_{\substack{k \\ -\infty}}^{+\infty} \sum_l C_{hkl} \int_{-1/2}^{+1/2} e^{2\pi i (h - h')u} \, du$$
$$\times \int_{-1/2}^{+1/2} e^{2\pi i (k - k')v} \, dv \int_{-1/2}^{+1/2} e^{2\pi i (l - l')w} \, dw.$$

And, as each integral has the value of the period for $h = h'$, etc., and zero otherwise,

$$\int_{V_c} f(\mathbf{r}) e^{-2\pi i (h'u + k'v + l'w)} \, dV_{\mathbf{r}} = V_c C_{h'k'l'}. \qquad (2\text{--}31)$$

We can greatly simplify Eq. (2–29) by using the reciprocal vectors, $\mathbf{b}_i$, that were so useful in crystallographic calculations. Consider:

$$\mathbf{r}_{hkl}^* = h\mathbf{b}_1 + k\mathbf{b}_2 + l\mathbf{b}_3,$$

and

$$\mathbf{r} = u\mathbf{a}_1 + v\mathbf{a}_2 + w\mathbf{a}_3.$$
$$\mathbf{r} \cdot \mathbf{r}^* = hu + kv + lw.$$

Therefore,

$$f(\mathbf{r}) = \sum_h \sum_{\substack{k \\ -\infty}}^{+\infty} \sum_l C_{hkl} e^{2\pi i (\mathbf{r} \cdot \mathbf{r}^*)}. \qquad (2\text{--}32)$$

The sum in Eq. (2–32) is a set of plane waves in real space. That is, the planes of constant amplitude are defined by $\mathbf{r} \cdot \mathbf{r}^* = \text{constant}$[1] and maximum amplitude is for $\mathbf{r} \cdot \mathbf{r}^*$ an integer. The waves have their fronts perpendicular to $\mathbf{r}^*$—i.e., normal to (hkl) planes—and each has a wavelength d_{hkl}. Thus $\mathbf{r} \cdot \mathbf{r}^*$ is merely the projection of $\mathbf{r}$ on the unit normal to the wave divided by the wavelength (d_{hkl}), and this times 2π is the phase angle for that particular position $\mathbf{r}$ in real space, for the hkl wave. In carrying out the triple sum many harmonics, nh, nk, nl, must be included because the sum is from minus infinity to plus infinity. Then $\mathbf{r}^*$ should be thought of as representing nh, nk, nl, even if such planes do not really exist. The spacing of such planes is d_{hkl}/n.

The Fourier transforms for a three-dimensional function can be written:

$$f(\mathbf{r}) = \int F(\mathbf{s})e^{2\pi i \mathbf{s} \cdot \mathbf{r}} \, dV_{\mathbf{s}}, \qquad (2\text{–}33a)$$

$$F(\mathbf{s}) = \int f(\mathbf{r})e^{-2\pi i \mathbf{s} \cdot \mathbf{r}} \, dV_{\mathbf{r}}. \qquad (2\text{–}33b)$$

In Figure 2–21 is sketched the plane hkl and a vector perpendicular to it, i.e., in the direction of $\mathbf{r}^*$. Points are indicated for n/d_{hkl}. There is a periodic repetition of the point at n/d_{hkl}—i.e., the phase is $n2\pi$ at each point if we think in terms of a wave along the $\mathbf{r}^*$ direction. Let $\mathbf{s}$ be a continuous vector along $\mathbf{r}^*$. The maximum amplitude (A) of the wave along $\mathbf{s}$ might be some physical quantity as we shall see shortly, such as the electron density $\rho_{\mathbf{r}}$ at $\mathbf{r}$ in the plane, or more generally in a small

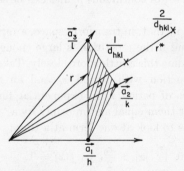

Figure 2–21. (After M. J. Buerger, *Crystal Structure Analysis*, John Wiley, New York, 1960.)

[1] This is the equation of a plane, for if we define $\mathbf{n}$ as a unit normal to a plane of spacing d_{hkl}, $\mathbf{n} \cdot \mathbf{r} = d_{hkl}$. $\mathbf{r}^*$ is just a unit normal vector times a constant $(1/d_{hkl})$.

volume centered on a point in the plane. Thus, if some point $\mathbf{r}$ scatters a plane wave with an amplitude depending on electron density,

$$A(\mathbf{s}) = \rho_{\mathbf{r}}\,dV_{\mathbf{r}}e^{-2\pi i\mathbf{r}\cdot\mathbf{s}},$$

and the total amplitude is

$$A_T(\mathbf{s}) = \int \rho_{\mathbf{r}}e^{-2\pi i\mathbf{r}\cdot\mathbf{s}}\,dv_{\mathbf{r}},$$

which is just the Fourier transform of the electron density and our amplitude is a function of this reciprocal or transform space.

Define a delta function $\delta(\mathbf{r})$ (known as the Dirac delta function) for which $\delta(\mathbf{r}) = 0$ for $\mathbf{r} \neq 0$, $\delta(\mathbf{r}) = \infty$ for $\mathbf{r} = 0$ and $\int \delta(\mathbf{r})\,dv_{\mathbf{r}} = 1$. We can then represent a lattice row by $\sum \delta(\mathbf{r} - m\mathbf{a})$.

Transforming this,

$$F(\mathbf{s}) = \int_{-\infty}^{+\infty} \sum_m \delta(\mathbf{r} - m\mathbf{a})e^{-2\pi i\mathbf{s}\cdot\mathbf{r}}\,d\mathbf{r}.$$

Making the substitution $\mathbf{r}_1 = \mathbf{r} - m\mathbf{a}$ and remembering that $\delta(\mathbf{r}_1)$ has a value only for $\mathbf{r}_1 = 0$,

$$F(s) = \sum_{m=0}^{N-1} e^{-2\pi i\mathbf{s}\cdot m\mathbf{a}} = \frac{\sin \pi\mathbf{s}\cdot N\mathbf{a}}{\sin \pi\mathbf{s}\cdot\mathbf{a}}\, e^{-2\pi i\mathbf{s}\cdot(N-1)\mathbf{a}/2}.$$

We have found that this kind of function is zero (for large N) except for $\mathbf{s}\cdot\mathbf{a} = h$; i.e., for $|\mathbf{s}| = \dfrac{h}{|\mathbf{a}|\cos(s, a)}$. The transform of a row of points is then a set of planes perpendicular to $\mathbf{a}$, spaced $1/a$ apart.[2] Conversely, the reciprocal of a set of continuous planes can be shown to be a lattice row.

This also shows us that, in transform space, a repeating δ function is a sum of waves and if the repetition is large enough this sum is quite sharp. Let us examine this a little more closely. Take a one-dimensional periodic delta function with period x_0 and an infinite set of one-dimensional waves of period x_0 in exponential form. They must be equal, so let us set them equal and multiply by a "potential" function that will permit us to look at one term at a time:

$$f(x) = 0, \quad |x| > \frac{x_0}{2}, \quad f(x) = 1, \quad |x| < \frac{x_0}{2}.$$

[2] The wave $\exp[-2\pi i\mathbf{s}\cdot m\mathbf{a}]$ can be written $\exp\left[\dfrac{-2\pi i\mathbf{s}\cdot m\mathbf{n}}{1/|\mathbf{a}|}\right]$ where $\mathbf{n}$ is a vector in the direction of $\mathbf{a}$. This is clearly a *plane* wave with fronts normal to $\mathbf{a}$ and with a wavelength $1/a$. The addition of many waves like this leads to sharp planes in $\mathbf{s}$ space.

Now let us transform both functions times $f(x)$ and set them equal:

$$\int_{-\infty}^{+\infty} \sum_{-\infty}^{\infty} \delta(x - nx_0)f(x)e^{(-2\pi imx/x_0)} \, dx$$
$$= \int_{-\infty}^{+\infty} \sum_{-\infty}^{+\infty} C_n f(x)e^{-2\pi i(m-n)x/x_0} \, dx.$$

Multiplication by $f(x)$ "destroys" all δ functions but the one nearest the origin, and s has values for m/x_0 only, because the functions are periodic. Therefore,

$$\int_{-\infty}^{+\infty} \delta(x)e^{(-2\pi imx/x_0)} \, dx = \sum_n C_n \int_{-\infty}^{+\infty} f(x)e^{-2\pi i(m-n)x/x_0} \, dx.$$

We can remove the exponential term in the integral on the left, because the δ function is so sharp, and give it a value at the center of $\delta(x)$— i.e., at $x = 0$. The remaining integral is the area of the δ function, equal to unity. Therefore,

$$1 = \sum_n C_n \int_{-\infty}^{+\infty} f(x)e^{-2\pi i(m-n)x/x_0)} \, dx$$
$$= \sum_n C_n x_0 \frac{\sin \pi(m - n)}{\pi(m - n)}.$$

Now $\dfrac{\sin \pi(m - n)}{\pi(m - n)}$ equals zero for integral values of m and n except for $m = n$ when it is unity.

Thus $C_m = 1/x_0$, and

$$\sum \delta(x - nx_0) = 1/x_0 \sum e^{(2\pi inx/x_0)},$$

or similarly

$$\sum \delta\left(s - \frac{n}{x_0}\right) = x_0 \sum e^{-2\pi inx_0 s}.$$

(For a three-dimensional function x_0 is replaced by the volume of the unit cell.) This shows us that an infinite sum of waves in one space can be represented by a δ function, which in turn is also in transform space, a δ function. The periodicity in one space is the inverse of the periodicity in the other.

A plane lattice can be represented by $\sum \delta[\mathbf{r} - (m\mathbf{a}_1 + n\mathbf{a}_2)]$.

$$F(s) = \int \sum_m \sum_n \delta[\mathbf{r} - (m\mathbf{a}_1 + n\mathbf{a}_2)]e^{-2\pi i s \cdot \mathbf{r}} dA_{\mathbf{r}}.$$

Therefore,

$$F(s) = \sum_n e^{-2\pi i s \cdot ma_1} \sum_n e^{-2\pi i s \cdot na_2}.$$

This function is the intersection of the two sets of planes represented by the two sums—a series of lines perpendicular to the original plane lattice. For a three-dimensional delta function we can expect the transform to consist of points which are produced by intersections of three sets of waves—i.e., a lattice in s space. In Figure 2–22, the three sets of planes of constant amplitude are sketched perpendicular to a_1, a_2, a_3 and spaced $1/a_1$, $1/a_2$, $1/a_3$ apart. The planes perpendicular to a_1 and a_2 intersect in the vertical lines shown. It is clear that the spacing along the vertical axis $|b_3^*| = (1/|a_3| \cos \gamma)$. This is what we

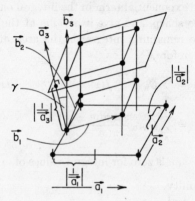

Figure 2–22.   A reciprocal lattice. (After P. P. Ewald in *Fifty Years of X-Ray Diffraction*, N. V. A. Oosthoek's Uitgeversmaatschaapij, Utrecht, The Netherlands, 1962.)

would calculate from the definition of the reciprocal axis b_3. The transform of a three-dimensional lattice is its reciprocal lattice!

The delta function is also useful in sectioning—i.e., $\delta(x - x_3)f(x_1 x_2 x_3)$ is a section through $f(x_i)$ at x_3.

Multiple transforms are interesting. If

$$F(s) = \int f(r)e^{-2\pi i s \cdot r} \, dV_r = T,$$

then if we operate on $F(s)$ by T^{-1},

$$\int F(s)e^{+2\pi i s \cdot r} \, dV_s = f(r) = T^{-1}T.$$

But if we transform twice in the same sense; i.e., without changing the sign,

$$\int F(\mathbf{s})e^{-2\pi i \mathbf{s}\cdot\mathbf{r}}\,dV_{\mathbf{s}} = \int F(\mathbf{s})e^{+2\pi i(-\mathbf{r})\cdot(\mathbf{s})}\,dV_{\mathbf{s}} = TT = f(-\mathbf{r}),$$

which is the function inverted through the origin.

There is one other function that we shall find useful—the convolution. It is defined as

$$f(\mathbf{x}) \times g(\mathbf{x}) = \int_{-\infty}^{+\infty} f(\mathbf{u})g(\mathbf{x} - \mathbf{u})\,dV_{\mathbf{u}}. \qquad (2\text{–}33)$$

We can see what this function physically means by considering two functions, as in Figure 2–23. If $f(\mathbf{x})$ is very sharp compared with $g(\mathbf{x})$,

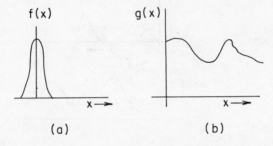

Figure 2–23.   (After A. Guinier, *X-Ray Diffraction*, W. H. Freeman and Co., San Francisco, 1963.)

we can factor $g(\mathbf{x})$ out in our convolution and write:

$$f(\mathbf{x}) \times g(\mathbf{x}) = g(\mathbf{x}) \int f(\mathbf{u})\,dV_{\mathbf{u}}.$$

That is, we are multiplying each point of $g(\mathbf{x})$ by the area of $f(\mathbf{x})$.

More generally we can consider $f(\mathbf{u})$ as divided into small volumes and if we reproduce $g(\mathbf{x})$ at $(\mathbf{x} - \mathbf{u})$, multiplying by $f(\mathbf{u})$ at that point and summing for all values of $(\mathbf{u})$, we have the convolution. This is illustrated in Figure 2–24.

A physically important phenomenon will in fact illustrate this meaning. Suppose a slit in a measuring system can be described by a function $f(y)$, and the true function is to be measured by $g(z)$ (Figure 2-25). The slit takes any element $g(z)\,dz$, as it "sees" it, and spreads it out into a function of the form of $f(y)$. Some point on this spread out function is a contribution $dh(x)$ to the measured function. Therefore we can write,

$$\frac{dh(x)}{g(z)\,dz} = \frac{f(y)}{\text{area of } f(y) = A_y},$$

$$dh(x) = \frac{1}{A_y}\ g(z)f(y)\ dz.$$

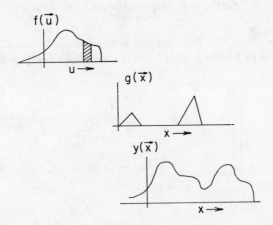

Figure 2-24.   Graphical illustration of the convolution

$$y(x) = \int f(u)g(x-u)dV_u$$

(After H. Lipson and C. A. Taylor, *Fourier Transforms and X-Ray Diffraction*, G. Bell and Sons, London, 1958.)

Letting $y = x - z$,

$$h(x) = \frac{1}{A_y} \int g(z)f(x - z)\ dz.$$

Our resulting function $h(x)$ is proportional to a convolution of the slit function and the true function. This is actually a very good way to visualize convolutions for setting up an analytical treatment. For example, suppose we wish to convolute two triangles. The situation as one triangle ($f(x_2)$) passes over another ($f(x_1)$) is illustrated in Figure 2-26(a). In the range to $-x_1$ the convolution is simply the integral of

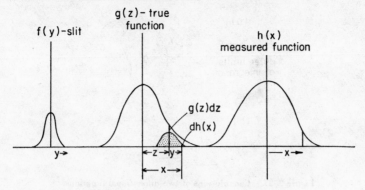

Figure 2–25. How a slit affects a function.

the product of the two functions. As soon as the "moving" triangle has its center displaced from $(-x_1) + (-x_2)$ to $-x_1$ the situation is as in Figure 2–26(b); three integrals are involved.

Consider the two-dimensional convolution of two small areas

$$\int f(u_1, u_2) g(x_1 - u_1, x_2 - u_2)\, du_1 du_2.$$

This again, as shown in Figure 2–27(a), is an integration over the area of overlap of the two functions, indicated by the dotted lines. If the two functions to be convoluted are two dimensional, the convolution can result in a three-dimensional function, if and only if the two are not functions of the same two dimensions, as illustrated in Figure 2–27(b).

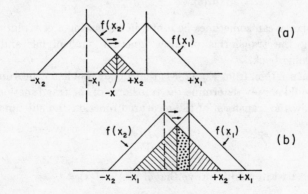

Figure 2–26. Convoluting two triangles.

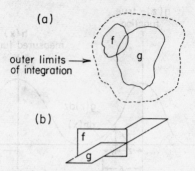

Figure 2-27. Convolutions of two-dimensional functions.

The transform of the convolution $y(\mathbf{x})$ is

$$Y(\mathbf{s}) = \int y(\mathbf{x}) e^{-2\pi i \mathbf{s} \cdot \mathbf{x}} \, dV_{\mathbf{x}}$$

$$\int = \int f(\mathbf{u}) g(\mathbf{x} - \mathbf{u}) e^{-2\pi i \mathbf{s} \cdot \mathbf{x}} \, dV_{\mathbf{x}} \, dV_{\mathbf{u}}.$$

Let $\mathbf{x} - \mathbf{u} = \mathbf{w}$

$$Y(\mathbf{s}) = \int \int f(\mathbf{u}) g(\mathbf{w}) e^{-2\pi i [\mathbf{s} \cdot (\mathbf{w} + \mathbf{u})]} \, dV_{\mathbf{u}} \, dV_{\mathbf{w}}$$

$$= \int f(\mathbf{u}) e^{-2\pi i \mathbf{s} \cdot \mathbf{u}} \, dV_{\mathbf{u}} \int g(\mathbf{w} e^{-2\pi i \mathbf{s} \cdot \mathbf{w}}) \, dV_{\mathbf{w}}$$

$$= F(\mathbf{s}) G(\mathbf{s}). \tag{2-34}$$

This property can sometimes be useful in evaluating a convolution, by obtaining the transforms of each function, multiplying and then transforming back.

We can see then from Eq. (2–34) that in our problem concerning the slit we could simply determine the transform of the true function $G(s)$, if we know the transform of the measured function and slit function.

$$G(s) = \frac{H(s)}{F(s)}.$$

The reader can readily prove that if $y(\mathbf{x}) = f(\mathbf{x}) g(\mathbf{x})$,

$$Y(\mathbf{s}) = F(\mathbf{s}) * G(\mathbf{s}). \tag{2-35}$$

It also follows from Eqs. (2–34) and (2–35) that

$$|G(s)|^2 = G(s)G^*(s) = \int g(x)xg(-x)e^{-2\pi i s \cdot x}\, dV_x, \qquad (2\text{–}36a)$$

$$|g(x)|^2 = g(x)g^*(x) = \int G(s)xG(-s)e^{+2\pi i s \cdot x}\, dV_{(s)}. \qquad (2\text{–}36b)$$

That is, in Eq. (2–36a), the square of the modulus of $G(s)$ is the transform of the convolution of the function $g(x)$ and the same function inverted through the origin. We have seen that the diffracted amplitude times its complex conjugate is the intensity we can measure in diffraction. $|G(s)|^2$ is then the form of what we can measure in a diffraction experiment; we can see that $|G(s)|^2$ refers to the structure with a center of symmetry even if there is not one!

Finally, we get some interesting results, if we combine delta functions and the convolution—e.g., the convolution of $f(x)$ and $\sum_n \delta(x - x_n)$:

$$y(x) = \int g(u) \sum_n \delta(x - u)\, du.$$

Let $x - u = x_n$; then,

$$u = x - x_n,$$

and

$$du = dx_n.$$

$$y(x) = \sum g(x - x_n) \int \delta(x_n)\, dx_n.$$

The function $g(x)$ is repeated at the points x_n by convoluting it with $\sum \delta(x - x_n)$.

The Practical Matter of Handling Experimental Curves in Terms of Fourier Methods

Before we return to our study of diffraction we will consider the problem of dealing with measured functions which cannot readily be represented analytically. How can we determine the coefficients of Fourier series, transforms, convolutions, etc. Let us set for ourselves the problem of actually determining the true function, in our problem concerning measuring with a slit. Our true function could be a diffraction peak from a small number of periodic scattering elements, and we

could determine the slit function from an experiment with a large
number of such elements, where the diffraction peak is very much
sharper than our slit function.

The cosine and sine function are plotted in Figure 2–28. It is not

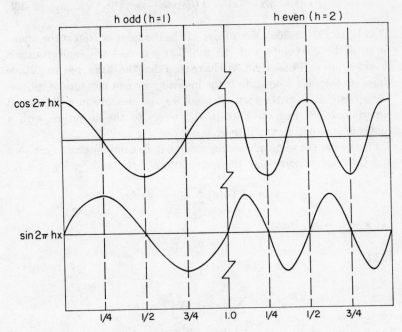

Figure 2–28.   (After M. J. Buerger, *Crystal Structure Analysis*, John Wiley, New
York, 1960.)

necessary to evaluate the sine or cosine function beyond $x = 1/4$,
because of the symmetry of the functions; we can see that for

$$x = 1/2 \text{ to } 1/4, \qquad x = 0 \text{ to } 1/4$$

$$h \text{ even} \begin{cases} \cos 2\pi h(1/2 - x) = \cos 2\pi hx \\ \sin 2\pi h(1/2 - x) = -\sin 2\pi hx \end{cases}$$

$$h \text{ odd} \begin{cases} \cos 2\pi h(1/2 - x) = -\cos 2\pi hx \\ \sin 2\pi h(1/2 - x) = \sin 2\pi hx. \end{cases}$$

If we wish to carry out sums of cosine and sine terms, we can do this separately for terms with h even and for terms with h odd.

Let

$$CE = \cos 2\pi hx, \quad h \text{ even } x = 0 \text{ to } 1/4$$

$$CO = \cos 2\pi hx, \quad h \text{ odd } x = 0 \text{ to } 1/4$$

$$SE = \sin 2\pi hx, \quad h \text{ even } x = 0 \text{ to } 1/4$$

$$SO = \sin 2\pi hx, \quad h \text{ odd } x = 0 \text{ to } 1/4.$$

Then, for $x = 0$ to $1/4$,

$$\sum C = \sum (CE + CO),$$
$$\sum S = \sum (SE + SO); \qquad (2\text{-}37a)$$

for $x = 1/2$ to $1/4$,

$$\sum C = \sum (CE - CO),$$
$$\sum S = \sum (SO - SE); \qquad (2\text{-}37b)$$

for $x = 1/2$ to $3/4$,

$$\sum C = \sum (CE - CO),$$
$$\sum S = \sum (SE - SO); \qquad (2\text{-}37c)$$

for $x = 1$ to $3/4$,

$$\sum C = \sum (CE + CO),$$
$$\sum S = \sum (-SE - SO). \qquad (2\text{-}37d)$$

If we refer to a Fourier series in the form of Eq. (2–12) we can see that summing the terms to evaluate $f(x)$ at a given x still involves considerable labor. Time-saving devices have been developed, and we shall use one of these to evaluate our problem—the Beevers-Lipson strips.[3] We consider this method because it is quick and easy to use for short problems and because it is quite analogous to the type of program that can be developed for a computer when the problem is long enough or if the problem has to be repeated often. Values of A_n are assumed, from 0 to 100, in units of 1 and from 100 to 900 in units of 100. The argument $2\pi hx/a$ is written $2\pi nt/120$ where n and t are integers corresponding to h and x, respectively—i.e., in terms of 3 degree steps. As we do not

[3] C. A. Beevers (1952), *Acta Cryst.*, 5, 670.

need calculation of an argument above 90 degrees, the calculations have been carried out for these 108 values of A (and for $-A$ values) for 30 sine terms ($n = 1 - 30$) and 31 cosine terms ($n = 0 - 30$), or $61 \times 216 = 13{,}176$ calculations! Each value of A_n and n is placed on one strip of paper, values for t from 0 to 30 are then calculated (408,456 calculations in all!) and each strip is arranged as in Figure 2–29. This is

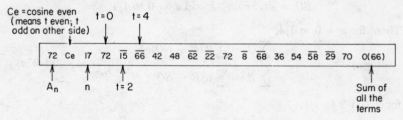

Figure 2–29.   A Lipson-Beevers strip for the term $72 \cos (2\pi 17 t.120)$.

certainly a useful tabulation to have! These strips are arranged in compartments, all strips of the same n but different A_n's in the same compartment. To evaluate a function if we know its coefficients we just take the even and odd coefficients (even and odd values of n), pull the corresponding strips, sum them separately, and obtain values for $f(t)$; $t = 0, 1, 2, 3, \ldots, 30$ correspond to $(x) = 0$ to $1/4$, so that:

$$\text{cosine part of } f(t) = \sum (CE + CO),$$

$t = 60, 59, 58, \ldots$, corresponds to $x = 1/2$ to $1/4$

$$\sum (CE - CO), \ldots, \quad \text{etc.}$$

To determine the transform or the coefficients of a function we know is much the same problem. For example, if we replace the integral to determine the cosine coefficients by a sum,

$$A_n = \frac{1}{a} \int_{-a/2}^{+a/2} f(x) \cos 2\pi nx/a \, dx = \frac{1}{a} \sum f(x) \cos 2\pi nx/a \, \Delta x.$$

Let $x/a = t/120$ (the function is divided into 120 parts), i.e., $a = 120$. Thus,

$$A_n = \frac{a}{120} \frac{1}{a} \sum_{-30}^{+30} f(t) \cos 2\pi \frac{nt}{120}. \qquad (2\text{--}38)$$

We then arrive at a form suitable for use with the strips. The function, as shown in Figure 2–30, is read for t values from -30 to $+30$. The rest of the interval from -60 to -30 and from $+30$ to $+60$ is zero. As the

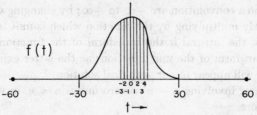

f(t)

-60   -30 $\begin{smallmatrix}-2\,0\,2\,4\\-3\,-1\ 1\ 3\end{smallmatrix}$ 30   60

t →

Figure 2–30.   Layout of $f(t)$ for determining its coefficients with Lipson-Beevers strips.

cosine does not change sign for plus and minus values of t, $\cos 2\pi nt/120$ will have the same value for both values of t so that we can add $f(t)$ and $f(-t)$.[4] The sum is the amplitude of a strip, and we have 31 terms corresponding to the 31 values for t. We interchange t and n so that all the different values $f(t)$ are in the same compartment, and each strip has values of n, 0–30 on one side, 1–29 on the other, and we sum as in Figure 2–31.

Finally to obtain a true function from our measured function and a slit function, both of which exist over the range a, we merely write the functions as Fourier series. The functions are not periodic, but the series represents them in the region a. The series repeat the functions periodically, but that is of no concern to us if they are correctly given in the range a; we shall just ignore the repeating parts.

$$h(x) = \int f(x_1)g(x - x_1)\,dx_1 = \int \sum F_n e^{(+2\pi i n x_1/a)}$$
$$\times \sum G_{n'} e^{[+2\pi i n'(x - x_1)/a]}\,dx_1$$
$$= \int_{-a/2}^{+a/2} \sum_n F_n \sum_{n'} G_{n'} e^{+2\pi i(n-n')(x_1/a)} e^{(+2\pi i n' x/a)}\,dx_1.$$

t
↓

f(o) CE 0	
f(+t₁) + f(−t₁)CE 1	
f(+t₂) + f(−t₂)CE 2	

sum = An, n =   0 2 4 — — — — — — — — — — —30

Figure 2–31.   Setting up strips for determining the Fourier coefficients of $f(t)$.

[4] For sine terms we subtract these two.

The limits on a convolution are $-\infty$ to $+\infty$; by changing the limits we are effectively multiplying by the function which is unit from $-a/2$ to $+a/2$. Thus, the integral is the transform of the function convoluted with the transform of the unit function; as the latter exhibits oscillations, these will appear in our graphical solution.

The integral involving $n - n'$ is zero unless $n = n'$ in which case it is a. Therefore,

$$h(x) = a \sum F_n G_n e^{(+2\pi inx/a)} = \sum H_n e^{(+2\pi inx/a)}.$$

Therefore, to obtain the coefficients of the true function $g(x)$,

$$G_n = \frac{H_n}{aF_n}. \tag{2–38a}$$

To separate this into sine and cosine coefficients, so that we can use the strips, we can write

$$G_r(n) + iG_i(n) = \frac{H_r(n) + iH(n)}{F_r(n) + iF_i(n)} \cdot \left(\frac{1}{a}\right).$$

$$G_r(n) + iG_i(n) = \frac{H_r(n) + iH_i(n)}{F_r(n) + iF_i(n)} \cdot \left(\frac{1}{a}\right).$$

And multiplying top and bottom of the right-hand side by $F_r(n) - iF_i(n)$,

$$G_r(n) = \frac{H_r(n)F_r(n) + H_i(n)F_i(n)}{F_r^2(n) + F_i^2(n)} \cdot \left(\frac{1}{a}\right). \tag{2–38b}$$

$$G_i(n) = \frac{H_i(n)F_r(n) - H_r(n)F_i(n)}{F_r^2(n) + F_i^2(n)} \cdot \left(\frac{1}{a}\right). \tag{2–38c}$$

If the measured functions are symmetrical, the sine terms of the series vanish and we have

$$G_r(n) = \frac{H_r(n)}{aF_r(n)}. \tag{2–38d}$$

In other words, if the slit and measured functions are symmetrical so is the true function.

With these coefficients then, we can synthesize the true peak. For the cosine terms in the general series [Eq. (2–15)] representing our function, this is done as in Figure 2–32.

If you wish to have the true function in absolute terms, instead of just its shape, *it is vital to keep track of all the constants in front of the sums in evaluating the coefficients of each function!* An easy way to do this is to choose a function for which the Fourier coefficients can be readily evaluated analytically and with the same period as the unknown. Carrying this function through with the strips and comparing to the analytical solution yields the true normalization factor. In using the strips, for highest accuracy, if a function has a value at the first division from the maximum of say 3.0, multiply all values by 100 and thus strips for values of the function as low as 0.01 will be included. That is, expand the scale to make use of all the strips, but keep track of the expansion!

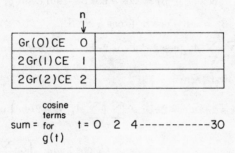

Figure 2–32. Resynthesizing a function after correcting for the slit.

It often happens that it is not convenient to use the same period for the slit function and measured function, because the latter is so much broader; if we did use the same period, with the sharper function we would waste many of our 60 intervals as zero. Suppose then that we choose 1/4 the interval for the sharper function—i.e., $a' = a/4$. As we wish to compare coefficients for equal values of the argument in the sine and cosine terms,

$$\frac{2\pi n x}{a} = \frac{2\pi n' x'}{a'} = \frac{2\pi n' x'}{a/4} = \frac{2\pi 4 n' x'}{a}.$$

We must compare the fourth coefficient of the sharper function with the first of the broader one, the eighth with the second, etc., in other words, $na = n'a'$. We can therefore choose whatever interval we please for each function, plot the coefficients versus na for each function and compare at equal values of na.

In order to demonstrate the method of handling two- or three-dimensional functions, we shall consider here the evaluation of a two-dimensional function whose coefficients are known:

$$f(\mathbf{r}) = \sum_{-\infty}^{+\infty}{}_h \sum_{k}^{\infty} C_{hk} e^{+2\pi i(hu + kv)},$$

$$C_{hk} = A_{hk} - iB_{hk}.$$

Expanding, and recalling that $C_{hk} = C_{hk}^*$ for a general sum,

$$f(\mathbf{r}) = \sum_{h}^{+\infty} \sum_{k}^{\infty} [A_{hk} \cos 2\pi(hu + kv) + B_{hk} \sin 2\pi(hu + kv)].$$

As

$$\cos(\alpha + \beta) = \cos \alpha \cos \beta - \sin \alpha \sin \beta,$$

and $\sin(\alpha + \beta) = \sin \alpha \cos \beta + \cos \alpha \sin \beta$:

$$f(\mathbf{r}) = \sum_{h} \sum_{k} A_{hk}[\cos 2\pi hu \cos 2\pi kv - \sin 2\pi hu \sin 2\pi kv \ldots].$$

Consider the first term:

$$\sum_{h} \sum_{k} A_{hk} \cos 2\pi hu \cos 2\pi kv = \sum_{h} \left(\sum_{h} A_{hk} \cos 2\pi kv \right) \cos 2\pi hu$$

$$= \sum_{h} C_h \cos 2\pi hu \quad \left(\text{or} \sum_{k} D_k \cos 2\pi kv \right).$$

Thus, we can carry out a sum in one dimension for all values of k with h held constant and then repeat this for each value of h. To reduce the effort, if k varies from 0 to 30 and h, 0 to 15, the sum over k should be evaluated first. First, lay out the coefficients in a table as in Figure 2–33. For each column, carry out the sum and evaluate the function versus v as for a one-dimensional function. Therefore, results can be

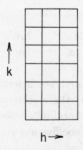

Figure 2–33. Two-dimensional Fourier coefficients, A_{hk}.

represented in a table of values of the function versus h and v, as shown in Figure 2–34.

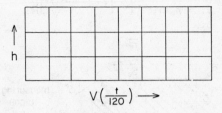

Figure 2–34. $\sum_k A_{hk} \cos 2\pi kv$ for various h's.

Now sum over vertical columns—i.e., for constant v—for various u values and our result is a series of values of $f(\mathbf{r})$ for u and v, Figure 2–35. The process is repeated in a like manner for other terms in the original two-dimensional function.

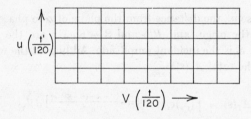

Figure 2–35. Tabulated values of $\sum_h \sum_k A_{hk} \cos 2\pi kv \cos 2\pi hu$.

Reformulation of the Diffraction Problem

We are now ready to make use of the tools we have just learned to analyze diffraction from a three-dimensional body. Consider a chunk of matter. A beam of radiation of wavelength λ, defined in direction by the unit vector $\mathbf{S}o$ is incident at 0, Figure 2–36. This beam is scattered by all the elements in the chunk, and we wish to find the resultant amplitude at some plane of observation P, at a distance R from the crystal and in the direction defined by $\mathbf{S}$. The incoming rays are assumed to be all in phase when they reach the vertical line through 0.

The instantaneous value of the wave, A_s, at P from the material with density ρ_r of scattering "effectiveness" at the end of $\mathbf{r}$, is

$$A_{\mathbf{s}} = \rho_{\mathbf{r}}\, d\nu_{\mathbf{r}} e^{2\pi i\left\{vt - \left[\frac{Y + R + (\mathbf{S} - \mathbf{S}o)\cdot\mathbf{r}}{\lambda}\right]\right\}}\boldsymbol{\epsilon}_I,$$

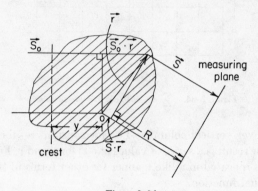

Figure 2–36.

where Y represents the distance from the plane of zero phase when the beam reaches the origin and R/λ and $\mathbf{S} - \mathbf{S}o/\lambda\cdot\mathbf{r}$ are the additional phase changes, $\boldsymbol{\epsilon}_I$ is the incident amplitude. Adding all the waves from the material, the total $A_T(\mathbf{s})$:

$$A_T(\mathbf{s}) = \int (\rho_{\mathbf{r}})\boldsymbol{\epsilon}_I e^{+2\pi i\left[vt - \frac{(Y + R + (\mathbf{S} - \mathbf{S}o)\cdot\mathbf{r})}{\lambda}\right]}\, dV_{\mathbf{r}}.$$

Letting $\dfrac{\mathbf{S} - \mathbf{S}o}{\lambda} = \mathbf{s}$,

$$A_T(\mathbf{s}) = e^{2\pi i\frac{[vt - (Y + R)/\lambda]}{\lambda}}\boldsymbol{\epsilon}_I \int \rho_{\mathbf{r}} e^{-2\pi i\mathbf{s}\cdot\mathbf{r}}\, dV_{\mathbf{r}}. \qquad (2\text{–}39)$$

(We can factor R from the expression if the object is quite small compared to R.) The total amplitude is proportional to the Fourier transform of the density of the "scattering effectiveness." In our measurement of the intensity, $A(\mathbf{s})A^*(\mathbf{s})$, the exponential term before the integral drops out. Also, considering $\boldsymbol{\epsilon}_I$ as some wave (of form λe^{ix}) only the magnitude of the incident field will appear. We now have to specify the appropriate function for $\rho_{\mathbf{r}}$. We can consider this term as the product of the scattering per unit scattering element times the density of scattering elements. Suppose the scattering is due to the electrons around an atom. Then the first part of the product, the scattering per electron, can be included as a constant k. We shall discuss this constant in a later chapter. The second part is the electron density $\rho'(\mathbf{r})$. Consider a group of n atoms. Let $\mathbf{r}_n$ be the vector to the nth atom. Then, $\mathbf{r}$ is the vector to some point around the atom from the origin of the coordinates, as in Figure 2–37.

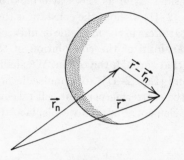

Figure 2–37.

For the most part in this book we shall be interested in crystalline materials. Thus,

$$\rho'(\mathbf{r}) = \sum_n \rho(\mathbf{r} - \mathbf{r}_n);$$

$\rho'(\mathbf{r})$ is a convolution of the scattering density around one atom and a delta function representing the lattice, and $\mathbf{r}_n$ is a triply periodic vector; i.e., $\sum_n$ is a sum in three dimensions, a triple sum.

$$A_T(\mathbf{s}) = k \sum_n \int \rho'(\mathbf{r} - \mathbf{r}_n)e^{-2\pi i \mathbf{s} \cdot \mathbf{r}} \, dV_{\mathbf{r}}.$$

Multiplying by $e^{-(2\pi i \mathbf{s} \cdot \mathbf{r}_n - 2\pi i \mathbf{s} \cdot \mathbf{r}_n)}$,

$$A_T(\mathbf{s}) = k \sum \left(\int \rho'(\mathbf{r} - \mathbf{r}_n)e^{-2\pi i \mathbf{s} \cdot (\mathbf{r} - \mathbf{r}_n)} \right) dV_r e^{-2\pi i \mathbf{s} \cdot \mathbf{r}_n}. \qquad (2\text{–}40)$$

The term in parentheses is the scattering per atom relative to the unit scattering, and we shall write it as f_n. If the scattering is due to the electrons, for example, then the scattering of an atom relative to the scattering of an electron is *the atomic scattering factor*, f_n. Equation (2–40) can thus be simplified to

$$A_T(\mathbf{s}) = k \sum_n f_n e^{-2\pi i \mathbf{s} \cdot \mathbf{r}_n}. \qquad (2\text{–}41)$$

The scattering factor per atom could have an imaginary term which we have so far ignored (see Eq. 2–40); we shall look at this later. If f_n is real, then in measuring $A(s)A^*(s) = |A(s)|^2$ we can only determine the modulus $|A(s)|$, and as we have seen this means that the structure will express itself in our measurement as if it was centrosymmetric, even if it is not.

Suppose we consider $\mathbf{A}_T(s)$ as the scattering from one molecule or unit cell. Then Eq. (2–41) without the constant is the Fourier transform of the density of scatterers in the molecule *or* unit cell and the intensity, $|A_T(s)|^2$, is the transform of the convolution of the density and the same density inverted through the origin. We shall call the amplitude per unit of structure [Eq. (2–41)] (one molecule or cell) the structure factor $F(s)$. It is the scattering per unit cell relative to the scattering by one scattering element. Suppose we displace the molecule or unit cell by $\mathbf{a}$:[6]

$$F_a(s) = \sum_n^{N-1} f_n e^{-2\pi(\mathbf{r}_n + \mathbf{a}) \cdot \mathbf{s}}$$

$$= e^{-2\pi i \mathbf{a} \cdot \mathbf{s}} \sum_n f n e^{-2\pi i \mathbf{s} \cdot \mathbf{r}_n}$$

$$= e^{-2\pi i \mathbf{a} \cdot \mathbf{s}} F_T(s).$$

There is an exponential term due to the displacement of the molecule (depending on the value of a). However, when we measure the *intensity* this term disappears; although there will be regions of high and low intensity we cannot get the *absolute* position of a group of atoms from such a measurement. If we now consider two molecules or units separated by $\mathbf{a}$:

$$A_T(s) = F(s) + F_a(s)$$

$$= F(s)(1 + e^{-2\pi i \mathbf{s} \cdot \mathbf{a}})$$

$$= \begin{cases} 2F(s) & \text{for } \mathbf{s} \cdot \mathbf{a} = 0, 1, 2, \ldots \\ 0 & \text{for } \mathbf{s} \cdot \mathbf{a} = 1/2, 3/2, \ldots, \end{cases}$$

---

[6] We drop the constant k, for simplicity. We are then writing the amplitude in terms of the scattering per unit scatterer, e.g., scattering per electron; in this case our amplitude is in "electron units."

and the total intensity I_T:

$$= \begin{cases} 4|F(\mathbf{s})|^2 & \text{for } \mathbf{s}\cdot\mathbf{a} = 0, 1, 2 \\ 0 & \text{for } \mathbf{s}\cdot\mathbf{a} = 1/2, 3/2, \ldots. \end{cases}$$

The maximum intensity is four times that for one molecule, at some places in $\mathbf{s}$ space; the intensity disappears for $\mathbf{s}\cdot\mathbf{a} = 1/2, 3/2$, etc. If we have a row of this atom group, periodically spaced, $\mathbf{a}$ apart:

$$A_T(\mathbf{s}) = F(\mathbf{s}) \sum_{m=0}^{N-1} e^{-2\pi i \mathbf{s}\cdot m\mathbf{a}}.$$

We have already seen that such a sum, for large N, is a periodic delta function with spacing $1/|\mathbf{a}|$. It can also be evaluated by summing the waves with a complex diagram, and the result we know is:

$$A_T(\mathbf{s}) = F(\mathbf{s}) \frac{\sin \pi \mathbf{s}\cdot N\mathbf{a}}{\sin \pi \mathbf{s}\cdot \mathbf{a}} e^{-\pi i \mathbf{s}\cdot(N-1)\mathbf{a}}.$$

As we saw before, for large N, this function is essentially zero when $\mathbf{s}\cdot N\mathbf{a}$ is an integer, but has a value N for $\mathbf{s}\cdot\mathbf{a}$ an integer—i.e., the condition for large diffracted amplitude is $\mathbf{s}\cdot\mathbf{a} = h$. The trigonometric term, as we have seen, represents a periodic set of planes of maximum amplitude normal to $\mathbf{a}$ and with period $1/|\mathbf{a}|$. The diffraction condition represents cone 3 of diffracted intensity whose axes are in the direction of $\mathbf{a}$.

For a three-dimensional crystal, consisting of rows of groups of atoms in three directions, we can write immediately that

$$A_T(\mathbf{s}) = F(\mathbf{s}) \frac{\sin \pi \mathbf{s}\cdot N_1\mathbf{a}_1}{\sin \pi \mathbf{s}\cdot \mathbf{a}_1} \frac{\sin \pi \mathbf{s}\cdot N_2\mathbf{a}_2}{\sin \pi \mathbf{s}\cdot \mathbf{a}_2} \frac{\sin \pi \mathbf{s}\cdot N_3\mathbf{a}_3}{\sin \pi \mathbf{s}\cdot \mathbf{a}_3}$$
$$\times e^{-\pi i \mathbf{s}\cdot[(N_1-1)\mathbf{a}_1 + (N_2-1)\mathbf{a}_2 + (N_3-1)\mathbf{a}_3]}, \quad (2\text{–}42a)$$

$$A_T(\mathbf{s})A_T^*(\mathbf{s}) = I_T = |F(\mathbf{s})|^2 \frac{\sin^2 \pi \mathbf{s}\cdot N_1\mathbf{a}_1}{\sin^2 \pi \mathbf{s}\cdot \mathbf{a}_1} \frac{\sin^2 \pi \mathbf{s}\cdot N_2\mathbf{a}_2}{\sin \pi \mathbf{s}\cdot \mathbf{a}_2} \frac{\sin^2 \pi \mathbf{s}\cdot N_3\mathbf{a}_3}{\sin^2 \pi \mathbf{s}\cdot \mathbf{a}_3}.$$
$$(2\text{–}42b)$$

For diffraction from a three-dimensional crystal, we have three conditions that must be satisfied simultaneously:

$$\begin{cases} \mathbf{s}\cdot\mathbf{a}_1 = h \\ \mathbf{s}\cdot\mathbf{a}_2 = k \\ \mathbf{s}\cdot\mathbf{a}_3 = l. \end{cases} \quad (2\text{–}43)$$

These are the three conditions that Laue recognized must hold while thinking over the interaction of short wavelength rays in a three-dimensional solid. In two dimensions, we have only two such conditions and two interference terms ($\sin^2 nx/\sin^2 x$) in the expression for $A_T(s)A_T^*(s)$. Each interference term represents in s space a periodic set of planes perpendicular to a_i and with period $1/|a_i|$. Values for the product of two such terms occur along lines perpendicular to the plane a_1, a_2. Geometrically then, diffraction occurs for a two-dimensional lattice when the sphere of reflection of radius $1/\lambda$ intersects these lines, as in Figure 2–38. In other words, there are two sets of the cones

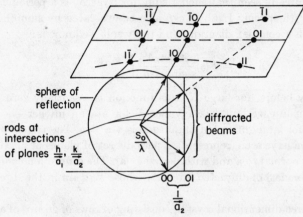

Figure 2–38.   Diffraction from a two-dimensional structure. (After E. A. Wood, *J. Appl. Phys.*, **35**, 1306, 1964.)

found for one dimension, one cone around each row and at their intersections we have a strong diffracted intensity; on a film there will be strong spots, as shown in Figure 2–38. These intersections are indexed h, k according to the particular intersection of cones from the planes $h/|a_1|$, $k/|a_2|$.

In three dimensions, we have three sets of planes, spaced $h/|a_1|$, $k/|a_2|$, and $l/|a_3|$ perpendicular to a_1, a_2, a_3 and hence points of intersection where the interference terms have a value other than zero. The sphere of reflection must touch a point for diffraction, as in Figure 2–39(b). $S - S_0/\lambda$ must equal r_{hkl}^*. There are then three sets of diffraction cones, and only at their common intersections is there strong diffraction, Figure 2–39(a).

These intersections do not occur frequently, in fact generally not at

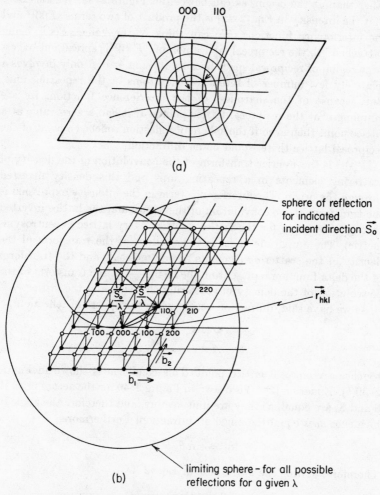

Figure 2–39. Diffraction from a three-dimensional structure. (Note that a diffraction spot is given without parentheses; this convention will be used throughout the text.)

all. We have to tilt the incident beam or the crystal or change λ to cause an intersection (if $|\mathbf{a}_1|$, $|\mathbf{a}_2|$, $|\mathbf{a}_3|$ are not equal the cones will contract and expand at different rates with λ).

In the one and two dimensional case there are always intersections, if $2/\lambda > 1/|\mathbf{a}|$. Otherwise the sphere cannot touch the rows of planes other than at the origin, as can be seen in Figure 2–38. We also note that the intensity in Eq. (2–42) is the product of two terms $|F(s)|^2$ and the interference functions. We can think of the value $|F(s)|^2$ being "attached" to the reciprocal lattice points. $|F(s)|^2$ is spread out over a large region of reciprocal space because its sum at best only involves a relatively few number of terms for the atoms in the repeating unit. But because of the sharpness of the interference function, we are sampling it at the reciprocal lattice points. If it had a zero value at a lattice point then even if the sphere of reflection touched a point of the reciprocal lattice there would be no diffraction.

$|F(s)|^2$ is the Fourier transform of the convolution of the density of scattering elements in a repeating unit and this density inverted through the origin. The interference term in the intensity expression is the transform of the convolution of the lattice and the lattice inverted through the origin (or the lattice itself as every lattice is centrosymmetric). The amplitude $A_T(s)$ is the product of the transform of the density of the scattering elements in one molecule and the transform of the delta function representing the lattice—i.e., the transform of the convolution of the density of scattering elements and the lattice.

As we have said, diffraction occurs when the sphere of reflection

$$\frac{S - S_0}{\lambda} = r^*_{hkl} \tag{2–44}$$

touches a reciprocal lattice point. This condition is shown in Figure 2–39(b). Equation (2–44) is drawn in Figure 2–40 for the actual crystal. S and S_0 are equal, as they are unit vectors, and therefore the angle of incidence *does* equal the angle of diffraction! Furthermore,

$$|S| = \sin \theta = |So|.$$

Therefore, writing the magnitude of Eq. (2–44):

$$\frac{2 \sin \theta}{\lambda} = \frac{1}{d_{hkl}},$$

or

$$\lambda = 2d_{hkl} \sin \theta.$$

Bragg's law is, in fact, quite correct! The reason this equation is not in the form $n\lambda = 2d \sin \theta$ can be seen by rewriting this for m

$$\lambda = \frac{2d}{n} \sin \theta = \frac{2 \sin \theta}{n/d_{hkl}} = \frac{2 \sin \theta}{r^*_{nhnknl}}.$$

That is, the second order from say a (111) plane is represented in reciprocal or Fourier space by the point at the end of the vector r^*_{hkl} with hkl (222). It is in this way that all the harmonics are included in a Fourier representation of a lattice, as we have already seen. Higher order "reflections" are commonly indexed in reciprocal space by the notation $nhnknl$ rather than writing "nth" order of hkl.

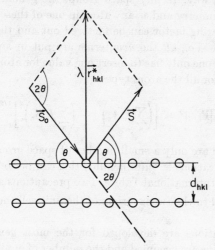

Figure 2–40.

Finally some comments on the calculation of the structure factor are appropriate.

$$F(\mathbf{s})_{\text{unit cell}} = \sum f_n e^{-2\pi i \mathbf{s} \cdot \mathbf{r}_n}.$$

Now if diffraction can only occur for $\mathbf{s} = \mathbf{r}^*$ and we write $\mathbf{r}_n$ as $u_n\mathbf{a}_1 + v_n\mathbf{a}_2 + w_n\mathbf{a}_3$,

$$\mathbf{F}_{hkl} = \sum_n f_n e^{-2\pi i(hu_n + kv_n + lw_n)}. \qquad (2\text{–}45a)$$

If the f's are real the structure will *appear* centrosymmetric; expanding Eq. (2–45a) in sines and cosines:

$$|\mathbf{F}_{hkl}| = \left[\left(\sum_n f_n \cos 2\pi hu_n + kv_n + lw_n\right)^2 \right.$$
$$\left. + \left(\sum_n f_n \sin 2\pi(hu_n + kv_n + lw_n)\right)^2\right]^{1/2}. \qquad (2\text{–}45b)$$

$|F_{hkl}| = |F_{hkl}|$, even if the structure is not really centrosymmetric. That is, as we can only measure $|F_{hkl}|$, all the terms that are imaginary are lost and this is the same thing that would happen if for every atom u, v, w there was another like it at exactly $\bar{u}$, $\bar{v}$, $\bar{w}$.

Sometimes it is relatively easy to write this out for a simple structure, but if there are many atoms it is a tedious job. This can be simplified in the following way. In any space group, the general equipoint will have certain symmetry and as any atom in one of these will be in all of them, the scattering factor can be factored out and the trigonometric terms simplified—i.e., all the uvw terms are put in and the equation simplified. Then one only has to insert one value for atom uvw, multiply by f_n, and sum for all the atom types:

$$|\mathbf{F}_{hkl}|^2 = \left[\left(\sum_n f_n A_n\right)^2 + \left(\sum_n f_n B_n\right)^2\right]^{1/2}. \qquad (2\text{–}45c)$$

Because there are only a small number of space groups a tabulation of these simplifications is quite helpful; this can be found at the back of Vol. 1 of the International Tables. Two precautions are necessary.

1. Be careful to choose the origin of the unit cell the same as in the tables.

2. The equations are developed for the most general equipoint. If *special* positions are occupied and the number of equivalent positions is reduced, the symmetry factors must be multiplied by

$$\frac{\text{rank of equipoint}}{\text{rank of general equipoint}}.$$

Summary

We have seen that the diffracted *intensity* depends on the structure of the *unit* doing the scattering and that the *positions* of diffraction peaks are determined by the *arrangement* of these units. The scattered amplitude and intensity can be expressed simply in terms of Fourier transform space and for a periodic structure, this results in a reciprocal lattice. Attached to each point in this lattice is a term involving the scattering per repeating unit—the structure factor. Diffraction occurs when a sphere of reflection of radius $1/\lambda$ intersects the reciprocal lattice provided the structure factor has a non-zero value at that point. The orientation of the direct beam relative to the crystal (or vice versa) and the wavelength determines what intersections, if any, will in fact occur. The structure factor extends over a large region of reciprocal space, but we are sampling it at the reciprocal lattice.

Several problems need further attention. First, we have seen that we seem to lose certain information in measuring the intensity. Specifically, we do not know if the structure is centrosymmetric. Second, we have assumed that there is conservation of momentum in scattering and third that radiation scattered by one row or plane does not rescatter from other rows or planes as it leaves the crystal.

In the next chapter we shall examine the production or radiation suitable for diffraction from materials. Then we shall examine more closely the required geometry for diffraction and the methods to obtain this geometry. After this we shall consider the evaluation of the interaction of various radiations on matter and the scattering per unit scattering element and some other factors which affect the actual intensity. Finally we shall consider the determination of structure and some effects of imperfections. In each of these we shall develop appropriate techniques. The last assumption is left until the very end merely because it has been demonstrated experimentally that it is satisfactory for x-rays and neutrons, except in certain special cases and suffices, qualitatively at least, for electron diffraction. Because of imperfections in most crystals, subgrains with slight tilts between them (often called mosaic structure), multiple scattering does not usually occur—or it can be deliberately avoided by introducing these imperfections. The small size of these regions (0.1μ) is why R can be factored from the integral in Eq. (2.39).

We shall find the Fourier methods more and more helpful as we proceed.

SUGGESTED REFERENCES

1. R. P. Stuart, *Fourier Analysis* (Methuen and Co., Ltd., London, 1961).
2. P. P. Ewald, *Fifty Years of X-Ray Diffraction* (N.V. A. Oosthoek's Uitgevers-maatschappij, Utrecht, The Netherlands, 1962).
3. *Tables of Integral Transforms*, Vol. 1, Bateman Manuscript Project (McGraw Hill Book Co., New York, 1954).
4. A. Guinier, *X-Ray Diffraction* (W. H. Freeman and Co., San Francisco, 1963).
5. R. W. James, *The Optical Principles of the Diffraction of X-Rays* (G. Bell and Sons, London, 1950).

PROBLEMS

1. Explain the numerical values of the amplitudes in Figure 2–6.

2. Calculate the height of the second and third maxima relative to the main maxima for $\dfrac{\sin^2 N\,\beta/2}{\sin^2 \beta/2}$ for $N = 4,\ 8,\ 16$.

3.* For a row of scattering elements, with the incident beam normal to the row:

    (a) What is the angular difference between a peak and its first zero? How will this vary with N? With order?

    (b) If the diffracted beam is fixed, what is the angular difference between a peak and its first maximum and how does this vary with N, order? Repeat (a) and (b) with planes instead of rows.

4. By considering the interference function, evaluate the sums:

$$\sum n \cos nx, \qquad \sum n \sin nx.$$

5.* Put the following sums for R in as simple form as possible. Evaluate and sketch the result.

    (a) $e^{2\pi i x_1} + e^{2\pi i x_2} = H e^{2\pi i y} = R.$

    (b) $f_1 e^{2\pi i x_1} + f_2 e^{2\pi i x_2} = H e^{2\pi i y} = R.$

    (c) $f_1 e^{2\pi i x_1} + f_2 e^{2\pi i x_2} + f_3 e^{2\pi i x_3} = H e^{2\pi i y} = R.$

6. Find the first four sine and cosine coefficients of the Fourier series representing the function $f(x)$.

$$f(x) = 1, \quad |x| < a/2$$
$$= -1, \quad a > |x| > a/2.$$

Plot the sum of these terms.

7. Consider the function shown below; its amplitude is unity and the base line is zero.

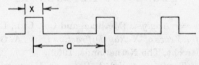

Problem 2–7.

Evaluate the coefficients of a Fourier series representing this.

* These problems will be used in later discussions and should be solved now.

8. Consider the function

$$f(x) = 1, \quad x > 0$$
$$= 0, \quad x < 0.$$

Determine its transform.

9. Take the Fourier transform of a one-dimensional Gaussian function. Discuss the result.

10. Consider the functions $f(x)$, a triangle with a 6-in. base, 1.5 in. altitude, and $g(x) = 3$ for $|x| < 1.5$ in. $g(x) = 0$ for $|x| > 1.5$ in.
    (a) Convolute these two functions analytically and plot the results.
    (b) Convolute these two functions using Lipson-Beevers strips if they are available.

11.* By considering its effect on one atom, show how $F(s)$, $|F(s)|^2$ are changed by 4, 4_1, 4_2 axes along the a_3 direction. For example, for what hkl value is $|F(s)| = 0$? Sketch the results in three-dimensional reciprocal space.

12.* Show the effect of a $c/2$ glide on (100) and a (100) mirror on $F(s)$, $|F(s)|^2$. For what hkl values is $|F(s)|^2 = 0$? Sketch the results in three-dimensional reciprocal space.

13. Derive an expression for $F(s)$ for a base centered unit cell. Sketch reciprocal space and compare to a primitive cell.

14.* Assuming one atom per lattice point and all atoms in the unit cell identical, evaluate $F(s)$, $|F(s)|^2$ for the following lattices.
    (a) Simple cubic.
    (b) Body-centered cubic.
    (c) Face-centered cubic.
    Sketch the results in three-dimensional reciprocal space and indicate the unit cells in this reciprocal space. For what values of hkl does $|F_{hkl}|^2$ vanish?

15.* Compare your results in any of the previous three examples with Tables 4–18 (p. 53) and 4.19 (p. 54) of Vol. I of the International Tables. Then examine space group $C\,2/m\,2/m\,2/m$. Note the conditions for reflection on the right-hand side of the page.
    (a) Find out from the text what the parentheses on certain of the conditions mean.
    (b) Indicate what symmetry elements give rise to each condition —including the special conditions.

* These problems will be used in later discussions and should be solved now.

16. Evaluate $F(s)$, $|F(s)|^2$ for a hexagonal close-packed unit cell with one atom per lattice point and all atoms identical. For what values of hkl does $|F_{hkl}|^2$ vanish? Sketch the results in three-dimensional reciprocal space.

17. Evaluate $F(s)$, $|F(s)|^2$ for NaCl.

18. In the structure of diamond there are carbon atoms at 000, 1/4, 1/4, 1/4, and other positions given by face-centered translations added to these. Evaluate $F(s)$, $|F(s)|^2$. For what values of hkl is $|F_{hkl}|^2 = 0$?

19. In the diamond structure outlined in the previous example, suppose the 000 atom is S and the 1/4, 1/4, 1/4 atom is Zn. (This is known as zinc blende.) Evaluate $F(s)$, $|F(s)|^2$. For what values of hkl does $|F_{hkl}|^2$ vanish?

20. Evaluate in as simple a form as possible the structure factor for the rank 4 equipoint in the two-dimensional space group pmg. (See *coordinates* in the International Tables, Vol. I. Remember that there is a table of structure factors at the end of this volume so that you can check you answer.)

21. Evaluate in as simple a form as possible the structure factor for space group $Pmm2$. Check your answer with the International Tables.

22. By using the International Tables write an expression for the intensity of the 222 peak from normal spinel, AB_2O_4, in terms of $f_A \cdot f_b, f_0$.

23. Uranium is orthorhombic, with four atoms per unit cell in positions:

u	v	w
0	y	1/4
0	$-y$	3/4
1/2	$1/2 + y$	1/4
1/2	$1/2 - y$	3/4

(a) What is the unit cell?

(b) For what reflections will $F(s)$ vanish regardless of y?

24. (a) Suppose that in a unit cell of a crystal there are six identical atoms in an octahedral array with a fourfold axis along a_3. Choosing the origin at the center of the octahedron, derive an expression for $|F(s)|^2$. Sketch the result for an hko reflection.

(b) Suppose the octahedron moves around the a_3 axis relative to the corners of the unit cell: show how the sampling of the structure factor will change on a $(h_1 h_2 o)$ plane in reciprocal space.

25.* An f.c.c. crystal often twins by shear on a {111}. Consider twins on one of the planes in this form and index "extra" spots in reciprocal space as a result of this twinning, in terms of the axes of the matrix (i.e., sketch the reciprocal space of the twin-matrix composite). How then might you detect twinning?

26. At one stage in precipitation in some alloys we can imagine the solute distributed sinusoidally with wave number q. Consider a one-dimensional lattice of points P apart and average density of scattering material ρ:

(a) Calculate the appearance of the diffraction pattern and sketch your result.

(b) How will the result be affected by the value of q? Sketch the result.

(c) Suppose the wave is finite—i.e., of length A. How will this length affect the result? That is, if the wave is not the length of the crystal but smaller, what effect will be produced?

(d) If there is only half a wavelength, of the wave, how will the pattern be affected?

(e) If any extra diffraction affects are too close to the main peak to be detected, using Parseval's theorem how much will the intensity of the fundamental peaks be affected?

(f) If the wave is not a pure cosine wave, but say a square wave, how will the pattern be affected?

(g) If there are three waves in each of the three $\langle 100 \rangle$ in a cubic crystal, what will the pattern look like? (Besides being important in materials, this problem has many important analogies. Frequency and time form Fourier sets like real and reciprocal space. If s is frequency and r is time, this problem is one on amplitude modulation.)

27.* The electron density in a crystal is periodic.

(a) Write a Fourier series for the electron density.

(b) Set up an equation for the coefficients. What is this equation in terms of what you know about diffraction?

(c) How could you obtain plots of the electron density? Will there be any problems?

* These problems will be used in later discussions and should be solved now.

28.* If the sphere of reflection has a radius $1/\lambda$, then, in three dimensions, only the points within the limiting sphere of radius $2/\lambda$ can ever diffract. Discuss how this limitation will affect electron density plots.

29.* Convolute the expression for electron density in Problem 27 with the density inverted through the origin.

(a) Will there be any problem in obtaining the information for this function?

(b) Where will peaks occur in such a pattern? (*Hint:* Look at the original convolution integral, not the result.)

(c) Is this function centrosymmetric?

(d) Suppose there are two identical atoms in a unit cell on either side of a mirror plane. How would their Patterson function appear? What form of the Patterson function will be most useful to get the distance of the atoms relative to the mirror plane? Assume the plane is perpendicular to the a_3 axis of the unit cell.

(e) Using the Patterson function how could you then get the x, y, coordinates of these atoms?

---

* These problems will be used in later discussions and should be solved now.

3 *The Production of Radiation Useful for Studying the Structures of Materials*

The radiation we need must be the same order of magnitude as the spacing of units in a periodic arrangement, and as we know (from diffraction studies) that these spacings are of the order of 1 Å (10^{-8} cm), we wish to examine sources of radiation of this wavelength.

X-Rays

Röntgen discovered, in the summer of 1895, that in an evacuated tube in which a voltage was applied across two metal plates unknown or "x"-rays emerged, penetrated matter, and exposed film. Experiments to examine the nature of these rays (whether they were particles or electromagnetic radiation), however, were difficult. Ruled grating experiments gave poor diffraction patterns that were hard to resolve and therefore not definitive; they did suggest, however, that the rays were waves of quite small wavelength. Very closely spaced gratings were hard to make at the time, but it was these experiments that suggested to Laue that x-rays might diffract from crystals. As we shall see in Chapter 5, x-rays could be polarized like other electromagnetic waves. (Their amplitude of variation could be made to lie in only one direction perpendicular to its propagation direction.) But they could also eject electrons when they impinged on a material as in a particle collision. Experiments to reflect x-rays also proved fruitless at first. (We shall see why, also in Chapter 5.) However, after some time, it became clear from polarization, the failure of the rays to be

deflected by electric or magnetic fields—that the rays were electromagnetic radiation. The emission of electrons when x-rays impinged
on them (the photoelectric effect) was explained by Einstein as being
due to the fact that radiation was quantized into energy packets. Later
experiments (such as Laue's) proved that the wavelength of x-rays was
indeed of the same magnitude of the periodicity in crystals and that
this was the order of angstroms (Å).

At the time, x-ray tubes were difficult to operate. Their operation
depended on ionization of the gas in the tube by a high voltage, followed

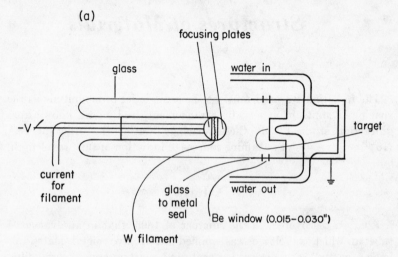

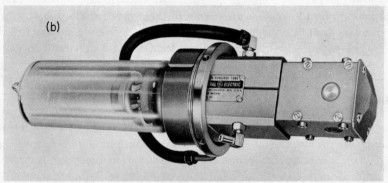

Figure 3–1.   (a) Schematic of an x-ray tube (the recess in the glass is to avoid
contact of high voltage with the body). (b) An actual tube. (*Courtesy
of General Electric Co., X-Ray Department.*)

by emission of electrons (cathode rays) at one metal plate by the bombardment of the ions, their acceleration to the other (positive) plate, where x-rays were emitted. The control of gas pressure, tube purity, target cleanliness, etc., made operation of such tubes a tedious and nerve-racking affair. Current and voltage in the tube were dependent on each other. Today we use tubes in which the electrons are emitted by heated tungsten filaments, allowing separate control of current and voltage, as in Figure 3–1. The voltage and current to such a tube are usually supplied by a transformer after stabilizing the (a-c) line voltage (variations in line voltage drastically affect emission from the hot cathode). Valve tubes are used with circuitry so that when the a-c voltage is in the wrong direction for "pulling" the electrons to the target, the valve tubes do not permit the voltage to stress the x-ray tube. A condenser in the circuit between filament and target provides voltage during this reverse cycle reducing the variations to a slight ripple. Safety circuits are usually included to shut off the unit if the voltage or current exceeds the ratings for the x-ray tube, or if the water flow (which cools the target) stops.

Typically, stabilization will keep the x-ray output so constant that two intensity readings 24 hours apart will differ by at most 0.3 to 3 per cent. The intensity at the sample is of the order of 10^9 cps.

Suppose we set up a sodium chloride crystal in the form of a cube with known d_{200} spacing, increase the voltage to the x-ray in steps, keeping the current constant, and examine intensity versus 2θ. The result is shown in Figure 3–2. First we note that there is a range of λ's; diffraction starts at some minimum angle, corresponding to a minimum wavelength λ_{min}, and occurs for a wide range of angles. Here, λ_{min} is characteristic of the tube voltage, and λ_{max} is the maximum wavelength

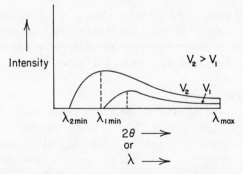

Figure 3–2. The white spectrum and the effect of voltage (V).

that will reach the counter without absorption in the air. (It is indeed one of the fortunate feats of nature that x-rays of the right wavelength for diffraction from crystals are not completely absorbed in air! If vacuum paths were needed, as in electron diffraction, the fact that crystals are periodic arrangements of groups of atoms, and that these arrangements can be studied, might still be in doubt!) Second, it can be shown that the area under each curve of "white" or continuous radiation is:

$$\text{Area } \alpha V^{1.5 \text{ to } 2} Z^2,$$

where Z is the atomic number of the target. Electrons accelerated by the voltage across the tube decelerate as they approach collision with the target. In order to understand why radiation is produced when the charge is decelerated, let us look at the electric field around a single moving charge:

$$\epsilon = qK \left[\frac{\mathbf{e}_{r'}}{r'^2} + \frac{r'}{c} \frac{d}{dt} \left(\frac{\mathbf{e}_{r'}}{r'^2} \right) + \frac{1}{c^2} \frac{d^2}{dt^2} \mathbf{e}'_r \right], \qquad (3\text{-}1a)$$

where q is the charge, K is a constant, t is time, r is the distance from the charge to where we are observing it, and $\mathbf{e}_{r'}$ is a unit vector pointing in

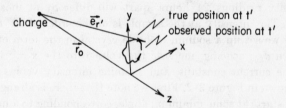

Figure 3–3. (Adapted from R. P. Feynman, R. B. Leighton and M. Sands, *The Feynman Lectures on Physics*, Vol. I., Addison-Wesley Co., Reading, Mass., 1963.)

the direction of observation from the charge. A field cannot propagate faster than c, the speed of light, and it therefore takes some time (r/c) for the information about the charge to reach us; we are observing the field from the charge where it was, not where it is, and the prime reminds us of this.

The first term is just the (stationary) field from the charge. The displacements are small and $\mathbf{e}_{r'}$ does not move much. As shown in Figure 3–3, if r is large compared to x, y, z, the z component of displacement is not important compared to the x and y components; if we are looking at the charge at a small angle to the z axis, the component of the unit vector $\mathbf{e}_{r'}$ in the z direction does not change appreciably as the charge moves in or out. The z displacement does not affect the x or y components of motion either. We can see this in the following way. At time t' the actual positions are

$$x(t'), \quad y(t'), \quad \text{and} \quad r(t') \cong r_0 + z(t').$$

The angular displacement in the x direction is x/r, and this is one of the components we want to describe, the unit vector's motion in Eq. (3–1a).

$$\frac{d(x/r)}{dt} = \frac{dx}{dt}\frac{1}{r} - \frac{dz}{dt}\frac{x}{r^2},$$

$$\frac{d^2(x/r)}{dt^2} = \frac{d^2x}{dt^2}\frac{1}{r} - 2\frac{dx}{dt}\frac{dz}{dt}\frac{1}{r^2} - x\frac{d}{dt}\left(\frac{dz/dt}{r^2}\right).$$

If r_0 is large, the terms in z are not important; when r_0 *is* large, only the last term in Eq. (3–1a) is important, so we can write the field due to acceleration in the x direction for *a* negative electron:

$$\epsilon_x = \frac{-Kq}{c^2r_0}\frac{d^2x}{dt^2} = \frac{-Kq}{c^2r_0}\mathbf{a}_x\left(t' - \frac{r_0}{c} - \frac{z(t')}{c}\right) \qquad (3\text{–}1b)$$

and similarly for the field due to motion in the y direction. z does affect the fields, even if it does not appreciably affect the displacements, but the effect is through the time of observation; we will see only the effect of the accelerations perpendicular to us, but the values of $\mathbf{a}_x, \mathbf{a}_y$ are affected by z'. The term $t' - r_0/c - z(t')/c$, the retardation, can be written as $ct' - r_0 - z(t') = ct$, where t is a "retarded" time. What this equation says is that if we have the actual displacements as a function of time, say as in Figure 3–4(a), we take these and displace them by r_0

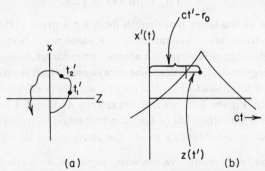

(a)   (b)

Figure 3–4.   (Adapted from R. P. Feynman, R. B. Leighton, and M. Sands, *The Feynman Lectures on Physics*, Vol. I., Addison-Wesley Co., Reading, Mass., 1963.)

and $z(t')$ as in Figure 3–4(b). The more rapid the oscillation the sharper the cusp in this figure, and in taking the second derivative of the curve, to get the term $\mathbf{a}_x$, a sudden rise in the field occurs.

Now when a charge such as an electron comes near the target in an x-ray tube, its path is altered by the charges around atoms, i.e., the electrons, and also these atomic electrons are made to move. Both motions give rise to pulses of radiation and this "Bremsstrahlung" is x-radiation.

We shall discuss other aspects of this equation for the field from an oscillating charge (Chapter 5), but there is one other point worth noticing now. If we decrease t by $-\Delta t$, it is the same as increasing by $\Delta r = +c\,\Delta t$; the field at greater distances comes from the motion at earlier times. Also, the field is the same if we add $\Delta r = c\,\Delta t$, after a time Δt. This is why we have been considering traveling waves from the source in studying diffraction.

If we assume that all the potential energy of the applied voltage across the tube goes into kinetic energy of an electron, and this in turn is converted to radiation in one encounter with an atom in the target,

$$Ve = \frac{1}{2}\,mv^2 = \frac{hc}{\lambda}\,^1$$

where V is the applied voltage, e the electronic charge, m the electronic mass, h is Planck's constant, and c is the velocity of light. In mks units:

$$\lambda \text{ (in Å)} \times 10^{10} V \text{ (in kv)} \times 1000 = \frac{2.99 \times 10^8 \times 6.62 \times 10^{-34}}{1.6 \times 10^{-19}},$$

or

$$\lambda \text{ (in Å)}\ V \text{ (in kv)} = 12.4. \tag{3–2}$$

This tells us the short wavelength limit for a given voltage, but not all the electrons are decelerated in the same way. Some lose their energy in glancing collisions with atoms in the target, losing only some of their energy in each collision. The x-rays coming off from some depth in the target are absorbed on their way out. These effects account for the curve in Figure 3–2, with a maximum at about $1.5\lambda_{\min}$. If the target were a very thin foil (a few hundred angstroms thick) minimizing absorption, the intensity would rise sharply and then fall.

[1] We could use, more exactly, the relativistic expression for the electron's kinetic energy $\left(\dfrac{m_0}{\sqrt{1 - v^2/c^2}} - m_0\right)c^2$. However, at the voltages used, generally 50 kv, this changes the electron's velocity by 10 per cent or less.

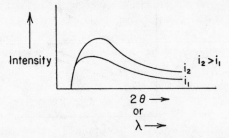

Figure 3–5.   The white spectrum and the effect of current.

Now, if we return to our experiment, hold the voltage constant, but raise the current (i), as shown in Figure 3–5, the curve is "lifted" vertically without any change in its fundamental features. *Altering the voltage changes the complete spectrum but current changes only the number of events, not their type, and thus alters only the intensity.*

If we now continue to raise the voltage above a certain level, sharp lines appear superimposed on the "Bremsstrahlung," as shown in Figure 3–6. In 1913, Moseley, following up some earlier work by Sir W. H. Bragg, showed that the square root of the frequency of these sharp lines was *characteristic* of the atomic number of the target. This is illustrated in Figure 3–7. (He determined these frequencies by measuring the x-ray wavelengths with a crystal of known lattice parameters.) Moseley was aware of the atomic model that Bohr had just proposed, in which electrons were assumed to travel in definite orbits around the nucleus. For the simple case of a circular orbit, balancing the force on an electron of mass m from the Z positive

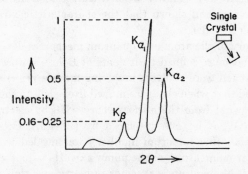

Figure 3–6.   The white and characteristic spectrum. K_{α_1} has a higher energy than K_{α_2} (or K_β) and therefore a smaller λ; hence it diffracts at a smaller 2θ.

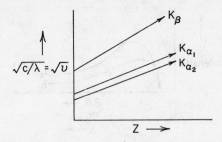

Figure 3–7. Moseley's Law, $\sqrt{\nu} \propto z$ (ν is frequency).

charges on the nucleus with the centripetal force and assuming that the momentum in an orbit was "quantized"—i.e., equal to nh (where n is an integer)—Bohr had shown that the total energy of an orbit was

$$E = \frac{-2\pi^2 m Z^2 e^4}{n^2 h^2}.$$

He also stated that when an electron moved from one level to another energy was absorbed or emitted in discrete packets or quanta of frequency ν:

$$E_1 - E_2 = h\nu,$$

$$\nu = \frac{E_1 - E_2}{h} = \frac{2\pi^2 m Z^2 e^4}{h^2}\left(\frac{1}{n_2^2} - \frac{1}{n_1^2}\right).$$

Therefore,

$$\sqrt{\nu} = KZ\left(\frac{1}{n_2^2} - \frac{1}{n_1^2}\right)^{1/2}. \tag{3–3}$$

Thus each of Moseley's lines was for a transition from one shell to a lower one, and he had shown that the characteristic x-radiation was proof for Bohr's model.

As the theory of the atom and quantum mechanics developed, many corrections and more refined treatments of Bohr's simple (but revolutionary) approach were evolved, involving fewer a priori assumptions. It was realized that when electrons moved from shell to shell, they were shielded somewhat from the nuclear charge, Ze, by electrons in shells ahead of it (i.e., Z is to be replaced by $(Z - \delta)$). Orbits could be elliptical and another quantum number l was needed to describe the orbital angular momentum, or the minor axis. Its values were found to be 0 to $n - 1$. Momentum is a vector property and thus it was found that the orientation of the orbit relative to some axis in space was quantized with a quantum number m_l (with values $-l$ to $+l$). The electron spins around an axis and has a magnetic field. Thus m_s was found to be the quantum number describing this field, which could be only in two directions, opposed or aligned to an applied field; m_s was found to have a value $+1/2$ or $-1/2$. No two electrons could have the same set of quantum numbers (the Pauli exclusion principle), analogous to the fact that no two objects can occupy the same space at the same time. In Figure 3–8 an energy-level diagram for an atom is presented.

These levels are named or lettered after spectra that had been found and labeled prior to the knowledge of the level diagram, such as the x-ray spectra. In this way the explanation of the emitted spectra was linked closely to the names in use.

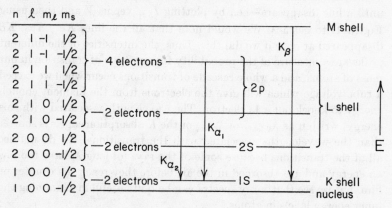

Figure 3–8.   Schematic of the energy levels of electrons in atoms showing the transitions that give rise to the characteristic peaks. Transitions from the L and M shells to a vacant state in the K shell; other transitions (to L or M shells) then occur also.

The interaction of spin and orbital angular momentum, or these with external electrostatic fields, splits levels of the same n and l into different energy levels m_l. Completed shells have no net angular momentum. (A magnetic field splits levels of the same n, l, m_l into different levels for the two values of m_s.) Transitions are possible for

$$\Delta l = \pm 1,$$
$$\Delta m_l = \pm 1, 0.$$

Thus, if electrons in an x-ray tube eject an inner electron from the K shell of a target atom, splitting of the $n = 2$ levels is aided as an electron leaves this level to lower its energy by moving to the K (or $1s$)

level. The L level is shown split in this fashion. The three transitions that correspond to the peaks found in Figure 3–6 are shown. From this diagram,

$$h\nu_{Ka_1} = \frac{hc}{\lambda_{Ka_1}} = \frac{hc}{\lambda_{\text{ionization}}} - \frac{hc}{\lambda_{\text{ionization}}},$$
$$K \text{ shell} \qquad L \text{ shell}$$

or

$$\frac{1}{\lambda_{Ka_1}} = \frac{1}{\lambda_{K \text{ ioniz.}}} - \frac{1}{\lambda_{L \text{ ioniz.}}}. \qquad (3\text{–}4)$$

We can measure the ionization potential by lowering the voltage until a line disappears—i.e., by plotting I_{Ka_1} versus V and then using Eq. (3–1) to get a λ. We would note that all the lines $K\alpha_1$, $K\alpha_2$, $K\beta$ disappeared at once if we did this. Thus, the intensities of the different peaks are a measure of the probability for any type of transition in our mass of atoms, and a whole cascade of transitions occur when we exceed a tube voltage which will give the electrons from the filament enough energy to knock out a $1s$ electron. The wavelength associated with this energy, written as $\lambda_{K \text{ ioniz.}}$ or $\lambda_{K \text{ abs}}$ or the K absorption edge,[2] is shorter than the wavelengths associated with the transitions. We do not see all of the transitions because some of the rays (of long λ) have too low an energy and are absorbed in the air before they reach the counter or film, but we see that x-ray spectra can be quite useful in examining the inner energy levels in atoms.

If the electrons have only enough energy to knock L electrons out, we get only spectra associated with transitions to the L level. Examination of a table of wavelengths of various spectra, as well as the ionization λ's (see pp. 60–65 in Vol. III of the International Tables) shows that as the atomic number goes up (i.e., as the positive charge on the nucleus increases) the K ionization potential increases (the nucleus has more positive charge to hold the inner electrons), and the wavelengths associated with this ionization and the K spectra decrease. With some materials such as W, with the usual operating voltage of 50 kv, we see only the L spectra from the tube. Because of the higher energy of this spectrum for targets of high atomic numbers, the L spectrum can reach the recording device.

[2] These are often referred to as the wavelength for the K absorption edge or $\lambda_{K \text{ abs}}$ obviously because of the sudden rise in absorption of an x-ray beam when its λ has this value for the absorbing material.

Because the sharp peaks in the distribution *are* characteristic and depend only on the types of atoms not the structure or state, they can serve as a means for chemical analysis. This has become a very powerful tool in industry. Two schemes for this are illustrated in Figure 3–9. In (*a*) the sample is bombarded as a target by electrons inside a tube which can be opened to change the target. In (*b*) x-rays are used to cause the ionization so that the specimen can be outside the tube, allowing for more rapid sample exchange and a greater variety of sizes and shapes of specimens. (Note (and explain) the differences in the spectra in Figure 3–9(*a*) and (*b*).) Vacuum paths are often used to increase the number of elements that can be analyzed.

In general, after a qualitative analysis reveals the elements, the method must be calibrated for quantitative work by comparing peak

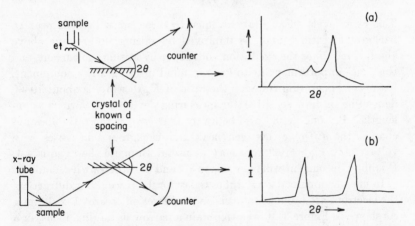

Figure 3–9. Two schemes for fluorescent analysis: (*a*) Sample fluoresced by electrons and, (*b*) sample fluoresced by x-rays.

intensities to intensities from samples of known composition—not by comparing directly to the intensity from a pure piece of each element. There are two basic reasons for this:

1. The K_β or K_α from one element may excite radiation from another, diminishing radiation from the first and enhancing that from the second (if the latter is energetic enough to reach the counter).

2. Because longer λ's are less penetrating, less radiation will come from say iron in silver than iron in aluminum.

The intensity of a characteristic peak is

$$I_{\text{char.}} = ki(V - V_{k \text{ excitation}})^n, \qquad (3\text{--}5)$$

where $n \approx 3/2$. Now

$$i = \frac{\text{power to tube}}{V} = \frac{P}{V}.$$

Therefore,

$$I_{\text{char.}} = \frac{kP(V - V_k)^{3/2}}{V}.$$

The ratio (R) of the intensity of a characteristic peak to the total white radiation including the fact that $P \alpha V$ is:

$$R = \frac{[k'(V - V_k)^{3/2}V]/V}{Z^2 V^2}, \tag{3-6}$$

$$= \frac{k'(V - V_k)^{3/2}}{Z^2 V^2}. \tag{3-7}$$

This ratio levels off at V about equal to three times V_k. The peak to background ratio cannot be improved by raising the voltage above about three times the excitation voltage, or by raising the current, and this is an important point to keep in mind in using x-ray equipment. (At normal operating voltages, the ratio of K_α to white is about 10–60 depending on how sensitive our measuring device is to various wavelengths.) But one should also be aware that even if the ratio does not change, the *difference* between peak and background increases with voltage, and higher voltages may be useful. Suppose the ratio is 4/1. Doubling the current will raise this to 8/2 and the *difference* has doubled.

In most commercial x-ray tubes today for fluorescence or diffraction, the electrons are brought to focus on the target on an area 1×10 mm. As shown in Figure 3–10 we can obtain a narrow beam (line focus) or a square spot (spot focus) depending on how we look at the target (the "take-off" angle). By electromagnetic fields, the electrons can be focused to about a micron or somewhat less and then analysis can be carried out over very tiny regions—grains, inclusions, etc. Scattered electrons and x-rays can be used to image the area.

The slits in Figure 3–10 reduce the horizontal and vertical angular divergence of a beam to the order of a degree so that all parts of the radiation used fulfill the Bragg condition very close to the same position on a film or at a counter, to keep the peaks sharp. A range of sizes from a tenth of a degree up to a few degrees is usually available, so that one can get more intensity, if necessary (with a loss in resolution). With a pinhole near the tube, one can get a picture of the distribution of x-rays across the target, i.e., how uniformly the electrons hit the target. This

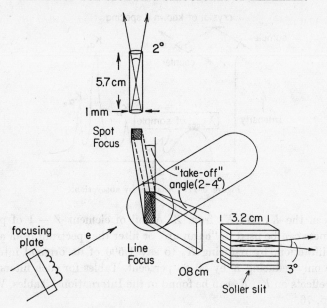

Figure 3–10. Spot and line focus from an x-ray tube and typical slits for limiting
divergence (divergence shown by arrows).

is important to know because a very nonuniform x-ray distribution can
severely distort a peak and it is best to be aware of possible distortions
other than those from the diffracting material. Such distortions, if they
are really from the material being studied, can tell us something about
the internal structure as we shall see in Chapter 8.

If we pass x-radiation through a specimen, it will be absorbed as
heat motion of the atoms, scattering and by ionization. We shall discuss
these interactions in detail in a later chapter, but at this point, it is
worth mentioning that because of ionization there is another method of
analysis. If we pass an x-ray beam from a tube through a specimen and
then analyze it with a crystal, the result may look like that in Figure
3–11. The sharp drop in transmitted intensity occurs for the K (or L)
excitation of an element in the specimen.[3] Its position is *characteristic*
of the type of atom (not the state of aggregation), and the drop may be
used for qualitative analysis or for quantitative analysis as we shall see
soon. (It is also a way to measure $\lambda_{K \text{ abs}}$ or $\lambda_{L \text{ abs}}$.)

For a target of atomic number, Z, the drop for element $Z - 1$ is

[3] The absorbed energy is given off in all directions as the K (or L) spectrum of the
element, which is why the transmitted beam has less intensity.

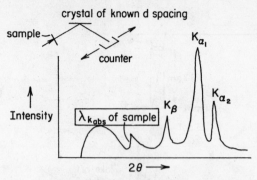

Figure 3–11. Analysis by absorption.

between the K_β and K_α from Z. A foil of element $Z - 1$ of proper thickness can be used to "clean up" or filter the spectrum from a tube for diffraction, by reducing K_β to say 1/500 of its original intensity while only reducing K by 50–60 per cent. Tables for such filters with their effects on K_α, K_β can be found in the International Tables, Vol. 3, pp. 75, 76.

Although it is generally not necessary, except for very weak scattering effects, we can get a very clean spectrum from an x-ray tube by diffracting one λ from a crystal. Even if there were not any sharp spectral lines, such a technique would allow us to choose one λ for diffraction from another crystal. Fortunately the characteristic lines are strong and sharp so that this additional complication is not usually required. (In fact, the Braggs assumed a sharp peak in their work on sodium chloride, for the spectrum had not yet been examined.)

To give some idea of the dimensions of diffraction equipment, Figure 3–12(a) shows a film arrangement and Figure 3–12(b) a counter unit.

X-ray quanta are packets or pulses of energy and our study of Fourier analysis shows us that they are made up of many independent waves. Our treatment of diffraction takes each one of these as an incident wave and adds the diffraction from them. It is because of the independence of the waves in the packet that we can do this.

Actually $K\alpha_1$ has a wavelength spread of the order $\Delta\lambda/\lambda = 0.5 \times 10^{-3}$ due to the range of wavelengths present in the wave packet. To see how this affects the angular spread of a diffraction peak, we differentiate Bragg's law:

$$d(\lambda) = d \cos \theta d(2\theta)$$

(a)

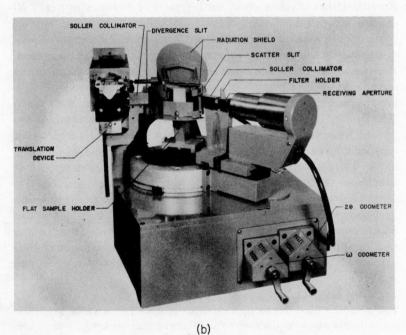

(b)

Figure 3-12. (a) A film unit. (The length of the track under the camera is about
fifteen inches.) *Courtesy of General Electric Co., X-Ray Department.*
(b) Diffractometer. One side of the unit is about fifteen inches long.
(Courtesy of Picker Corp.)

(2θ is the variable we usually measure—the angle between the incident and diffracted rays) or,

$$d(2\theta) = \frac{d(\lambda)}{d \cos \theta} \quad \text{and as} \quad \frac{1}{d} = \frac{2 \sin \theta}{\lambda},$$

$$d(2\theta) = 2 \frac{d(\lambda)}{\lambda} \cdot \tan \theta.$$

Multiplying by $360/2\pi$ to convert to degrees 2θ,

$$d(2\theta) = \frac{720}{2\pi} \frac{d(\lambda)}{\lambda} \tan \theta. \tag{3-8}$$

For a low angle peak, say at $2\theta = 30$ degrees,

$$d(2\theta) = 0.015 \text{ degrees } 2\theta,$$

and at $2\theta = 160$ degrees,

$$d(2\theta) = 0.34 \text{ degrees } 2\theta.$$

At large angles this effect is a very significant contribution to the breadth. Other effects such as small crystal or mosaic size (small N) can also broaden the peaks.

Wavelengths have been determined both by ruled grating experiments and by using density and crystal diffraction, as the Braggs did. Because at the time most of the measurements were made there was an error in Avogadro's number, there was a difference in the wavelength for the two types of measurements; calling the latter "kx" units, 1 kx unit $\simeq 1.00202$ Å. There is a difference of 0.2 per cent. At the present time, lengths and hence d spacings can be measured to six significant figures, but the accuracy in the last place of the conversion is not well established; it could be 1.00206, so that the accuracy can at best be only 1 part in 25,000. Precision can of course be higher, but it is always necessary to state the wavelength used as well as the precision in measurements if they are supposed to be of an accuracy higher than 0.2 per cent, so that when this matter is settled the data can be adjusted, and the differences between reports of spacings from different investigators can be properly judged.[4] This has not always been done, and

[4] If the specimen whose d spacings are being reported is an alloy of metals, or ceramic materials, do not forget to give the error in the chemical analysis also. This is usually much higher than the error in the x-ray measurement! These points should not keep the reader from realizing that even with these uncertainties, the determination of d spacings and lattice parameters is one of the most precise and accurate physical measurements that can be made.

care should be taken in examining the literature to ascertain the units, or λ. (The values in the International Tables are in angstroms.) One should also state how the position of a peak was measured! The center of gravity of a peak and its maximum can be quite different. Most tabulated values for λ correspond to the maximum in the wavelength distribution.

The x-rays from a target are incoherent. We can see why by examining the result of adding two waves of the same amplitude emitted at different times so that their phases are different (see Problem 2–5a). The result is of the form

$$I = A_T^2 = 2A_1^2 + 2A_1 \cos (\varphi_1 - \varphi_2).$$

It takes about 10^{-8} sec for an atom to give off radiation. Thus at any one small region of the target during the seconds or minutes it takes us to make a measurement there is a great range in phases, and the cosine term averages to zero; the intensity *appears* as if it is simply the sum of the intensities of independent sources. Suppose it happens that two atoms on the target emit at the same time—i.e., with the same phase— and suppose they are 10^{-2} cm apart or $10^6 \lambda$, then even in the small angular range (1 degree or so) that we view the target, the phase angle difference varies greatly so that the cosine term goes through many cycles. The *average* intensity we measure over this region *appears* to be coming from independent sources.

Neutrons

We now know that all particles have wave properties associated with their momentum (mv) according to the relation proposed by De Broglie:

$$\lambda = \frac{h}{mv}. \tag{3–9}$$

In most research reactors the neutrons from fission collide with atoms in the reactor, particularly with water (usually heavy water because of its lower neutron absorption) or graphite and emerge from a port or tube with an rms velocity related to the temperature of the reactor, as if it were a monatomic gas:

$$\frac{1}{2} mv^2 = \frac{3}{2} kT.$$

Therefore from Eq. (3–9),

$$\lambda = \left(\frac{h^2}{3mkT}\right)^{1/2}. \tag{3-10}$$

As the mass of a neutron is 10^{-24} gms, at 0°C and 100°C the λ's are 1.6 Å and 1.3 Å—just right for diffraction from crystals. The actual number of neutrons $v\,d\lambda$ between λ and $\lambda + d\lambda$ will be of the form

$$v\,d(\lambda) = \frac{2N}{\lambda}\left(\frac{E}{kT}\right)^2 e^{-E/kT}, \tag{3-11}$$

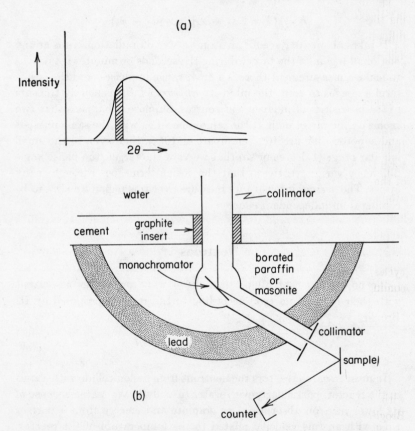

Figure 3–13. (a) Spectrum from a thermal nuclear reactor. Shaded region is chosen by a monochromator. (b) A typical port for neutron diffraction. (Adapted from G. E. Bacon, *Neutron Diffraction*, 2nd Ed., Clarendon Press, Oxford, 1962.)

where N is the total number of neutrons of all λ's per second. (Typical fluxes at a reactor core are 10^{12} to 10^{14} neutrons/cm^2/sec.) E is the energy of any one neutron of wavelength λ. The distribution of the spectrum from a crystal will look like that in Figure 3–13(a).

It is *necessary* in this case to use a monochromator crystal to choose a wavelength for diffraction because of the lack of any sharp intense spectra. In general, if one wavelength is desired for diffraction it is better to choose a λ to the left of the maximum, so that $\lambda/2$, which will diffract in second order at the position for first order from λ, is minimized, or to use a crystal whose structure factor is zero for the second order.[5] To see the effect of the spread in energies on the shape of peak, let $E = (3/2)\, kT$. Then $v\, d\lambda = N/\lambda$. If the angular range over which the monochromator diffracts strongly due to mosaic is say $\Delta 2\theta$, the range of λ's reflected is $d(\lambda)$:

$$d(\lambda) = d \cos \theta\, \Delta 2\theta,$$

or the total beam from the monochromator, N_T,

$$N_T = \frac{N}{\lambda}\, d \cos \theta\, \Delta 2\theta\, KF^2$$

$$= N\, \frac{\cot \theta}{2}\, KF^2\, \Delta 2\theta. \tag{3–12}$$

The more mosaic the crystal the more divergent its beam will be, but also the higher the flux to the specimen. This intensity also is greater for a low-angle reflection from the monochromator. Hence, if possible, a monochromator should be chosen that has a large enough d spacing to diffract the peak in the neutron distribution at low angles, and of course it should have a large structure factor for this diffraction; if resolution needs to be sacrificed for intensity, a crystal with a large mosaic is required.

A typical arrangement for neutron diffraction is shown in Figure 3–13(b). The hydrogen in the paraffin or masonite slows down any fast neutrons which are then absorbed in the boron. The γ or x-rays from the pile are absorbed by the lead. This is for safety and to reduce the background. At the reactor face a typical neutron beam is the order of an inch or two inches square (to get adequate intensity). The collimator to the crystal monochromator is about 4 to 5 feet long, and will be of wood with cadmium plated steel channel (cadmium absorbs neutrons). There will be vertical plates spaced about 1/4 to 1/2 of an inch apart so

[5] This effect occurs with x-rays also ($\lambda/2$ is in the white spectrum), and the same solution will work.

that the horizontal divergence is of the order of 1/4 to 1/2 degrees and the vertical divergence is about 1 degree. A lead shutter and facilities for filling the collimator tube with water may be installed so that one can remove the shielding and get at the monochromator, or it can be removed from a hole at the top of the shielding which is normally plugged. External controls will be available for tilting the mono-chromator to orient it. The entire monochromator assembly, shielding and exit collimator, may be mounted on a rotating plate to allow a choice of λ, or there may be plugs in various places on the outside shield to obtain different λ's. The counter will be typically a 2-in. diameter, 1-ft long cylinder filled with BF_3 enriched in the isotope B^{10}. (We shall discuss counters more later; however, this isotope emits alpha particles on absorption of neutrons, which ionize the gas, causing a pulse as in a gas-filled x-ray counter.) When covered with shielding it will weigh several hundred pounds! The goniometer to move the counter is usually much more massive than an x-ray goniometer, weighing several tons.

Knowing the collimator's dimensions we can estimate what area of the neutron source is being seen and hence the neutrons per second coming from the collimator; then when we know how to calculate the diffracted intensity in absolute units (KF^2 in Eq. (3–12)), we shall find that the counting rate from the monochromator is 10^6 to 10^8 counts per minute—orders of magnitude lower than with x-rays. An examination of the pattern requires a great deal of time. Because a pile, unlike an x-ray generator, cannot be stabilized electronically, the beam from the monochromator is counted by a small low absorbing counter in the beam's path, and counts from the specimen are measured for a fixed number of counts into this monitor counter.[6]

There is a promising technique for reducing the counting time. No monochromator is used, but instead all the neutrons from the collimator are allowed to strike the specimen. These are taken from the reactor with a chopper—a rotating disk with a slot in it (really an aluminum disk covered with highly absorbing cadmium except in one sector). Because neutrons with different energies will have different veloci-ties, higher wavelengths will reach the specimen at later times. The sample does not move, i.e. θ is fixed, and the various reflections are examined because of the varying λ, using a counter and an electronic device which records only the counts in a short time interval or in a certain energy range (a multichannel analyzer).

[6] This can also be done with x-rays to improve the stability. The fluorescence from a thin foil in the x-ray beam to the sample can be used.

It is also possible to use film methods in neutron diffraction. However, the beam dimensions and low collimation required to achieve adequate intensity do not yield good resolution. Film methods are now mainly used for examining the uniformity of the beam from a monochromator, or the location of the beam with respect to a specimen or set of slits. In general, these film methods employ a high speed film such as Polaroid; a screen is placed before the film of gadolinium, which emits γ rays (higher energy x-rays), or of zinc sulfide including some of a B^{10} or Li^6 isotope, which emit alpha particles on absorption of a neutron. In the latter case the alpha particles cause light flashes in the sulfide which then expose the film. In the former the gamma rays strike the film.

Electrons

The diffraction of electrons was first demonstrated in 1927 (nine years before diffraction of neutrons was demonstrated).

Using the De Broglie relationship for electrons, equating the applied field Ve to the kinetic energy of the electron as in deriving Eq. (3–2), neglecting relativistic corrections:

$$\lambda_A = \frac{12.3}{\sqrt{V_{\text{volts}}}}, \tag{3–13a}$$

where V is the accelerating voltage to which the electrons have been subjected. At very high voltages, 50 kv or more, relativistic corrections are required:

$$m = \frac{m_0}{\sqrt{1 - v^2/c^2}} \quad \text{or} \quad (mv) = \sqrt{(mc)^2 - (m_0 c)^2}.$$

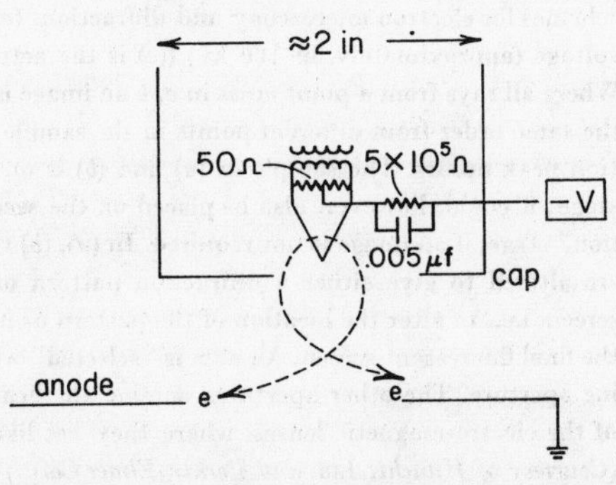

Figure 3–14.   Self-biasing electron gun. (Adapted from C. E. Hall, *Introduction to Electron Microscopy*, McGraw-Hill Book Co., New York, 1953.)

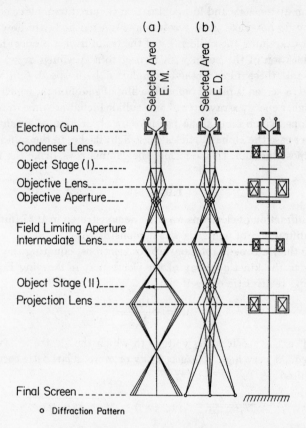

Electron Gun

Condenser Lens

Object Stage (I)

Objective Lens
Objective Aperture

Field Limiting Aperture
Intermediate Lens

Object Stage (II)

Projection Lens

Final Screen

o Diffraction Pattern

Figure 3–15.   Schemes for electron microscopy and diffraction. (a), (b), (c): High
voltage (approximately 50–100 kv) ((c) is the actual microscope).
Where all rays from a point cross in a, b an image is formed; where
the same order from different points in the sample cross, a diffraction peak occurs. The sample in (a) and (b) is on the first object
stage; it could, however, also be placed on the second or "diffraction" stage, if an image is not required. In (a), (b) the lens currents
are altered to give either a diffraction pattern or image on the
screen, i.e., to alter the location of the pattern or image relative to
the final fluorescent screen. An area is "selected" with a field limiting aperture. The other apertures confine the beam to the center
of the electro-magnetic lenses, where they act like optical lenses.
(Courtesy of Hitachi, Ltd. and Perkin-Elmer Corp.) (d) Low voltage
(100 volts). (Adapted from L. Germer, Physics Today, 17, 1964.)

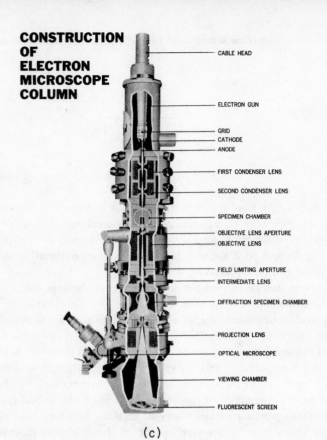

CONSTRUCTION OF ELECTRON MICROSCOPE COLUMN

CABLE HEAD

ELECTRON GUN

GRID
CATHODE
ANODE

FIRST CONDENSER LENS

SECOND CONDENSER LENS

SPECIMEN CHAMBER

OBJECTIVE LENS APERTURE
OBJECTIVE LENS

FIELD LIMITING APERTURE
INTERMEDIATE LENS

DIFFRACTION SPECIMEN CHAMBER

PROJECTION LENS

OPTICAL MICROSCOPE

VIEWING CHAMBER

FLUORESCENT SCREEN

(c)

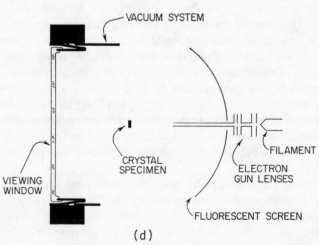

VACUUM SYSTEM

CRYSTAL
SPECIMEN

FILAMENT

ELECTRON
GUN LENSES

VIEWING
WINDOW

FLUORESCENT SCREEN

(d)

Also,

$$(m - m_0)c^2 = Ve \quad \text{or} \quad m = m_0 + \frac{Ve}{c^2}.$$

Therefore,

$$mv = \sqrt{2m_0 Ve + \frac{e^2}{c^2} V^2},$$

$$\lambda = \frac{12.3}{\sqrt{V + 10^{-6} V^2}}. \tag{3-13b}$$

The wavelength thus varies from about 1 Å at 150 v to about 0.03 Å at 100 kv, the highest voltage now in general use. At these high voltages the diffraction angles will be quite small, several orders appearing from 0 to 2 degrees 2θ. To a good approximation $\sin \theta$ in Bragg's law can be replaced by θ.

Diffraction can be carried out in transmission through thin foils, or by glancing incidence from thicker specimens.

A typical arrangement for an electron source uses an undoped fine W wire operating at 2400°K to produce a small flux of thermally emitted electrons; a typical electron "gun" is shown in Figure 3–14.

The negative potential to the cap or "Wehnelt cylinder" around the filament increases as the current to the filament increases, so that at some filament current the beam current through the anode remains constant; the heating of the filament and the negative bias are in balance. There is a "cross-over" point of the electrons that is the effective source point. The beam intensity can be controlled by the depth of the filament inside the cylinder. A filament may last up to a week or two in continuous operation. Voltages are controlled very precisely electronically. From this source point, the beam is controlled by a series of electromagnetic lenses. Typical arrangements are shown in Figure 3–15. An aperture may be used to isolate a small fraction of the field for diffraction, as small as a few tens of angstroms. (Note that if the aperture blocks many of the orders of diffraction, the image will not be perfect; from Chapter 2, Problem 23 the structure can be represented by a Fourier series, and if terms are eliminated the picture is not perfect.)

The pattern is focused to be sharp, but must be calibrated for a given setting of the lenses or magnification with the diffraction pattern from a known specimen, if d spacings are desired. In calibrating, it is necessary to measure distances to spots of known d spacing in several directions, to correct for any eccentricity of the lenses.

Now that we have examined the general production of radiation for diffraction, we turn to the geometry of recording diffraction patterns. Then we shall see the relative advantages of using any one of these radiations. The reader is to be warned that all three of these radiations are dangerous; just as they ionize gases in counters, so can they ionize atoms in the body, and the beams cannot be seen except with fluorescent screens. Caution is required to avoid placing parts of the body in the direct or diffracted beams. With reasonable care and shielding of equipment, one will not expose himself to no more than that from cosmic radiation. High energy electrons can cause x-rays when they strike parts of equipment, and neutrons can make some substances radioactive —thus all parts of an experimental arrangement should be carefully thought out. It is a good idea to have a portable counter on hand to look for stray radiation and to always keep away from the source.

SUGGESTED READINGS

1. H. P. Klug and L. E. Alexander, *X-Ray Diffraction Procedures* (John Wiley, New York, 1954).
2. G. E. Bacon, *Neutron Diffraction*, 2nd Ed. (Clarendon Press, Oxford, 1962).
3. G. Thomas, *Transmission Electron Microscopy of Metals* (John Wiley, New York, 1962).

PROBLEMS

1. A copper target x-ray tube is run at 40-kv peak (full wave rectified) and a tube current of 20 ma so that the power input P is

$$P = \int_0^{T/2} \frac{V \sin 2\pi\, t/T \cdot i\, dt}{T/2}.$$

The efficiency of an x-ray tube is so low that only of the order of 1 per cent of the energy is converted to x-rays.

(a) If there were no dissipation of heat by water cooling, conduction, radiation, etc., how long would it take a 100-gram copper target to start to melt?

    (b)   If the target is cooled by a water supply of 2 liters per minute, how much does the temperature of the water rise?

    (c)   What problems do you think might occur with an x-ray tube after long use?

2. A copper x-ray tube, with the filament 5 cm from the anode, is operating at 50 kv, 10 ma.

    (a)   Find the acceleration of the electrons to the anode.

    (b)   Find their maximum velocity if classical theory holds, and with relativistic corrections.

    (c)   Draw a sketch of the spectrum from the tube giving λ_{K_β}, $\lambda_{K_{\alpha_1}}$, $\lambda_{K_{\alpha_2}}$.

    (d)   What is the excitation voltage for the tube?

3. (a)   To hold the output for the characteristic lines to ±0.5 per cent, how well must the voltage of an x-ray tube and its current be stabilized?

    (b)   With this stability how much will the maximum in the distribution of the white radiation vary?

4. To hold the wavelength in electron diffraction to four significant figures, how well must the current and voltage be stabilized?

5. Calculate the angles (θ) for electron diffraction for the first four orders of the (200) from a crystal of copper at

    (a)   50 kv

    (b)   100 v

    (c)   100 kv

    (d)   If the distance from the sample to the film is about 2 ft, what will be the distance to these orders on the film (from the center)? Sketch the experimental arrangement with particular attention to the required orientation of the crystal with respect to incident and diffracted beams.

6. With CuK_α x-radiation and a distance from the sample to a film of 5.73 cm, how far from the direct beam will the 200 and 400 from a crystal of iron appear? How far with MoK_α? Sketch the arrangement with particular attention to the required orientation of the crystal to the incident and diffracted beam to permit these diffraction peaks.

7. As part of an industrial research program, you have cast a Cu–Zn alloy, and you are fairly sure it is 50 wt-per cent zinc. In order to check this and get an accurate value, you send a sample to your analytical laboratory for analysis. A few hours later someone calls

you and says the alloy is 55.0 per cent copper. He says he has done the analysis with x-ray fluorescent techniques. You check his patterns and notice the CuK_α, CuK_β, ZnK_α, and ZnK_β. The CuK_β is about 1/5 the CuK_α but the ZnK_β is very much weaker (see p. 71, the International Tables, Vol. III). The analyst says he has determined the composition by comparing the intensities of the K_α lines from the alloy with those from the pure metals. Is there anything wrong? What do you recommend he do?

8. An x-ray film is taken by scattering white radiation from an amorphous material. The film is made of AgBr. Look up the excitation wavelengths and sketch how the blackening of the film might appear.

4 *Recording the Diffraction Pattern*

As we have just seen, the diffraction pattern can be recorded by film or counter with x-rays, principally by counter with neutrons, and by film with electrons. In Chapter 2 it was pointed out that diffraction from a three-dimensional structure required some freedom in choice of λ, or relative orientation of the beam and crystal. The reason for this is easily seen: if the interatomic spacings are of the order of say 4 Å, the reciprocal lattice is 0.25 Å^{-1} on edge and the radius of the reflecting sphere for 1-Å radiation is 1 Å^{-1}. The curvature of the sphere is important relative to the lattice, and some freedom is required for the sphere to intersect the reciprocal lattice. With high energy electrons of say 0.03 Å, the radius would be 34 Å^{-1}, which is large compared with the reciprocal lattice. In this case, essentially a planar section of reciprocal space is seen all at once, and some of the difficulty is removed.

We shall first discuss the methods for radiation of the order of 1 Å. These methods are based on the following:

1. Orienting a crystal relative to the beam for one diffraction spot with one λ, or for many spots, using a beam of many λ's.
*2. Oscillating the crystal using one λ.
3. Using a powder or polycrystalline specimen to provide many orientations all at once to a fixed λ.

We shall dwell on the procedure that is generally the most useful for each case. We shall discuss the method, how it affects intersections of reciprocal space, and then relate this to the actual appearance of the record. The record is a map and we shall have to learn something about the "mapping procedures" for each technique. That is, our record is not always the diffraction points in the reciprocal lattice but a map of them on a flat film or a cylindrical film.

148

Orienting a Crystal for One Diffraction Spot with One λ, Knowing a_1, a_2, a_3

In Figure 4–1 a plane is shown through a reciprocal lattice. We shall first examine a system with orthogonal axes. All planes above it are identical; only the l coordinate needs to be changed (of course, if the b_3 axis is not perpendicular to b_1 and b_2, higher layers are displaced and do

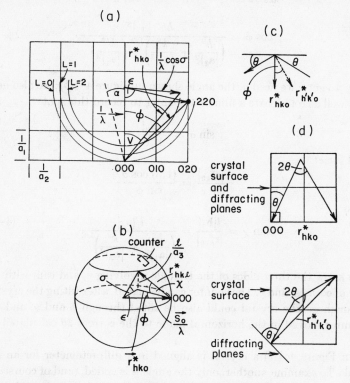

Figure 4–1.

not superimpose on the $b_1 - b_2$ plane). Over this plane is a set of circles, each representing a section of the reflecting sphere,[1] at the height of the next layer.

[1] It can be useful to prepare such circles to a given scale on transparent paper and to draw each reciprocal lattice for each crystal to the same scale in units λ/a_1, λ/a_2, λ/a_3 rather than $1/a_1$, etc. In this way, the transparency will be generally useful. This is merely saying that the condition for diffraction $(S - S_o)/\lambda = r^*_{hkl}$ can be written $S - S_0 = \lambda r^*_{hkl}$.

If we wish to examine the 221 diffraction spot, we must turn the crystal so that the sphere of reflection cuts through the 221 spot. This is equivalent in our drawing to moving the circular section representing the first layer so that it touches the 220 point. We can graphically then determine the angle α. This can also be done analytically. Now $\alpha = \phi - v$; ϕ is the angle between $\mathbf{r}^*_{\bar{1}00}$ and $\mathbf{r}^*_{220}$. Thus,

$$\mathbf{r}^*_{hk0} \cdot \mathbf{r}^*_{h'00} = hh'|\mathbf{b}_1|^2 = |\mathbf{r}^*_{hk0}||\mathbf{r}^*_{h'0}| \cos \phi,$$

or

$$\cos \phi = \frac{hh'/|\mathbf{a}_1|^2}{\left(\dfrac{h^2}{|\mathbf{a}_1|^2} + \dfrac{k^2}{|\mathbf{a}_2|^2}\right)^{1/2} \left(\dfrac{h'^2}{|\mathbf{a}_1|^2}\right)^{1/2}}. \qquad (4\text{-}1a)$$

Now to get v we need σ, the angle shown in Figure 4–1(b); we also need ε as well as σ to locate a film or a counter to record this spot:

$$\sin \sigma = \frac{l/|\mathbf{a}_3|}{1/\lambda},$$

and for ε:

$$\frac{|\mathbf{r}^*_{hk0}|}{\sin \varepsilon} = \frac{(1/\lambda) \cos \sigma}{\sin \phi}.$$

Also

$$\tan \chi = \frac{l|\mathbf{b}_3|}{|\mathbf{r}^*_{hk0}|} = \frac{l/|\mathbf{a}_3|}{\left(\dfrac{h^2}{|\mathbf{a}_1|^2} + \dfrac{k^2}{|\mathbf{a}_2|^2}\right)^{1/2}}. \qquad (4\text{-}1b)$$

We know the three sides of the triangle involving v, and can, with the law of cosines, find v. The counter can be placed, after tilting the crystal, through α. The crystal could also be tilted through ϕ and χ, and the counter moved in the horizontal plane to the correct 2θ calculated for d_{hkl}.

In Figure 4–1(c) a crystal is aligned in a diffractometer for an $hk0$ peak. To examine another, only the angle ϕ is ended, (and of course the angle θ is changed). This is shown schematically in (d), in reciprocal space. If we can identify a plane (say $hk0$) on a crystal and find its diffraction peak, then by simply tilting the crystal to ϕ, we find another reflection $h'k0$. If it is an $h'k'l'$ reflection we seek after the $hk0$, we must tilt through χ (Figure 4–1(b)) and then an angle like ϕ, the angle between the component of $r^*_{h'k'l'}$ on the $hk0$ plane, and r^*_{hk0}.

If the $\mathbf{a}_3$ axis is not perpendicular to $\mathbf{a}_1$ and $\mathbf{a}_2$ we must first locate the origin of any layer, which is displaced from the 000 point. We first recall that the $\mathbf{a}_3$ axis is *always* perpendicular to the $\mathbf{b}_1$, $\mathbf{b}_2$ plane, because

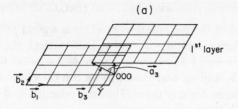

(a)

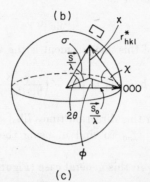

(b)

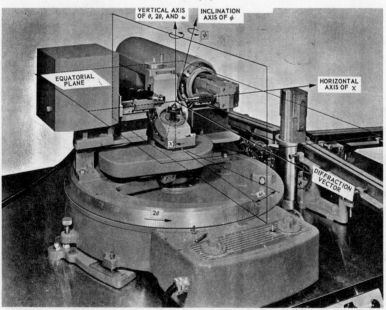

(c)

Figure 4-2 (a), (b), and (c): An attachment for locating reflections on a diffractometer. The G.E. eucentric goniometer. (Reprinted with permission of General Electric Co. X-Ray Department, Milwaukee, Wisconsin.)

of the definition of the reciprocal axes. (This is a good point to keep in mind. If we align a crystal with the $\mathbf{a}_3$ axis vertical, the $\mathbf{b}_1$, $\mathbf{b}_2$ planes are always horizontal.) As shown in Figure 4–2(a), what we need is the angle between $\mathbf{b}_3$ and $\mathbf{a}_3$, and from this we can calculate the *magnitude* of the displacement for any layer. Thus the magnitude of the displacement for the lth layer is

$$l|\mathbf{b}_3| \sin \gamma. \tag{4–1c}$$

The direction of this displacement is the vector

$$\mathbf{b}_3 - \mathbf{a}_3 = \left[\mathbf{b}_3 - \left(\frac{\mathbf{b}_1 \times \mathbf{b}_2}{\mathbf{b}_1 \cdot (\mathbf{b}_2 \times \mathbf{b}_3)}\right)\right]. \tag{4–1d}$$

A unit vector in this direction times $l|\mathbf{b}_3| \sin \gamma$ must be added to (or subtracted from) $\mathbf{r}^*_{hk0}$ to find α, using the procedure described for orthogonal axes.

For the angle χ in this general case (Figure 4–2(b)):

$$\sin \chi = \frac{\mathbf{x}}{|\mathbf{r}^*_{hkl}|}, \tag{4–1e}$$

where

$$\mathbf{x} = \frac{\mathbf{b}_1 \times \mathbf{b}_2}{|\mathbf{b}_1| |\mathbf{b}_2| \sin (\mathbf{b}_1 - \mathbf{b}_2)} \cdot \mathbf{r}^*_{hkl}, \quad \text{or} \quad \frac{\mathbf{a}_3}{|\mathbf{a}_3|} \cdot \mathbf{r}^*_{hkl}. \tag{4–1f}$$

The formulae for the other angles are also changed but these examples should suffice for the reader to work out the others.

These calculations are ideally suited for a computer; in many laboratories where work on crystal structures is the primary effort, the computer has been "attached" to the diffractometer, giving it its angular settings for a peak, collecting intensity data, and moving for the next peak.

A commercial device for locating a spot for diffraction is shown in Figure 4–2(c). The axes of the rotations intersect at a known point; if the x-ray beam is made to strike the crystal at this point, the crystal will not be displaced from the beam during the tilting.

Using a Range of Wavelengths

When we choose the alternative of using a range of wavelengths, say all those from an x-ray tube, we usually have wavelengths from the

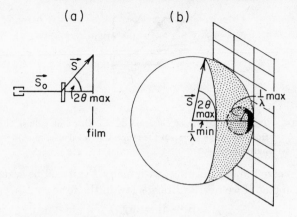

Figure 4–3.   Geometry for Laue patterns in transmission.

short-wave length limit to the longest wavelength from the tube that will reach the film or counter in air—about 2 Å. We therefore have a whole range of reflecting spheres, and all the spots between these spheres diffract. If we use a flat film as in Figure 4–3(a) and examine the pattern by transmission, there is a limitation on the fraction of the spots intercepted by the film; the situation in reciprocal space is given in Figure 4–3(b).

We would record only the shaded portion, due to the dimensions of the film. The situation for the "back-reflection" region is illustrated in Figure 4–4. Only the spheres for the extreme wavelengths in the spectrum are shown; all regions between these (shaded) can diffract.

How will the spots appear on the film? Because of the profusion of

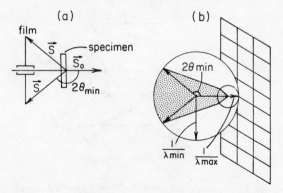

Figure 4–4.   Geometry for Laue patterns in back reflection.

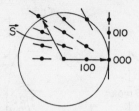

Figure 4–5.   The Ewald sphere of reflection drawn with unit radius. The lines
from the origin represent the range of λ's available in taking a Laue
pattern.

spheres involved in our drawings with many λ's, it will be easier to see
what is going on if we rewrite Bragg's law in the form:

$$\mathbf{S} - \mathbf{S}_o = \lambda \mathbf{r}_{hkl}^*.$$

Thus we can draw a sphere of unit radius, and the reciprocal lattice
points will be rods through the origin, of lengths given by the spread
of available λ's. This is shown in Figure 4–5. The spots are the lattice
points for $\lambda_{K\alpha_1}$. All the reciprocal lattice vectors that are normal to
planes in a zone lie in a plane of the reciprocal lattice normal to the
zone axis and passing through the origin of reciprocal space. These
rods then are in such planes, which intersect the sphere of reflection in a

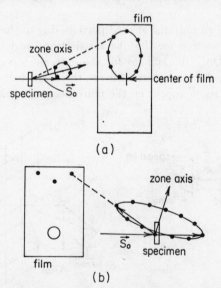

Figure 4–6.   (a) Transmission Laue pattern; ellipse of spots from a zone. (b) Back
reflection Laue pattern; hyperbola of spots from a zone.

circle. The diffraction spots from a zone will be in the form of a cone around the zone axis, with the incident beam as one edge of the cone. This is illustrated in Figure 4–6(a) and (b). Note that each spot in the cone will have a different wavelength at the intersection. That is, each plane chooses the correct λ (if it is available) from the continuous radiation. It is also possible to see, from Figure 4–5, that at the same 2θ the 330 *might* diffract due to one λ and the 220 due to $3\lambda/2$; i.e., the third order from the 110 due to λ might superimpose on the second order from $3\lambda/2$. Each spot may in general be made up of several harmonics.[2]

This "pass-filter" behavior of these Laue patterns was not recognized by the discoverers of diffraction from crystals. They set out to analyze these patterns in the following way.

As we know, diffraction is related to reciprocal space, and what we wish to plot from the Laue pattern, if we can, is reciprocal space—i.e., the normals to planes causing diffraction. We can calculate the position of these as shown in Figure 4–7 for a transmission pattern. We use a

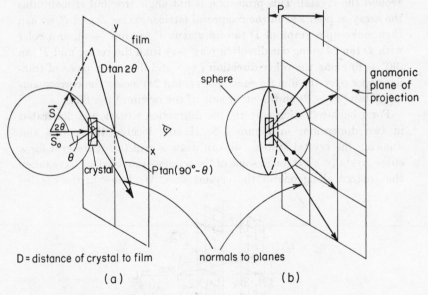

D = distance of crystal to film

(a)

normals to planes

(b)

Figure 4–7.   The gnomonic projection for the transmission Laue pattern.

[2] Note also in Figure 4–5 that a Laue spot can be at a lower or higher 2θ angle than a Bragg spot from the characteristic radiation. As the crystal is rotated, a Laue spot will move toward or away from the Bragg spot.

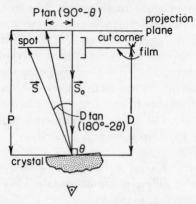

Figure 4–8.   Gnomonic projection for the back reflection Laue pattern. (After N. F. M. Henry, H. Lipson, and W. A. Wooster, *The Interpretation of X-ray Diffraction Photographs*, Macmillan and Co., London, 1961.)

"gnomonic" projection—a projection onto a plane tangent to a sphere around the crystal. This projection is not angle true but it maintains the array of points as in the reciprocal lattice. Fixing D and P, we can then make up a graph of $D \tan 2\theta$ versus $P \tan (90° - \theta)$, or a ruler with $D \tan 2\theta$ along one direction (say $-x$) from the center and $P \tan (90° - \theta)$ along the other direction $(+x)$, and then on a piece of tracing paper over the film for each spot ($D \tan 2\theta$) locate the corresponding $P \tan (90° - \theta)$ on the other side of the origin of the film.

For a back-reflection pattern, the diffraction situation is illustrated in two dimensions in Figure 4–8. Having located the points and knowing the crystal system, we can draw a grid (a square grid for a cubic crystal, e.g.) through some of the points—provided we have taken the pattern along one of the crystal axes. We know in the case of

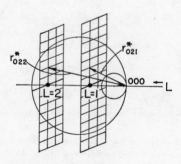

Figure 4–9.

transmission that many of the points will be of the form hkl as the first l layer of reciprocal space is cut by this method (but not the $hk0$ layer). Other points lie inside grid squares and are from layers of higher l, as shown in Figure 4–9. (In back-reflection, high index spots are close to the film's center but they are far from the center in transmission.) If we find an index referred to our two-dimensional grid of $1\frac{1}{2}$, $3\frac{1}{2}$ it means the point has indices 372—i.e., it comes from the second layer.

Let us consider a transmission Laue pattern taken along the $\mathbf{a}_3$ axis of a cubic crystal as shown in Figure 4–10. We now write the three Laue equations:

$$(\mathbf{S} - \mathbf{S}_o) \cdot \mathbf{a}_1 = h\lambda,$$

$$(\mathbf{S} - \mathbf{S}_o) \cdot \mathbf{a}_2 = k\lambda,$$

$$(\mathbf{S} - \mathbf{S}_o) \cdot \mathbf{a}_3 = l\lambda.$$

$$\mathbf{S}_o \cdot \mathbf{a}_1 = \mathbf{S}_o \cdot \mathbf{a}_2 = 0 \qquad \mathbf{S}_o \cdot \mathbf{a}_3 = -1.$$

Expanding,

$$\mathbf{S} \cdot \mathbf{a}_1 = h\lambda, \qquad |\mathbf{a}_1| \cos \alpha = h\lambda, \qquad \cos \alpha = \frac{h\lambda}{|\mathbf{a}_1|};$$

$$\mathbf{S} \cdot \mathbf{a}_2 = k\lambda, \qquad |\mathbf{a}_2| \cos \beta = k\lambda, \qquad \cos \beta = \frac{k\lambda}{|\mathbf{a}_2|};$$

$$\mathbf{S} \cdot \mathbf{a}_3 + |\mathbf{a}_3| = l\lambda, \qquad |\mathbf{a}_3| \cos \gamma + |\mathbf{a}_3| = l\lambda, \qquad \cos \gamma = \frac{l\lambda}{|\mathbf{a}_3|} - 1;$$

$$\cos^2 \alpha + \cos^2 \beta + \cos^2 \gamma = 1 = \frac{h^2\lambda^2}{|\mathbf{a}_1|^2} + \frac{k^2\lambda^2}{|\mathbf{a}_2|^2} + \frac{l^2\lambda^2}{|\mathbf{a}_3|^2} + 1 - \frac{2l\lambda}{|\mathbf{a}_3|}.$$

As $|\mathbf{a}_1| = |\mathbf{a}_2| = |\mathbf{a}_3|$ for a cubic crystal,

$$1 = \frac{\lambda^2}{|\mathbf{a}|^2} (h^2 + k^2 + l^2) + 1 - \frac{2l\lambda}{|\mathbf{a}|},$$

$$\frac{2l\lambda}{|\mathbf{a}|} = \frac{\lambda^2}{|\mathbf{a}|^2} (h^2 + k^2 + l^2),$$

$$\frac{\lambda}{|\mathbf{a}|} = \frac{2l}{h^2 + k^2 + l^2}.$$

We know hkl from idexing the gnomonic projection. The ratio λ/a was found by Laue to be a series of numbers, different for different spots.

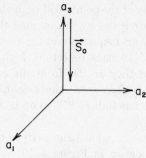

Figure 4–10.

Laue did not at first realize the "filtering" of the white radiation by three-dimensional gratings; he assumed that the various λ's were fluorescent radiation from the specimen, diffracting inside the crystal! He also did not realize that missing spots indicated the structure of the unit cell or repeating unit—i.e., a reciprocal point for which $F(\mathbf{s})$ was zero. Sir W. L. Bragg, however, noticed in one of Laue's papers that when the film was placed increasing distances behind the crystal, the Laue spots become elliptical. As rays should travel in straight lines, he realized this ellipticity must be the result of focusing. He visualized this process as in Figure 4–11, with each plane of a family choosing the appropriate λ; this drawing led to his famous equation and the first structure analyses.

As we shall see, there are more powerful methods for evaluating the structure of reciprocal space (we have already seen how Bragg used his equation), and Laue patterns are now mainly used in two ways.

1.   With a crystal whose structure is unknown, taking a Laue normal to a well-developed face will reveal certain aspects of the point group

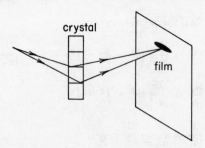

Figure 4–11.   The focusing action of crystal planes. (After P. P. Ewald, *Fifty Years of X-Ray Diffraction*, N. V. A. Oosthoek's Uitgeversmaatschappij Utrecht, The Netherlands, 1962.)

symmetry. That is, the symmetry of the pattern should be the symmetry of the point group—plus a center of symmetry (because, as we have seen, in an intensity measurement a center is added).

We can easily see that the point group symmetry is the same in reciprocal space as it is in real space. If we rotate a vector in real space, say $\mathbf{r}$, clockwise, this is equivalent to rotating $\mathbf{s} = (\mathbf{S} - \mathbf{S}o)/\lambda$ in the opposite sense in a transform as $\mathbf{s} \cdot \mathbf{r}$ is the same in the exponent. Thus the transform of a function will be the same for either operation, and a rotation symmetry in one space will appear in the other. Looking at this another way, any symmetry operation that takes a plane into

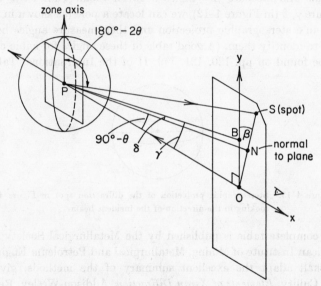

Figure 4–12.   (After B. D. Cullity, *Elements of X-Ray Diffraction*, Addison-Wesley, Reading, Mass., 1956.)

another plane, takes the normal into the normal of this second plane, and therefore the reciprocal lattice, made up of normals, will show the same point group symmetry as the crystal. As the Laue pattern is a "picture" of reciprocal space around the origin, we see point symmetry. However, a center of symmetry is added, so that of the 32 point groups, only 11 can be found by examining Laue patterns taken along important axes of the crystal (see p. 30, Vol. I of the International Tables and Problem 1–9).

2.   They are a valuable aid in determining the orientation of a crystal

grown in a container, so that the faces do not arise due to natural growth but rather due to the confines of the container. With this method we can determine the orientation before we test the crystal or cut it. We shall expand on this problem to see the techniques that have been developed to make it easier.

Consider first the back-reflecting technique (Figure 4–12). We wish to figure out some scheme—such that from a diffraction spot—we can locate the pole of the plane causing the spot, and identify the plane. Since our crystal might have any orientation, indexing the reciprocal space will be difficult. We can accomplish our goal if we can locate several normals and measure the angles between them. That is, if we can measure γ, δ (in Figure 4–12), we can locate a pole (as shown in Figure 4–13) in a stereographic projection and then measure angles between poles to identify them. (A good table of these angles for cubic crystals can be found on pp. 120, 121, Vol. II of the International Tables. A

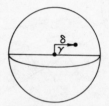

Figure 4–13. Stereographic projection of the diffraction spot in Figure 4–12, looking in the direction of the incident beam.

more complete table is published by the Metallurgical Society of the American Institute of Mining, Metallurgical and Petroleum Engineers.) We shall adapt the excellent summary of the methods, given by B. O. Cullity, *Elements of X-ray Diffraction*, Addison-Wesley, Reading, Mass., 1956. From the drawing in Figure 4–12, for the given diffraction spot,

$$x = \text{OS} \sin \beta; \qquad y = \text{OS} \cos \beta; \qquad \frac{x}{y} = \tan \beta, \qquad (4\text{–}2a)$$

$$\text{OS} = \text{OP} \tan (180^\circ - 2\theta) = (x^2 + y^2)^{1/2}, \qquad (4\text{–}2b)$$

$$\tan \beta = \frac{\text{BN}}{\text{BO}} = \frac{\text{PB} \tan \delta}{\text{PB} \sin \gamma} = \frac{\tan \delta}{\sin \gamma}, \qquad (4\text{–}2c)$$

$$\tan (90^\circ - \theta) = \frac{\text{BN}/\sin \beta}{\text{PB} \cos \gamma} = \frac{\text{PB} \tan \delta/\sin \beta}{\text{PB} \cos \gamma} = \frac{\tan \delta}{\sin \beta \cos \gamma}. \qquad (4\text{–}2d)$$

Here, OP is fixed experimentally. We can therefore determine γ, δ, the angles for the normal, from x, y, the position of the spot (or vice versa) in the following way:

1. Measure x, y.
2. Calculate β.
3. Calculate OS.

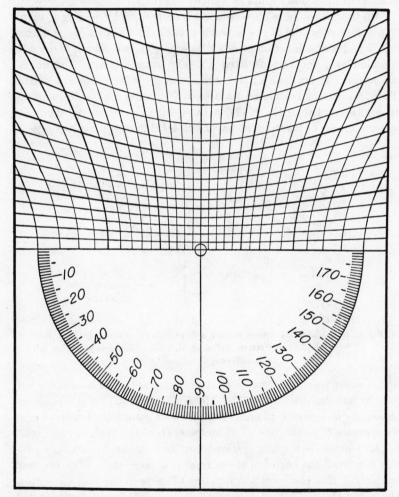

Figure 4–14. Greninger Net. From C. S. Barrett, *Structure of Metals*, 2nd edition. Copyright 1943, 1942 by the McGraw-Hill Book Co., Inc. Used by permission of McGraw-Hill Book Company.

4. Calculate $(180° - 2\theta)$ and hence $(90° - \theta)$.

5. Solve equations c and d simultaneously for γ, δ.

6. Locate the pole in stereographic projection.

7. Repeat for several poles and identify by measuring angles between them and comparing to a table for the system. (It is helpful to connect poles with great circles. Common intersections of these circles must be prominent poles and should be easier to identify.)

This process can be made considerably more rapid by making a "map" to place over the film of γ, δ for each x, y. First let us plot, using a fixed OP, x and y as a function of δ (for various γ's), and then x and y as a function of γ for various fixed δ's. For example, with constant γ, $x/y = \tan\beta = \tan\delta/\sin\gamma$; for each δ we get a value of x/y and β. Then x, y can be calculated for a fixed OP, using Eq. (4–2b), and x/y to get OS, and then Eq. (4–2b) with (4–2a) to get x, y. We then plot x, y on a piece of transparent paper and label it with its values of γ, δ,

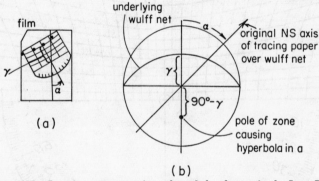

(a)

(b)

Figure 4–15.   Locating a zone causing a hyperbola of spots in the Laue Back Reflection Pattern. (After B. D. Cullity, *Elements of X-Ray Diffraction*, Addison-Wesley Co., Reading, Mass., 1956.)

and connect points of equal γ. Each resulting curve for constant γ will be a hyperbola—the locus of spots from planes in one zone. We can see this easily in Figure 4–12 and with the above equations. For fixed γ, as we increase δ, β, and $(90° - \theta)$ increase. Our map is shown in Figure 4–14. (The curves running vertically are for constant δ, varying γ.) We can then read the angles of the normal to a plane right from the spot by placing this plot over the film, on the side of the film away from the x-ray tube. (Cutting a corner before exposure, as shown in the figures, will help us keep track of the film's orientation.) Such a "net" is named after its inventor, Greninger, who devised it as part of his

Ph.D. thesis. Now we can locate each pole. Two poles will fix the orientation if we know the system, a third or fourth are a useful check.

As all planes having poles of the same γ lie in a zone, they lie on a great circle in a stereographic projection; we can therefore plot it or its pole, immediately. The net is placed *over* the film and rotated until one hyperbola of constant γ matches a hyperbola of spots. The direction and amount of rotation (indicated by the compass marked on the bottom of the net) are noted. As indicated in Figure 4–15, a tracing paper over a Wulff net is rotated *in the opposite sense* (why?) and the great circle located. This is much quicker and easier than reading each spot. The intersections of great circles and poles of these circles can be indexed by measuring the angles between them and comparing them to our table of angles between normals to planes. Angles between spots can be measured right on the film along a coincident hyperbola of the net, and the rotation angle between two hyperbolae is the angle between two planes or their great circles. With this in mind and some practice comparing the stereographic projection to the Laue pattern, the reader will soon be able to spot important symmetry axes and index spots right on the films without the projection. (Inking in the hyperbolae and/or spots on the film, or on a tracing, may make them stand out more clearly.)

Now let us consider the same analysis for the transmission method, as in Figure 4–16. Again we could seek equations to relate x, y to γ, δ, and watch to maintain our orientation during the analysis such that *we are looking in the direction in which the beam is going.* Figure 4–17 showed the Leonhardt chart for the analysis of these transmission patterns and a stereographic plot of one pole.

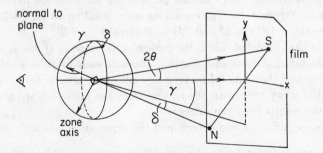

Figure 4–16. Indexing a transmission Laue pattern. (After B. D. Cullity, *Elements of X-Ray Diffraction*, Addison-Wesley Co., Reading, Mass., 1956.)

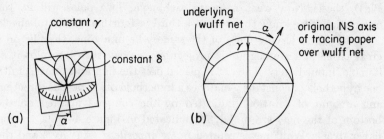

Figure 4–17.   Indexing an ellipse in a Transmission Laue Pattern. (*a*) Leonhardt chart. (After B. D. Cullity, *Elements of X-Ray Diffraction*, Addison-Wesley Co., Reading, Mass., 1956.)

If a chart is not available, there is another quick way to locate the poles, illustrated in Figure 4–18, for the back-reflection method.

$$OS = OC \tan (180° - 2\theta), \qquad (4\text{–}3a)$$

$$PD = TD \tan (45° - \theta/2) = 2r \tan (45° - \theta/2). \qquad (4\text{–}3b)$$

As triangle TUD is similar to triangle TMC,

$$R = 2r, \qquad (4\text{–}3c)$$

and

$$PD = R \tan (45° - \theta/2). \qquad (4\text{–}3d)$$

We make up a "stereographic" ruler, Figure 4–19, labeling PD in terms of OS. Once we *choose* OC, R, for the film and projection, we can calculate for a given OS, θ, Eq. (4–3*a*) and PD from Eq. (4–3*d*).

A stereographic ruler can also be used for transmission patterns, as shown in Figure 4–19. The equations corresponding to Eq. (4–3*a*) and (*d*) are OS = OC tan 2θ and PD = R tan (45° − $\theta/2$).

Note that *with the rulers, the projection is made as if one is looking into the beam.* (One is just plotting opposite ends of poles in the two methods and therefore for making any tilt of the crystal he faces away from the x-ray tube with the results from the nets—toward the tube with the results from the rulers.[3])

Suppose, after having determined the orientation, we wish to move

---

[3] With care in remembering the direction of projection, if transmission and back-reflection Laues are taken at the same time with one sample, a pole from the back-reflection pattern will appear inverted through the center in the transmission pattern, if the former is analyzed with a Greninger net, the latter with a ruler.

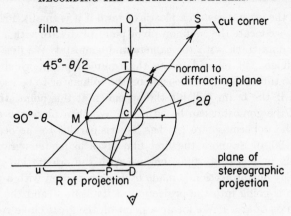

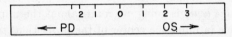

Figure 4–18. (After B. D. Cullity, *Elements of X-Ray Diffraction*, Addison-Wesley Co., Reading, Mass., 1956.)

the crystal to another orientation—e.g., to cut it. In order to examine the motions necessary to accomplish this, assume we mount a cubic crystal on a goniostat (a sturdy one if the crystal is to be held for a cut,

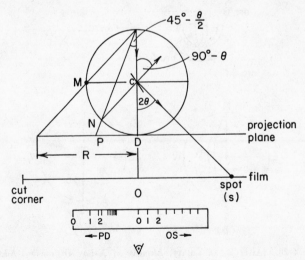

Figure 4–19. Construction of a stereographic ruler for a transmission pattern.

and with the crystal cast in a plastic or resin if it is small). Prior to the first film, we locate the common pivot point of the arc with a telescope mounted on a track with the camera and goniostat. We first focus on our specimen, tilt it, and locate the common point, which will not defocus on tilting. Then by focusing on the collimator to be used we can ascertain if the beam will hit the specimen at this point. If not, the height of the goniostat can be adjusted. We then place the goniostat so that the uppermost arc (A) has its axis parallel to the beam, as in Figure 4–20(a). Suppose the first film gives us a stereographic projection, as in Figure 4–20(b), but we wish the orientation in Figure 4–20(c). Say our projection is made by back reflection with a net—i.e., the beam is going into the projection at its center—and the center is also the axis of arc A. We locate a point on the great circle connecting 012 and 010 poles, 90 degrees from 012 (the point x in Figure 4–20(b)). In the final orientation, this point is to be the North pole. *Looking in the direction in which the beam* is going, we rotate about the upper axis A around a small circle (around the center of the projection) to bring x to the N–S axis. Rotation about this upper axis does not effect the lower axes B, C. We then rotate about axis B, the E–W axis, to bring x to the North pole, and then about axis C (the N–S axis) to bring (012) into the center.

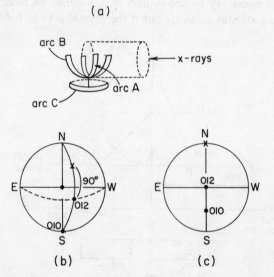

Figure 4–20. (After B. D. Cullity, *Elements of X-Ray Diffraction*, Addison-Wesley Co., Reading, Mass., 1956.)

If we wished to cut a surface parallel to (012), it would only be necessary to rotate the 012 pole into the center of the projection. This could be done with only two of the circles; a rotation first about the B axis to put (012) on the E–W axis, and then around C to put (012) in the center. The orientation should be checked with another Laue and then the goniostat is transferred to the bed of a milling machine or cut-off wheel where a track for the goniostat has been aligned accurately parallel to the cutting wheel. Dovetail tracks at the x-ray tube and on the bed of the cut-off wheel will provide for an accurate transfer.

This orientation could be done on the diffractometer as it can measure angles quite accurately, more accurately than the $\pm 1/4$–$1/2$ degree possible with the usual Laue methods (due to the size of the

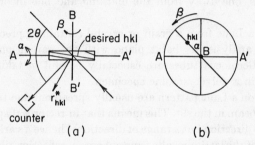

Figure 4–21.   Locating a plane in a crystal on the diffractometer. (After B. D. Cullity, *Elements of X-Ray Diffraction*, Addison-Wesley Co., Reading, Mass., 1956.)

spots and the interpolation of the nets). The counter is set at the 2θ for reflection from the plane desired, for the characteristic radiation of the tube, as in Figure 4–21. The specimen is then rotated α around AA′ and β around BB′ until the reflection is located. The normal to the desired plane is now bisecting the incident and diffracted beams $((\mathbf{S} - \mathbf{S}o)/\lambda = \mathbf{r}^*_{hkl})$. Imagining a stereographic sphere around the specimen, with BB′ through the center, the pole is located as in Figure 4–21(b). A narrow receiving slit in front of the counter can be added to refine the angles to a hundredth of a degree if necessary. At this point the specimen can be cut, or another pole located if orientation is desired. (Commercial counter units, in fact, came into being in the Second World War to satisfy a need for a rapid device for cutting crystals for piezoelectric devices.)

There are many uses for such orientation determinations, of which we shall describe briefly only three.

1.   For a single crystal being used, say for a tensile test, such an orientation determination perpendicular to the axis of the specimen locates the tensile axis as the N–S axis in the projection. After a small amount of deformation, slip markings on one or two surfaces will identify the slip plane. Laues can be taken for increasing strains and the tensile axis plotted, say in a standard (100) projection. Because the slip direction rotates into the tensile axis, an arc connecting successive positions of the tensile axis must pass through the pole on the great circle representing the slip plane which is the slip direction. When other slip planes and directions become active, these can be noted. The elongation can be measured.

2.   Unusual striations, which might be twins, can be identified by taking Laues, one away from the marking and one in or straddling the marking.

3.   With a Laue from a grain or crystal containing precipitate, and two surface analysis, its habit plane with the parent phase can be identified. Microfocus tubes are especially helpful in taking patterns from grains in a polycrystalline specimen.

The spots on a Laue pattern are usually spread out due to the divergence of the beam in the slit. This means that in reciprocal space S_o does not have one direction but a range of directions; hence a variation of the intersection of the lattice results from spheres of reflection tilted slightly. If the specimen is distorted, so that the planes are bent over a range of angles say around one axis, the reciprocal lattice exists over the range of these angles. Again there is a volume of intersection. If this is in excess of the divergence due to the beam, it can be recognized, and in simple cases the axis of rotation can be identified—e.g., if the spots spread along a hyperbola, the axis of tilt is the zone axis of the planes contributing to the hyperbola. If there is a mosaic, with subgrains tilted relative to each other, we can visualize this as discrete reciprocal lattices tilted slightly with respect to each other. If the tilt is 1–2 degrees or more, a Laue spot will be composed of small discrete spots.

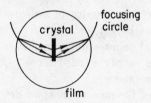

Figure 4–22.   Focusing action of a circular film.

With microfocus tubes or fine collimation, tilts of only a few minutes of arc can be readily detected.

If the spots are quite broad due to mosaic, or distorted due to severe deformation, it may be difficult to gather enough spots with a flat film in any reasonable time. This situation can be readily overcome by using a cylindrical film. As shown in Figure 4–22, focusing can be obtained at least in the horizontal plane by using a cylindrical film; the exposure will be greatly reduced as a result of the focusing. Charts for reading such films are described in Vol. 2 of the International Tables.

Some of the spots are formed partly with characteristic radiation. If the spots are spread out due to distortion, this more intense radiation will in a short time produce an arc as in Figure 4–23. A very long

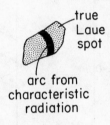

Figure 4–23.

exposure (≈ 2 days) will usually bring out the full spot in a heavily deformed specimen.

Finally it is important to remember that as white radiation is used for Laue patterns, and this is proportional to Z^2, it is best to use a tube with a high Z—unless the characteristic radiation, which is so much stronger than the white, will fluoresce the sample. Sometimes it can be helpful to cover the film or central portions of the film with aluminum foil to reduce blackening from such effects.

Oscillating Crystal Methods

Oscillating crystal methods are the most powerful of the diffraction techniques. Generally film techniques are employed with filtered radiation, followed by counter methods for precision intensity measurements. Although considerable attention is now being given to automating the diffractometer to enable it to do the entire process to be described, when a laboratory is not constantly doing work on structures, film methods still provide the advantage of a small record of a great number of spots.

The Rotating Crystal Method

A film is wrapped around the crystal in the form of a cylinder; filtered radiation is employed. The crystal is placed, with some prominent axis as the axis of the cylindrical film and rotated, as shown in Figure 4–24. The reflecting sphere cuts the reciprocal lattice (a) forming

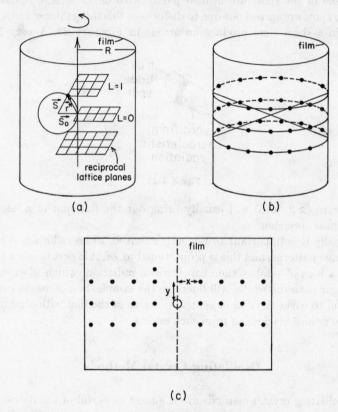

Figure 4–24. A rotation pattern.

horizontal layers of spots (b), (c) because an axis in real space is perpendicular to a plane in reciprocal space. In the full 360 degree rotation, the reflecting sphere generates a toroid, as shown in Figure 4–25. All

Section of toroid generated by rotation of Ewald sphere

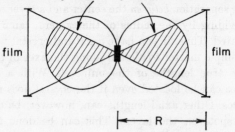

Figure 4–25. Shaded area is the region of reciprocal space seen during rotation.

the points within the toroid and the limits set by the film height and camera radius can diffract.

Consider the rotation axis as the $\mathbf{a}_3$ axis of the crystal. Then from the Laue conditions:

$$(\mathbf{S} - \mathbf{S}_o) \cdot \mathbf{a}_3 = l\lambda. \tag{4-4a}$$

$\mathbf{S}_o$ is perpendicular to $\mathbf{a}_3$; therefore

$$\mathbf{S} \cdot \mathbf{a}_3 = l\lambda, \tag{4-4b}$$

or

$$|\mathbf{a}_3| \cos \varphi = l\lambda, \tag{4-4c}$$

or

$$\sin \beta = \frac{l\lambda}{|\mathbf{a}_3|}.$$

The angles ϕ and β are shown in Figure 4–26. All spots with the same l, regardless of h, k, have the same β and lie on the same layer—i.e., each

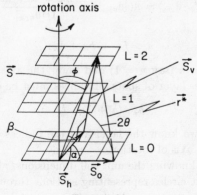

Figure 4–26.

cone of spots is for one l value, as can also be seen in Figure 4–24. By measuring the separation *between* the center and a layer or between two layers and dividing by the radius of the camera, $\tan \beta$ and then $|\mathbf{a}_3|$ can be calculated. Thus, if you have a natural crystal with prominent faces, it is a simple matter to align it along the axes of the crystal and determine the true lengths of the unit cell. With a Laue pattern, important axes can be located even if the crystal does not have well-developed faces. Other axial lengths can, however, be determined by indexing the spots on the layers. This can be done routinely with 1–2 per cent accuracy. Also, different symmetry elements in the unit cell result in zero intensity for certain spots; if we can figure out a scheme for indexing all of the spots, we could determine the other axes and which spots were missing, and this would give us information about the space group. In fact in Vol. I of the International Tables, under each space group, for each equipoint, the extinctions are listed to help us! We shall therefore consider how to index the spots.

If rotation is around the axis represented by $u\mathbf{a}_1 + v\mathbf{a}_2 + w\mathbf{a}_3$, this vector has a length that is the inverse of the distance of the planes (uvw) in reciprocal space. Let

$$\mathbf{d}_{uvw} = \frac{u\mathbf{a}_1 + v\mathbf{a}_2 + w\mathbf{a}_3}{1/|\mathbf{d}_{uvw}|}.$$

Then, $\mathbf{d}_{uvw}$ is a *unit* vector perpendicular to the reciprocal lattice layers—i.e., along the direction $[uvw]$. If we take the scalar product of $\mathbf{d}$ with an $\mathbf{r}^*_{hkl}$ (to a point in reciprocal space on a given layer), we obtain a relation involving the number (n) of layers to this spot:

$$\mathbf{r}^*_{hkl} \cdot \mathbf{d}_{uvw} = n(|\mathbf{d}_{uvw}|) = \frac{hu + kv + lw}{1/|\mathbf{d}_{uvw}|}, \qquad (4\text{–}5a)$$

or

$$n = hu + kv + lw. \qquad (4\text{–}5b)$$

If we have a layer n (say $n = 1$) and know the axis of rotation (say [110]), then on this layer of spots all indices must be of the form

$$h, \quad (\bar{h} + 1), \quad l.$$

Conversely, if we know the layer and the indices of two spots, we can determine the axis of rotation.

Next we could, knowing the unit cell dimensions, plot the reciprocal lattice and lay out circles representing sections through the reflecting sphere at various levels, as we did to orient a crystal for one diffraction

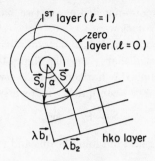

Figure 4–27.

spot. This is done in Figure 4–27, where α is the angle between S_o and the component of S on a horizontal plane—i.e., it is the angle determined by the distance x on the film (Figure 4–24(c)) and the radius (R) of the camera ($\alpha = x/R$). Thus, by calculating α for a spot on a given layer, the indices can be found.[4] However, in the usual experiment with this technique, the crystal is rotated continuously. The 360-degree rotation leads to an uncertainty; several spots may have the same α! For such uncertain spots, we can change the gearing on the camera and oscillate over a finite angular range to see which of the possible spots is the correct one. (This can also be done on the diffractometer using the instrument shown in Figure 4–2(c).) This oscillation is indicated in Figure 4–28. In (a) the oscillation is illustrated for a spot on the equator and in (b) for a spot on some l layer. The shaded area is the region of possible intersection. It is necessary to check all possible

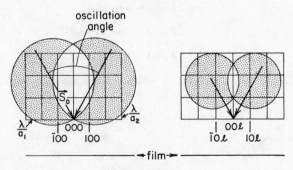

Figure 4–28.

[4] Note that an hk spot on successive layers (i.e., the 110, 111 ...) must move away from the center of the film.

indices for any given spot—not just one or two, as there may be several at one point in a full rotation.

The indexing of spots can be greatly simplified with the aid of a chart known as the *Bernal* chart. Consider Figure 4–26. If we can rapidly measure, from the film, the horizontal and vertical components of $\lambda \mathbf{r}^*$, $\lambda \mathbf{r}_h^*$, and $\lambda \mathbf{r}_v^*$, and φ, we can quickly index a spot. Now,

$$\mathbf{S} - \mathbf{S}_o = \lambda \mathbf{r}^*.$$

Breaking the incoming and outgoing beams and $\mathbf{r}^*$ into horizontal and vertical components:

$$\mathbf{S}_v - \mathbf{S}_{o_v} = \lambda \mathbf{r}_v^*.$$

$$|\mathbf{S}_{o_v}| = 0.$$

Therefore,

$$\mathbf{S}_v = \lambda \mathbf{r}_v,$$

and, referring to Figure 4–26:

$$\sin \beta = \frac{|\mathbf{S}_v|}{1} = \lambda |\mathbf{r}_v^*|; \qquad \tan \beta = \frac{y}{R} \quad \text{(See Figure 4.24.)}$$

As

$$2 \sin \theta = \lambda |\mathbf{r}^*|,$$

$$4 \sin^2 \theta = \lambda (|\mathbf{r}_h^*|^2 + |\mathbf{r}_v^*|^2).$$

The geometric situation in Figure 4–26 is that of a spherical right triangle so that

$$\cos 2\theta = \cos \alpha \cos \beta,$$

$$1 - \cos 2\theta = 1 - \cos \alpha \cos \beta,$$

$$2 \sin^2 \theta = 1 - \cos \alpha \cos \beta,$$

$$\lambda^2 (|\mathbf{r}_v^*|^2 + |\mathbf{r}_h^*|^2) = 2(1 - \cos \alpha \cos \beta).$$

But,

$$\lambda^2 |\mathbf{r}_v^*|^2 = \sin^2 \beta.$$

Therefore,

$$\sin^2 \beta + \lambda^2 r_h^{*2} = 2(1 - \cos \alpha \cos \beta). \qquad (4\text{–}6)$$

In addition,

$$\alpha = \frac{x}{R}$$

where as before, x is the horizontal distance from the center line of the

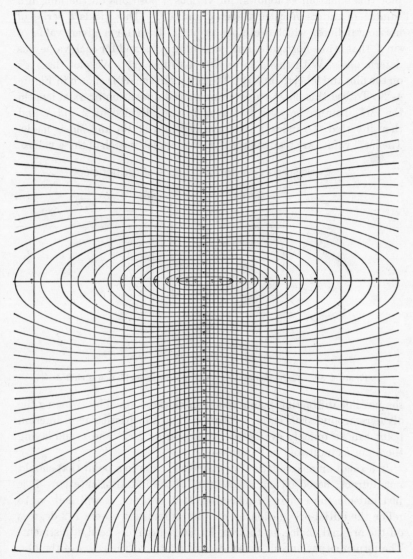

Figure 4–29.   Bernal chart. (Reprinted from N. F. M. Henry, H. Lipson, and W. A. Wooster, *The Interpretation of X-ray Diffraction Photographs*, Macmillan, London, 1951.)

film to a spot (i.e., along a layer) and R is the camera radius. We can plot this equation as follows: for various y positions on the film in a camera of radius R calculate $\sin \beta$ and $\lambda|\mathbf{r}_v^*|$. This yields a series of horizontal lines, which we label as $|\lambda \mathbf{r}_v^*|$. Then for a given value of $\sin \beta$, that is one horizontal line, pick values of x and for each value this determines α. With this α solve Eq. (4–6) for $\lambda|\mathbf{r}_h^*|$. We plot these x's on the film and label them $\lambda|\mathbf{r}_h^*|$. The completed chart is shown in Figure 4–29. To use this chart to determine a cell dimension or axial length, the $|\lambda \mathbf{r}_v^*|$ distance between two layers is read, divided by 2 and λ, and then inverted. To index layers, a scaled plot of $\lambda \mathbf{b}_1$ and $\lambda \mathbf{b}_2$ is made. The $|\lambda \mathbf{r}_h^*|$ values are read and, with a dividers set at each of these values,

Ewald spheres in extreme positions of oscillation

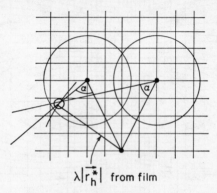

$\lambda |\overrightarrow{\mathbf{r}_h^*}|$ from film

Figure 4–30. The region causing a spot during an oscillation is circled.

the possible diffracting points can then be ascertained by swinging the dividers around 000. In an oscillation film, the particular diffraction point can be quickly evaluated by measuring $\lambda|\mathbf{r}_h^*|$ and α and laying them out as indicated in Figure 4–30.

In a small-angle oscillation we may come close to a point that should not diffract; based on our assumption of the initial orientation—it is just outside the sphere of reflection. If it appears, it will help us to refine the initial orientation by making us realize we were 1–2 degrees off the original choice, or that the lattice parameters need adjustment. The former situation will cause the spots out near the edges of the film to be wide, as shown (exaggerated) in Figure 4–31.

It is not always possible to completely determine the space group of a crystal; of the 230 only 50 can be determined without question. A rotation or oscillation introduces two mirror planes parallel to the oscillation axis. In addition there is the added center of symmetry (which might be determined by such external measurements as piezo-electricity or special x-ray techniques to be discussed later). It is sometimes necessary to use other methods to distinguish whether a screw rotation is left or right handed. Knowledge of the true point group can be helpful. Replacing screw axes and glide planes by rotation axes and reflection planes gives the point group, so that the latter may fix the space group. Your choice of unit cell may not correspond to that used in the International Tables, and it is often necessary to try interchanging the axes and re-examining extinctions and the tables to find the possible space groups. The various space group symbols for different choices of labeling the axes can also be found at the back of Vol. I of the International Tables, p. 543. The starting point in study of structure is the listing of the Laue point group (of

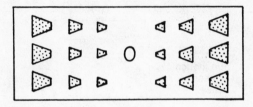

Figure 4–31. Rotation pattern—crystal poorly aligned.

the 11 three-dimensional Laue point groups that result when a center of symmetry is added to the 32, p. 30, Vol. I of the International Tables and Problem 1–9), the type of lattice and, with your choice of axes, the types of glide planes or screw axes present as indicated by the extinctions. These are given by Laue patterns along principal axes, and the crystal system, and extinctions are found from the oscillation and rotation films. Then the possible space groups can be reduced to only a few. Carefully examine pp. 53, 56, 347–352 of the International Tables, Vol. I and Problem 2–10–13. Starting on p. 347, the possible space groups for a given lattice, Laue point group, screw axes, glide planes, are given; these can then be examined individually to see which one (or two) fit the observed extinctions. A useful summarizing table, prepared by Dr. S. K. Dickinson Jr., is given in Appendix C. In a final analysis, accurate intensity measurements will be needed to check certain peaks and also to obtain the atomic positions; we shall examine how to do this later. Examples of the use of rotation films are given at the end of this chapter.

Weissenberg Methods

The several films necessary to eliminate uncertainties in the rotation can be eliminated in a simple manner, devised by Weissenberg; the method is illustrated by Figure 4–32.

The film is made to *move with* the rotation of the crystal so that spots at different rotations but with the same $|\lambda r_h^*|$ are not overlapping. A single layer line is isolated with a screen. The geometry of this selection is illustrated in Figure 4–33. (The Ewald or reflection sphere is of unit radius, so distances are not $\mathbf{b}_i$ but $\lambda \mathbf{b}_i$.) Let u be the complement of the angle between the direct beam and the rotation axis, v the complement of the apex angle of the cone representing a layer of spots. From such

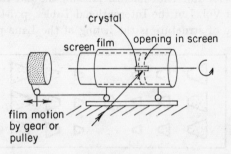

Figure 4–32.   Weissenberg camera. (After N. F. M. Henry, H. Lipson, W. A. Wooster, *The Interpretation of X-Ray Diffraction Photographs*, Macmillan Co., London, 1951.)

drawings and the radius of the camera, we can calculate the location of the screen relative to the direct beam. If the radius of the camera is r, the displacement for Figure 4–33(b) is $r \tan v$. One reason for using inclination methods is illustrated in Figure 4–34. We can see that there is a "blind spot" for $u = 0$. Points closer than $1 - \sqrt{1 - |\lambda r_v^*|^2}$ and further than $1 + \sqrt{1 - |\lambda r_v^*|^2}$ cannot be seen.

The geometry of the technique can be followed by examining reciprocal space and the moving film. This is done in Figure 4–35 looking down along the rotation axis. In (a) a lattice row passing through the origin is considered, and in (b) the row does not pass through the origin. Here, f is merely a proportional relationship—i.e., during rotation φ, translation is $f\varphi$; usually f is 1 mm for 2 degrees in φ; r is the radius of the camera. A Weissenberg pattern, then, looks like that shown in Figure 4–36. Charts are also available for reading these films.

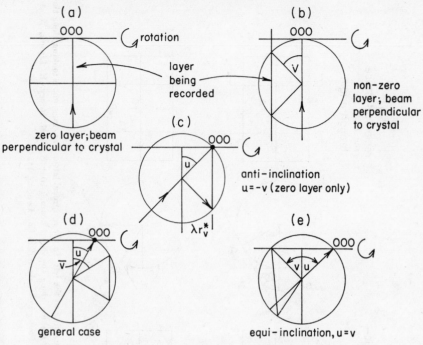

Figure 4–33. Some ways of using a Weissenberg camera. (After N. F. M. Henry, H. Lipson, W. A. Wooster, *The Interpretation of X-Ray Diffraction Photographs*, Macmillan Co., London, 1951.)

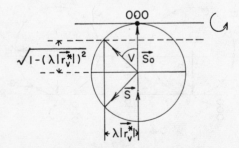

Figure 4–34. The blind region in a Weissenberg pattern. (After N. F. M. Henry, H. Lipson, W. A. Wooster, *The Interpretation of X-Ray Diffraction Photographs*, Macmillan Co., London, 1951.)

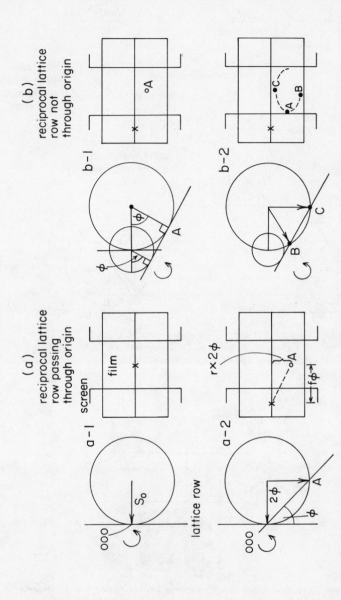

Figure 4-35. How the Weissenberg pattern forms. The film is moving to the left. In the reciprocal lattice drawings, one is looking along the rotation axis; in the sketches of the film, one is looking along the direct beam. (After N. F. M. Henry, H. Lipson, W. A. Wooster, *The Interpretation of X-Ray Diffraction Photographs*, Macmillan Co., London, 1951.)

180

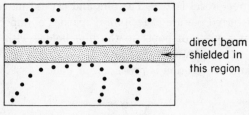

direct beam
shielded in
this region

Figure 4–36.

Precession Methods

Buerger and de Jong and Bouman pointed out that work would be considerably easier if one could really see a picture of the reciprocal lattice undistorted rather than getting involved in the geometry of the crystal motion and the film shape. They accomplished this with a flat film! We shall here discuss the precession method of Buerger. Imagine the crystal at the center of the reflecting sphere of unit radius. From the crystal we imagine some zone axis that is perpendicular to a layer in the reciprocal lattice of the crystal. We shall consider first a zero layer—i.e., a layer passing through the origin of the sphere of reflection—and we shall imagine the film attached to this layer but displaced from it. This situation is shown in Figure 4–37.

The real lattice direction precesses about the direct beam, and thus a small circle is cut by each of the reciprocal lattice planes which is perpendicular to this real lattice direction as it swings around the

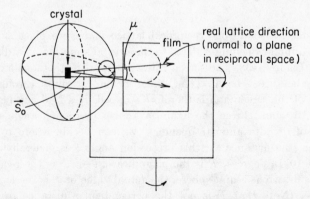

Figure 4–37.   The precession camera. The small circle around the lattice direction precesses around S_0. (After M. J. Buerger, ASXRED Monogr. No. 1 (1944) "The Photography of the Reciprocal Lattice".)

origin of the reciprocal lattice. The film and crystal move together so that an undistorted picture of reciprocal space is obtained. If a unit is available, put a piece of paper in the film holder with a layer of a lattice ruled on it and watch the motion. A series of pictures showing the camera and this motion is presented in Figure 4–39.

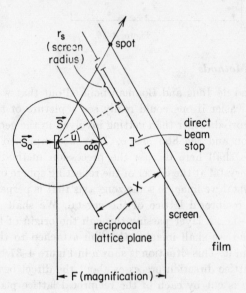

Figure 4–38.   (After M. J. Buerger, ASXRED Monogr. No. 1 (1944) "The Photography of the Reciprocal Lattice.")

In order to isolate one reciprocal lattice plane, we place a screen with an annular opening r_s, fixed to the crystal's motion at a distance x, as in Figure 4–38. The screen rotates normal to the zone axis and around the direct beam. (The direct beam can pass through the opening of the screen and is therefore stopped by a lead cup before it reaches the film.) From the figure, a known precession angle u, and screens of definite annular openings, we can decide where to place each one (the distance x); this precession angle u is generally of the order of 10–15 degrees. F is the magnification—i.e., as the reciprocal sphere is drawn as a unit sphere, the actual value of F is the length of one Å^{-1}. (Note that F is not the perpendicular distance from the crystal to the film but this distance over cos u.) A typical film and the reciprocal lattice obtained from it are shown in Figure 4–40. (The streaks through the spots are due to the fact that the film was over exposed.)

As with the rotation or Weissenberg cameras, in the precession technique the crystal can be orientated on a goniostat under an optical microscope, or with Laue patterns. However, alignment is also readily achieved by removing the screen and taking a photograph with unfiltered radiation. Sharp circles will appear marking the intersection of each layer of the lattice with the reciprocal sphere—i.e., the cut-off of possible reflection. If these circles are not centered on the direct beam then the crystal must be tilted slightly to correct for this. The amount of tilt can readily be determined graphically with the aid of a rough scale drawing as in Figure 4–39 or with formulae found in the manual supplied with the camera. Note that several zero layers can be quickly examined by choosing different normals—a choice which merely involves rotating the crystal around the axis normal to the precessing axis. This is a simple manipulation on the actual camera, as can be seen in Figure 4–39(a); it involves turning the large wheel on the left.

For nonzero layers, the situation is shown in Figure 4–41.

$$n\lambda d^* = (\cos u - \cos v);$$

v can be calculated for the nth layer if d^* is known. The film is moved closer to the crystal by $Fn\lambda d^*$ and the distance of the screen relative to the crystal readjusted so that $\tan v = r_s/x$. Combining these two equations:

$$n\lambda d^* = \left(\cos u - \cos \tan^{-1} \frac{r_s}{x}\right). \tag{4-7}$$

If the repeat distance is *not* known, a film is placed in the screen holder, without a screen; with filtered radiation continuous circles appear. From the radius of any circle (r_s) (other than the first layer circle) and the distance to the screen holder, r_s/x can be calculated, hence $n\lambda d^*$.

Nomographs are supplied with the unit to assist in choosing settings and selecting the screen, as only a fixed number of screens is supplied.

Although the area explored increases with the layer, there is a blind region (not recorded) as can be seen in Figure 4–42; this increases with the layer.

Molybdenum $K\alpha$ radiation is most desirable for all this single crystal film work, if the spots are not too close together, because the reflecting sphere is larger and more spots can be obtained on one record.

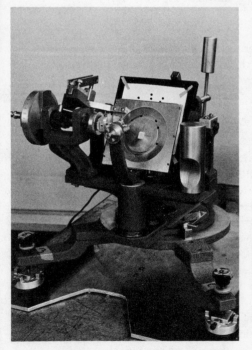

Figure 4–39. A precession camera with a grid showing through the screen at various positions of the camera.

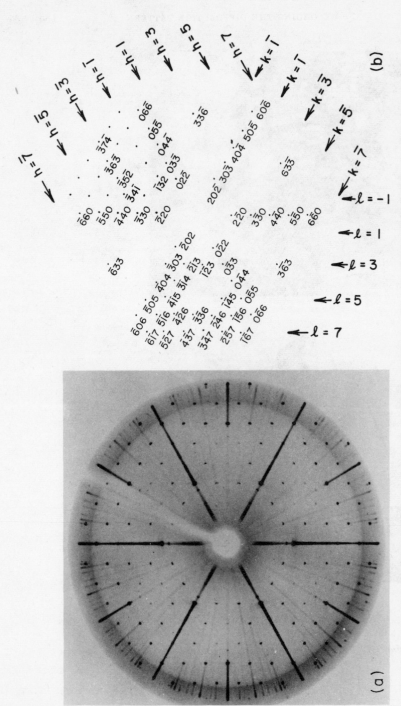

Figure 4-40. Typical precession film, taken by C. Fairhurst. Zero level of a (111) in cubic Ag-Hg; MoK_α, Zr filter, $u = 20°$, $r_s = 15$ mm, crystal to film, 42 mm (perpendicular to film). Over exposed to show streaking from white radiation.

186

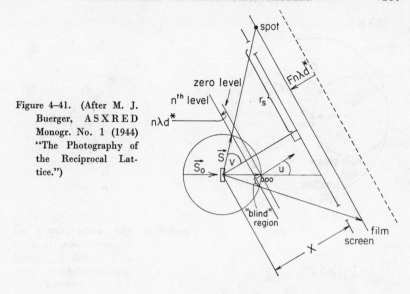

Figure 4–41. (After M. J. Buerger, ASXRED Monogr. No. 1 (1944) "The Photography of the Reciprocal Lattice.")

The Powder Method

In this method, we have many small crystals or grains arranged randomly, and we use one λ—generally filtered radiation. We can think of this random orientation then as one reciprocal lattice, with the Ewald sphere taking on all possible orientations around (000), as shown in Figure 4–42(a). The "limiting" sphere of radius $2/\lambda$ results. The number of possible points (neglecting points that do not diffract because $F(s) = 0$) is

$$\frac{4/3\ \pi(2/\lambda)^3}{\text{Volume primitive unit cell in rec. space}} = \frac{32\pi V_{u,c\ (\text{real space})}}{3\lambda^3}.$$

$$(4\text{–}8)$$

We can also visualize this collection of orientations by holding the Ewald sphere fixed and allowing each and every $\mathbf{r}^*_{hkl}$ to take on all possible orientations (Figure 4–42(b)). Each resultant sphere of radius $|\mathbf{r}^*_{hkl}|$ intersects the Ewald sphere in a small circle leading to a cone of diffracted radiation with the direct beam as its axis and with 2θ as its semi-apex angle. Thus the pattern depends only on $|\mathbf{r}^*_{hkl}|$, or on $1/d$; all planes of a form, such as {100} (i.e., (001), (100), (010), (100), etc.) will diffract at the same angle and superimpose on the same cone. The multiplicity will therefore reduce the number of cones. For example, if we have a triclinic crystal, as diffraction introduces a symmetry

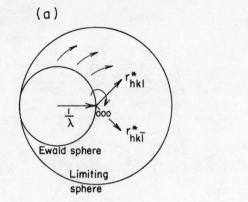

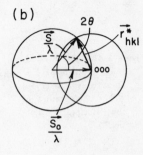

Figure 4–42. The powder pattern and reciprocal space. In (c), a strip of film is wrapped around the diffracted cones, which are centered on the direct beam, and have a semi-apex angle, 2θ.

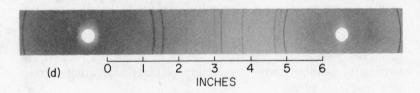

center, every form has a multiplicity of 2. If the crystal has a unit cell volume of 50 Å³ and we use CuKα radiation ($\lambda = 1.54$ Å), there will be 230 such cones. With a diamond cubic structure of the same volume per cell there will be only 5. Parseval's theorem can tell us something quite important here. In Chapter 2, Problem 27 we found that the electron density in a crystal was a Fourier series whose coefficients were the structure factors. If we redistribute the same atoms in a different crystal structure, but with the same volume per atom, so that the average electron density is the same, the *sum* of the squares of the coefficients (the structure factors squared) must remain the same; if there are nonzero coefficients, the remaining ones are larger, and the associated diffraction peaks have more intensity. We have a conservation of energy. There are fewer peaks but they are more intense.

As $\lambda = 2d \sin \theta$, we can write

$$\frac{1}{d^2} \frac{\lambda^2}{4} = \sin^2 \theta, \qquad (4\text{-}9a)$$

or

$$\frac{1}{d^2} = \frac{4}{\lambda^2} \sin^2 \theta = |r^*_{hkl}|^2. \qquad (4\text{-}9b)$$

As the powder pattern depends only on the magnitude of r^*_{hkl} for a given λ, it depends only on θ. Planes with the same d spacing, even if they have different indices, will also superimpose, as well as all those in one form. For example, for a cubic crystal,

$$\frac{1}{d^2} = \frac{h^2 + k^2 + l^2}{a^2} = |r^*_{hkl}|^2.$$

The $\{600\}$ and $\{442\}$ will superimpose. This lack of "directionality" seriously reduces the information readily obtained from a power pattern, although it is much easier to obtain a powder specimen. It is also easier to explore the information available in the pattern from a powder because the intensity is the same around the cone if the powder particles are randomly arranged. As shown in Figure 4–42(c), it is only necessary to wrap a narrow film around a powder rod or to move a counter around in one plane to record all the available information.[5] If a camera has a radius of 57.3 mm (so that around the circumference 1 mm = 1 degree 2θ), then the circular section of the cone at the film has a radius R equal to 57.3 mm $\times \sin 2\theta$. At $2\theta = 60$ degrees, the radius (R) is about 50 mm and the circumference $2\pi R \cong 300$ mm. The film is normally about 25-mm wide and therefore intercepts only about 1/12 of the cone on either side of the film. With a diffractometer, usually of radius 5.73 in. (so that 0.001 in. = 0.01 degree 2θ) and slit height of 0.5 in., only about 2 per cent of the cone is intercepted. Weak peaks can be completely missed and this can cause additional trouble in ferreting out the structure.

It is important to be sure that the powder is random, and to this end, brittle flat particles should never be pressed too hard in forming the sample. The powder should pass through at least a 250 mesh-screen to assure a continuous cone. A hard mortar and pestle or the device a dentist uses to prepare amalgams can be used to make the powder. (This is merely a small tube with a pestle which is vibrated rapidly.) The specimen, a rod for a camera (or a flat specimen for the diffracto-meter) is often rotated around the rod axis (or in the plane of the flat

[5] Occasionally a flat film perpendicular to the incident beam is used to get a series of circles; this is often referred to as a pinhole pattern.

face) to bring other particles into position for diffraction and to reduce spottiness in the pattern (or lack of reproducibility with a counter), a result of too coarse a grain or particle size.

Suppose we wish to determine if a sample is cubic and if so whether it is simple cubic (all values of h, k, l possible) body centered ($h + k + l = 2n$) or face centered (h, k, l all even or all odd). The peaks will appear at increasing values of 2θ as hkl increases [Eq. (4–9)]. For the three possible unit cells, the indices of the peaks are listed in Table 4–1.

Table 4–1

Simple Cubic			b.c.c.			f.c.c.		
	$\dfrac{\|\mathbf{r}_x^*\|^2}{\|\mathbf{r}_1^*\|^2}$			$\dfrac{\|\mathbf{r}_x^*\|^2}{\|\mathbf{r}_1^*\|^2}$			$\dfrac{\|\mathbf{r}_x^*\|^2}{\|\mathbf{r}_1^*\|^2}$	
hkl	$h^2+k^2+l^2$	*or*	hkl	$h^2+k^2+l^2$	*or*	hkl	$h^2+k^2+l^2$	*or*
		$\dfrac{\sin^2 \theta_x}{\sin^2 \theta_1}$						$\dfrac{\sin^2 \theta_x}{\sin^2 \theta_1}$
100	1	1	110	2	1	111	3	1
110	2	2	200	4	2	200	4	4/3
111	3	3	211	6	3	220	8	8/3
200	4	4	220	8	4	311	11	11/3
210	5	5	310	10	5	222	12	4
211	6	6	222	12	6	400	16	14/3
220	8	8	321	14	7	331	19	19/3
300	9	9	400	16	8	420	20	20/3

Note that even in the simple cubic, certain integral values of $h^2 + k^2 + l^2$ are missing. In both the simple and body-centered cubic cases, peaks are equally spaced in $\sin 2\theta$ (Eq. (4–9)) and also in 2θ because they are proportional over much of the 2θ range; thus we can readily discern whether the pattern is simple or body-centered cubic. The b.c.c. structure identifies itself by the presence of a value of $(\|\mathbf{r}_x^*\|^2)/(\|\mathbf{r}_1^*\|^2)$ of 7, which is not possible for the simple cubic.[6] The f.c.c. also yields a characteristic set of ratios. It is a simple matter to decide if the structures are cubic, and of which space lattice. The $\|\mathbf{r}^*\|^2$ or $\sin^2 \theta$ values are marked on the D scale of a slide rule, and the value of 1 on the C scale

[6] It is therefore important to use a radiation such that at least seven peaks appear on the pattern!

is placed over the first value. The numbers 2, 3, etc., will appear over the other values if the sample is simple or body-centered cubic; for the latter a value of 7 will be found. If this does not work, the value of 3 on the C scale is placed over the first $|\mathbf{r}^*|^2$ value and the numbers 4, 8, 11, etc., will appear over the other values, proving the sample is cubic and face centered.

If this does not work we can see if the structure is tetragonal:

$$\frac{1}{d^2} = \frac{h^2 + k^2}{a^2} + \frac{l^2}{c^2},$$

and

$$\frac{4}{\lambda^2} \sin^2 \theta = \frac{1}{a_1^2}(h^2 + k^2) + \frac{l^2}{a_3^2} = |\mathbf{r}_{hkl}^*|^2, \qquad (4\text{--}9c)$$

or

$$|\mathbf{r}_{hkl}^*|^2 = \frac{A}{a_1^2} + \frac{B}{a_3^2}.$$

Values of $|\mathbf{r}_{hkl}^*|^2$ are tabulated and all possible *differences are taken*. Many of these differences are just $\Delta A/a_1^2$, or $\Delta B/a_3^2$ (i.e., they have a common l or h, k). The commonly occurring differences can then be placed on the D scale of a slide rule and a match sought with integers on the C scale. Assume some of these are for peaks with a common l; ΔA can be 1, 2, 3, 4, 5, 6, 7, and 8. One looks for the most frequent differences to use with the slide rule. Thus a_1 can then be calculated and also $|\mathbf{r}^*|$ values for $hk0$ peaks. These are found in the list and indexed. Not all of the remaining differences will match with the integers on the C scale in this first step, as some of them are from peaks with common h, k but different l (i.e., due to ΔB not ΔA). There are less of these than peaks with the same l but different h, k. (Of course, some differences are for different hkl values.) ΔB can take on values 1, 3, 4, 5, 7, 8, and again the slide rule can be used to obtain a value for a_3. With a_3 and a_1 all the peaks can now be indexed by comparing calculated and measured $|\mathbf{r}_{hkl}^*|$ values, and from missing peaks the lattice can be determined.

If we fail to index the pattern at this point, we can try to see if we have a hexagonal cell in the same way. If this procedure does not work we can see if the crystal is orthorhombic, with a similar procedure. The problem is more difficult at this point because there are now three variables, a_1, a_2, a_3. Monoclinic or triclinic cells are very difficult.[7] It is generally better to spend some time trying to grow a single crystal.

---

[7] A scheme can be found in *The Powder Method* by L. V. Azároff and M. J. Buerger (McGraw-Hill, New York, 1958).

Keep in mind that finding a cell may not be an indication of the true system. Recall that there are many cells that describe the same lattice. This can be another problem in trying to elucidate the structure with a powder sample. (There is a systematic way for attempting to find the true lattice (see the book by Azároff and Buerger), but it has not gained general acceptance as yet.) If the material is brittle, examining the morphology of grains in the powder in a microscope may help to fix the true system, and this should always be done to ensure that only one phase is present.

Graphical aids have been devised to accomplish much the same indexing process for cubic hexagonal or tetragonal crystals, but in a more rapid fashion. (If you are doing considerable work with unknowns, it pays to purchase the charts, as they are available commercially.) As an example of these methods consider the tetragonal system:

$$\frac{1}{d^2} = \frac{1}{a^2}\left[h^2 + k^2 + \frac{l^2}{(c/a)^2}\right],$$

$$2\log d = 2\log a - \log\left[h^2 + k^2 + \frac{l^2}{(c/a)^2}\right]; \qquad (4\text{--}9d)$$

$2\log d_1 - 2\log d_2$ for a given c/a depends only on the (hkl) values for the two peaks d_1 and d_2, and c/a—*not* on a. A plot is made of $\log h^2 + k^2 + l^2/(c/a)^2$ as abscissa and c/a as ordinate, for various hkl's. As c/a varies, curves develop (Figure 4–43). From a powder pattern, d values are obtained and plotted on a log scale twice as big as that used in the graph and in the opposite sense, as indicated by Eq. (4–9d).

This piece of paper with the observed d values marked on it is now

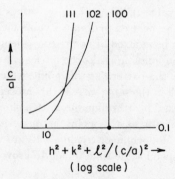

Figure 4–43.   Part of the Hull-Davey chart for indexing powder lines from a tetragonal crystal.

moved up and down and laterally on the graph until all the d values touch curves of the graph. All lines are then indexed from the chart and c/a and a obtained (Figure 4–44). That a can be determined can be seen from Eq. (4–9d); when $d = 1 \log d = 0$. When $h^2 + k^2 + l^2/(c/a)^2 = 1$, its log is zero, so that the difference in the origins (value $= 1$) of the two scales is simply $\log a$.

More accurate values of a can be obtained from the actual 2θ values after the lines are indexed. The absence of certain indices indicates the type of lattice. Charts like this are available for hexagonal and tetragonal materials.

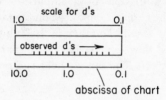

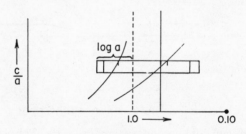

Figure 4–44.

There are several important experimental details. In a case where there are some lines giving special difficulty they may be from K_β, as filtered radiation is generally used and some of this could get through the filter. From Bragg's law we can see that for a fixed value of d:

$$\frac{\sin^2 \theta_\beta}{\sin^2 \theta_\alpha} = \frac{\lambda^2 K_\beta}{\lambda^2 K_\alpha}. \tag{4–10}$$

That is, if we multiply the $\sin^2 \theta$ value for the suspicious line by $(\lambda^2 K_\alpha)/(\lambda^2 K_\beta)$, if it is a K_β this will bring the $\sin^2 \theta$ value into coincidence with another line. A final check can be made by re-exposing the film (or re-recording with a counter) without the filter. The intensity of the suspected K_β line will increase considerably more than the K_α lines.

It is always necessary to choose a radiation that does not fluoresce the specimen, as this raises the background. If a nickel specimen is used with copper radiation filtered at the x-ray tube, the fluorescence (caused by copper K_β getting through the nickel filter d) can be quite high. A nickel tube is better. If enough filter material can be obtained to place over the film rather than just at the tube, a cobalt tube would be the best choice, because its filter, Fe, would absorb most of the fluorescence from the nickel sample. (Only a small piece of cobalt filter will be needed in front of a counter.)

With a crystal of known d spacing, we can check to see if there is any important radiation from impurities on the target—such as tungsten from the filament deposited on the target.

Particular care should be taken in designing the equipment and slits to avoid having the beam strike other materials that might give a confounding pattern. The sample holder, if one is used and if it will be

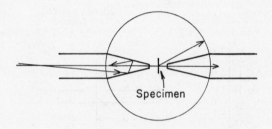

Figure 4–45. Tapered slits for a powder camera.

in the beam, should not give any pattern (i.e., it should be an amorphous material or one that gives no net scattering at all, which is possible as we shall see with neutrons). In camera designs for film work, the slit is brought as close as possible to the specimen to avoid air scattering by the incident beam, which would fog the film. A beam trap is provided. The main features of the slits of a good camera are shown in Figure 4–45 and most of the important points are available with commercial cameras. Note that both slits are tapered to minimize the lost angular region and to reduce scattering from inside the slits.

Air scattering can also be eliminated by evacuating the camera; this will also reduce the exposure time, as the absorption in air of the direct beam and the diffracted peaks is reduced, but this is only necessary when the scattering factors are quite low. Another factor contributing to the background when using filtered radiation is the overlapping Laue patterns of all the grains. This can be eliminated by using a monochromator. If this is done, as proposed by Guinier (see Figure 4–46), exposure times are not increased too much by the double reflection because the focusing allows us to use a broad region on the monochromator; the geometry produces sharp lines. Also such a monochromator will help to reduce fluorescence caused by the white

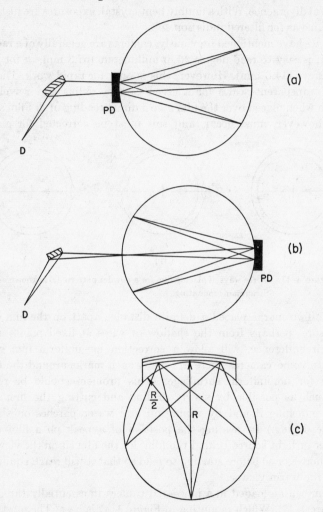

Figure 4–46. Focusing powder cameras with monochromators. *D* is the source, *PD* the specimen. The monochromator is bent as shown in (c). (After A. Guinier, *La Radio Crystallographie*, Dunod, Paris, 1956.)

radiation, always present even with properly selected filtered radiation. Note that to make the crystal focus it is bent so normals to various parts of the crystal come to a point, and then it is ground to fit the angle. To further reduce the exposure time, the crystal may be bent in the plane perpendicular to the drawing, minimizing losses due to vertical divergence. With a doubly bent crystal, exposures are just about the same as for filtered radiation.

As we have mentioned previously, cameras are generally of a radius so that it is easy to read degree 2θ in millimeters (57.3 mm, or for higher accuracy, 114.6 mm). However, this is only for rapid work. There are even transparent scales for a given camera radius and wavelength, which when placed over the film give a direct reading of d. Film shrinkage, however, must occur, and this must be corrected for accurate

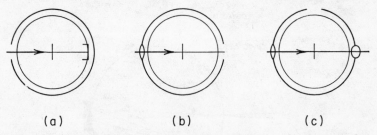

(a)   (b)   (c)

Figure 4–47.   Three ways of placing film for a powder pattern. (c) is known as the Straumanis mounting.

work. Two marks placed a definite distance apart on the film during exposure, perhaps from the shadow of wires at fixed points around the circumference, will allow a correction for uniform film shrinkage. In some cameras there are many such marks around the film to allow for nonuniform shrinkage. (This problem should be reduced as much as possible by slowly drilling and cutting the film rather than punching it and by wiping off any water patches on the film before drying.) In reading the position of a peak on a film with a viewer or light source behind the film, let the film sit on the viewer for 10 minutes or so before starting to read so that it will reach equilibrium with the warm viewer.

Film can be loaded in a powdered camera in essentially three ways (Figure 4–47). Which mounting in Figure 4–47 is best? The most interesting is (c), as fiducial reference points (whose spacing must be measured) are not necessary to correct for shrinkage. One merely splits the distance between corresponding peaks on both sides of the holes at the entrance and at the exit of the beam, and the distance, center to center, must be 180 degrees 2θ. If we differentiate Bragg's law we can see serious problems with the mounting in (a):

$$0 = 2d \cos \theta \, \Delta\theta + 2 \sin \theta \, \Delta d,$$

$$\Delta\theta = -\frac{\Delta d}{d} \tan \theta; \qquad \frac{d}{\Delta d} = -\frac{\tan \theta}{\Delta d} = \text{resolution}, \qquad (4\text{--}11)$$

i.e., the largest angular change for a small change in d is at high angles, and for some error $\Delta\theta$ in measurement, the error in d is smallest at large angles. But in the mounting in Figure 4–47(a) this high-angle region is where the film shrinkage would be most severe!

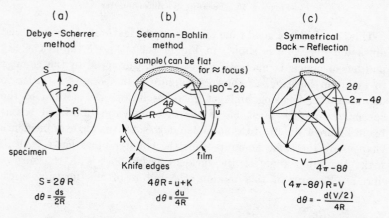

Figure 4–48. Various powder cameras and their resolution, (b) and (c) are focusing cameras. Incident and diffracted beams cut equal arcs on the circle so that if the incident beam is a line, the diffracted beam is a line.

There are different camera designs also (Figure 4–48). With both (b) and (c) large specimens can be used and even if they do not conform perfectly to the circle there will be some focusing. Thus polished and etched metallographic sections may be used. Note that if (a) (the Straumanis mounting) is used no reference marks are needed. None are needed in (c).

Using the general features of each camera, $d\theta$ is given for each design so that from Eq. (4–11) the resolution can be calculated. Notice that the focusing arrangements have twice the resolution of the Debye–Scherrer method, but cover only the high-angle regions.

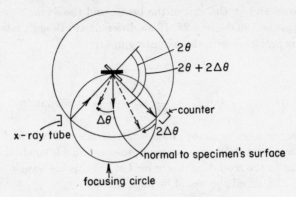

Figure 4–49. Focusing in a diffractometer.

This is probably a good time to examine the features of a commercial diffractometer. One is shown in Figure 4–2(c) and 3.12(b). The flat powder specimen is made to turn at half the speed of the counter to maintain focusing, as shown in Figure 4–49, because in order to maintain this focusing and get good resolution, the normal to the specimen's surface must bisect the incoming and diffracted beams (as in Figure 4–46(c)); if the specimen moves $\Delta\theta$, the angle of incidence changes by the same amount—thus the counter must move $2\Delta\theta$ to make the same angle as the incident beam does with the surface normal. Because of this motion, the radius of the focusing circle

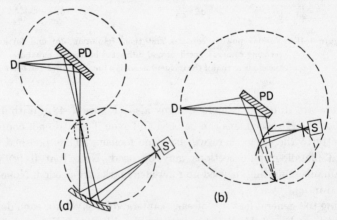

Figure 4–50. Monochromators with a diffractometer. In (a) and (b) S is the source (or counter) PD is the specimen and D the detector (or source). (After A. R. Lang, *Rev. Sci. Instr.* 27, 17, 1956.)

decreases with increasing θ. In Figure 4–50 are shown various ways to use a monochromator with a counter and maintain the focusing. Commercial units have mechanical features to allow the operator to make sure that at 0 degree 2θ the specimen surface is parallel to the beam's vertical direction and that the slits are parallel to the beam.[8]

What can we expect in terms of precision? The following systematic errors are possible:

1. If film is used, uniform film shrinkage (nonuniform shrinkage would be a random error).
2. Effective center of specimen is not the mechanical center due to absorption of beam in the specimen and the limit of accuracy in alignment.
3. Radius of camera or location of reference marks are not known accurately.
4. Incorrect location of the peak (the systematic error, not the random portion).
5. Temperature fluctuations.

We have already discussed (1), and (3) can be eliminated by using the Straumanis film mounting. As shown in Figure 4–51, (2) causes a peak displacement:

$$\frac{\sin \Delta 2\theta}{\delta/\sin \theta} = \frac{\sin (180° - 2\theta)}{R}.$$

Therefore,

$$\Delta 2\theta \cong \frac{-2\delta \cos \theta}{R},$$

$$\frac{\Delta d}{d} = -\frac{1}{\tan \theta} \Delta 2\theta = \frac{\cos \theta}{\sin \theta} \frac{2\delta \cos \theta}{R} = \frac{K \cos^2 \theta}{\sin \theta} = \frac{\Delta a}{a}. \quad (4\text{–}12)$$

Thus a lattice parameter calculated from a low angle line will have a greater error than one from a high angle line. By extrapolating parameters from lines at various angles versus $\cos^2 \theta/\sin \theta$ this error can be eliminated. In general, this is the largest error and thus the plotted values both with cameras and a diffractometer will be a straight line.

[8] The reader should realize that with a powder in a diffractometer, moving to maintain focusing, at the position for a 100 peak one is measuring intensity from those grains with {100} parallel to the surface of the flat powder compact; at the 110 peak, only those grains with {110} parallel to the surface.

Of particular difficulty is (4). One of the principal advantages of the diffractometer over a film is that a trace of the intensity distribution of a peak is given, whereas with a film one must estimate the center of a dark band. The intensity varies with angle across a peak because of geometric factors in the total intensity expression, as we shall see, and because λ dispersion is not symmetric. More important, the target distribution may not be uniform, and as a different section of the beam is seen at different angles with any of the methods, this will affect the shape. Soller slits, used on a diffractometer, cause asymmetry. These effects can be corrected for by using the center of gravity of a peak which can be determined from the trace on a diffractometer. The effects of various factors on the center of gravity can be treated analytically. However, the tails of a peak carry a heavy weight in such a procedure; they are difficult to determine and it is not at all certain that the peak

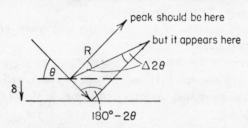

Figure 4–51.   Effect of sample displacement δ on peak position for a diffractometer.

maximum would not be the easiest and most useful quantity. It is hardly affected by dispersion and geometric factors, and one can choose a tube with a uniform target distribution.

Temperature is not too much of a problem these days; with film methods all peaks are being recorded at the same time. They will be slightly broadened by any temperature fluctuations but it is only necessary if one is reading the center of a line to know the mean temperature during an exposure. With a diffractometer, the room temperature must be carefully controlled or read at each peak. If there is only a 3-degree drift in room temperature during a recording of a material with a coefficient of expansion of say $10^{-5}/°C.$, the error in lattice parameter for two peaks, one at high angles and one at low angles, will be 3×10^{-5} or 0.003 per cent. Modern air-conditioning, however, can maintain much closer temperatures than this for a few hours.

With care and extrapolation, it is possible to have a *precision* in a parameter of $\pm 10^{-3}$ per cent. Routinely, with little care, 10^{-2} per cent is possible. There are few experimental measurements capable of this precision with as little effort!

Absolute accuracy is another question. A recent comparison of parameters determined on samples of a given material in laboratories throughout the world using all the same constants (wavelength, coefficient of expansion to correct to one temperature, etc.) showed that although the precision was high in each laboratory, the agreement in parameter was only within $\pm 10^{-2}$ per cent. Why this is so is not yet understood.[9]

The wavelength used should always be reported, since they are not yet known to an accuracy of better than 4×10^{-3} per cent as indicated in Chapter 3.

There are a great many uses for powder patterns, despite the fact that unless the structure is reasonably simple it will be difficult to determine with this technique.

Some of these uses are:

1. Determination of coefficient of expansion.

2. As the lattice parameter of a solid solution generally varies with solute additions, chemical analysis can be carried out from a master curve. For example, with a diffusion couple, layers may be taken off and the parameter determined to obtain the concentration profile.

3. In contrast to a solid solution, in a region of a phase diagram involving two solid phases the composition of both phases does not vary —only their amount. Thus by determining the parameter of one phase in a series of alloys of varying composition, it is easy to locate the solvus line. This method is in fact the most useful for phase boundaries involving solid state reactions, because they are sluggish, and heat evolution or length changes are not often satisfactory for accurately determining the alloy composition with the first small amount of a second phase. Quantitative metallography is also often not sufficiently accurate.

4. Defect structures (vacant sites, interstitials, etc.) can be detected by comparing the macroscopic density and that which is calculated from the lattice parameters and chemical composition.

5. One of the most important uses of powder patterns is in conjunction with the card systems kept up by American Society for Testing Materials. This is a collection of data on the d spacings and relative intensities of lines on powder patterns from a great variety of substances indexed in various ways.

First of all, there is a book (or deck) of cards, one for each substance

[9] W. Parrish, *Acta. Cryst.*, **13** (1960), 838–850.

with the d spacings and relative intensities of many peaks, and whatever is known about the space group, density, etc. Then there is an index to the cards called the Davey index, which lists all the substances alphabetically, and for each gives the location of the card and the three strongest lines. The Hanawalt index is listed according to the d-spacings of the three strongest peaks from which one can also locate the card. If two substances have the strongest line at the same d-spacing, the two are placed in order of the d-value of their second strongest peak, etc. Each substance is listed three times; if the three strongest peaks have d values d_1, d_2, d_3 (with d_1 the strongest) the substance can be found also under listing d_2, d_1, d_3, or under d_3, d_1, d_2. This helps if the powder is not random. Then there is the Fink index, which uses the eight strongest lines and the permutations of the six strongest. This is needed because in electron diffraction patterns the intensity variation is different and not as strongly varying as in x-ray patterns. The latest addition to these systems is the Matthews coordinate index. A series of large cards each with a different range of d-values, is punched with a hole for the d spacings of each substance, so that each card has rows and columns of holes. When a series of these are chosen that represent the intervals in which the d values fall for the unknown substance, a light placed underneath the stack will show through only certain holes. The coordinates of these locate the cards for possible substances. There are also cards which can be used to indicate the definite presence or absence of certain elements, which greatly help to reduce the number of possible substances.

For a single unknown phase these files provide a rapid procedure for identification; over 11,000 substances are covered. If the unknown contains more than one substance (look at the powder in the microscope), then one of the strongest lines may be an overlap of two lines from each of two substances, or two of the lines may be from one and the third from the other. In the latter case, we might look for one card based on two of the lines and one based on the third plus two of the other lines in the pattern. In the former case we might look for a card based on two of the three stronger lines and another card which contains two of the measured peaks other than the first three, but which also has a smaller peak at the position of the supposed overlap.

The various possible permutations involved in such a procedure must be tried, and chemical analysis can be helpful at this point in eliminating certain cases. (If there are three phases, without other information, the job is almost impossible.)

6.   The mechanical or magnetic properties of solid materials that are polycrystalline often depend on the texture or relative alignment of the grains. For example, the good magnetic properties of the iron–silicon sheet used in transformers depend on a high degree of alignment of grains, with $\langle 100 \rangle$ in the sheet. This is the direction of easy magnetization in a single crystal of iron–silicon, and hysteresis losses are reduced if the alignment is good. If there is texture in a specimen, then there will not be uniform intensity around the sphere of radius $|\mathbf{r}^*_{hkl}|$. Consider the 110 sphere in a cubic material in wire form, with (100) planes aligned nearly parallel to the axis of the wire in most of the grains. As shown in Figure 4–52(a), the $|\mathbf{r}^*_{110}|$ values are confined to being perpendicular to this $\langle 100 \rangle$ direction, or at 45 degrees to it, and the intersections result in the cone in Figure 4–52(b). This whole cone can be recorded in a pinhole pattern. A specimen may also be placed in a diffractometer; the counter is placed at the 2θ position say for a 110 peak. The specimen is then tilted, say α in Figure 4–42(c), and then the intensity is recorded

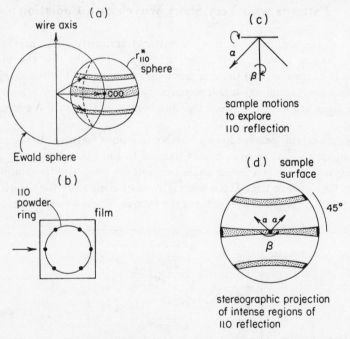

Figure 4–52.   Examining texture. (After L. V. Azároff, Norelco Reporter, **6**, 81, 1959.) Predominantly $\langle 100 \rangle$ along a wire axis and its influence on the 110 cone of reflection.

as β varies. Contour lines can then be drawn at values of equal intensity in a stereographic projection as in Figure 4–52(d). (Transmission through the specimen rather than reflection is necessary to record the outer edges of the projection.) The projection represents the distribution of $|r_{1\bar{1}0}^*|$ around the $|r_{1\bar{1}0}^*|$ sphere.

7. Accurate measurements of parameters can be made for any crystal structure, once the lattice is known.

8. Internal or "residual" stresses and strains can be measured; e.g., if a specimen is maintained in tension, planes perpendicular to the tensile axis have their spacing increased, whereas those parallel to the axis have their spacing decreased. The fractional *change* in spacing over that for an unloaded or stress-relieved specimen is a strain, and with the elastic constants this can be converted to stress.

We shall see some more uses after we study more about diffracted intensities.

Patterns with Very Short Wavelength Radiation

In electron diffraction, powder patterns are analyzed in much the same way as those just discussed, taking into account that the whole cone is intersected and that, as previously mentioned, it is necessary to correct for magnification and eccentricity with a known test specimen. The lines will be much closer together because of the small λ generally used.

Single crystal *patterns* have a number of unique features. As shown in Problem 2.3, lattice rows nearly parallel to the beam have very low resolution (there is a larger angle between the peak and its minimum than for higher orders). If the beam is incident along a row the associated cones will be broad at the center of the pattern. The net result is that the

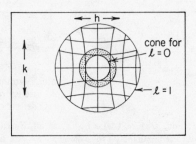

Figure 4–53.

spots are broadest nearest the center and there may be several spots for a "two-dimensional" *pattern* occurring, as in Figure 4–53.

As was pointed out at the beginning of this chapter, the sphere of reflection is quite large relative to the spacing of reciprocal space for electron diffraction. Because of mosaic or subgrains (regions of slight tilt) in the specimen, it is quite possible to record a whole plane of reciprocal space. For example, for a beam incident along an [001] in a cubic material we can ask what mosiac tilt will be required to record the 080 spot. Using Bragg's law in the form

$$\theta = \frac{\lambda}{2d}; \quad \text{for } \lambda = 0.05 \text{ Å}^{-1}, 080 \text{ will occur for } \theta = 2.6 \text{ degrees.}$$

Consider Figure 4–54, a drawing of the *okl* plane with the incident beam

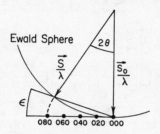

Figure 4–54.

along [001]; a mosaic tilt of only ± 2.6 degrees is required. The mosaic spread of the spot is $0.3a^*$ for this 080 spot. To see this, calculate ε from

$$\frac{\varepsilon}{|\mathbf{r^*}|} = \frac{2.6° \, 2\pi}{360}.$$

From the usual mosaic spread, with a single crystal pattern from within a grain in the sample, we are generally seeing a whole layer of the reciprocal lattice, especially with the short wavelengths at 50 kv and above. Because of the low angles of diffraction with these voltages in a transmission experiment, this layer is essentially perpendicular to the beam, so that if the spots can be indexed the cross product of any two in the pattern gives the reciprocal lattice vector normal to the surface of the film (and hence the {*hkl*} of the surface of the specimen if it is not tilted)—approximately, of course, due to the mosaic spread.

We generally know the material's structure and want only to know the orientation. Indexing of the spots can be done by comparing the

Table 4-2

Ratios of Reciprocal Lattice Vectors in the Cubic System — Prepared by O. Kimball*

	100	110	[111]	[200]	210	211	[220]	221 / 300	310	[311]	[222]	320	321	[400]	322 / 410	330 / 411	[331]	[420]
100	1	1.414	1.732	2.00	2.24	2.45	2.83	3.00	3.16	3.32	3.46	3.61	3.74	4.00	4.12	4.24	4.36	4.47
110	0.707	1	1.23	1.41	1.58	1.73	2.00	2.12	2.24	2.34	2.45	2.55	2.64	2.83	2.92	3.00	3.09	3.16
[111]	0.577	0.817	[1]	[1.15]	1.29	1.41	[1.64]	1.73	1.83	[1.92]	[2.00]	2.08	2.16	[2.31]	2.38	2.45	[2.52]	[2.58]
[200]	0.500	0.707	[0.866]	[1]	1.12	1.23	[1.41]	1.50	1.58	[1.66]	[1.73]	1.80	1.87	[2.00]	2.06	2.12	2.18	2.24
210	0.448	0.634	0.776	0.896	1	1.10	1.27	1.34	1.41	1.49	1.55	1.62	1.68	1.79	1.85	1.90	1.96	2.00
211	0.408	0.577	0.707	0.816	0.912	1	1.15	1.22	1.29	1.35	1.41	1.47	1.53	1.63	1.68	1.73	1.78	1.83
[220]	0.345	0.500	[0.612]	[0.707]	0.789	0.866	[1]	1.06	1.12	[1.17]	[1.22]	1.28	1.32	1.41	1.46	1.50	[1.54]	[1.58]
221 / 300	0.333	0.472	0.578	0.667	0.745	0.817	0.944	1	1.05	1.11	1.16	1.20	1.25	1.33	1.37	1.41	1.46	1.49
310	0.316	0.448	0.548	0.634	0.707	0.775	0.895	0.949	1	1.05	1.10	1.14	1.19	1.27	1.30	1.34	1.38	1.41
[311]	0.302	0.426	[0.522]	[0.604]	0.674	0.739	[0.854]	0.905	0.955	[1]	[1.05]	1.09	1.13	[1.21]	1.24	1.28	[1.31]	[1.35]
[222]	0.289	0.408	[0.500]	[0.578]	0.645	0.707	[0.817]	0.866	0.913	[0.957]	[1]	1.04	1.08	[1.15]	1.19	1.22	[1.26]	[1.29]
320	0.277	0.392	0.480	0.554	0.619	0.679	0.784	0.831	0.877	0.918	0.960	1	1.04	1.11	1.14	1.18	1.21	1.24
321	0.267	0.378	0.463	0.535	0.597	0.655	0.757	0.802	0.845	0.887	0.927	0.965	1	1.07	1.10	1.13	1.17	1.20
[400]	0.250	0.354	[0.433]	[0.500]	0.559	0.612	[0.707]	0.750	0.791	[0.830]	[0.866]	0.902	0.936	[1]	1.03	1.06	[1.09]	[1.12]
322 / 410	0.242	0.343	0.420	0.485	0.542	0.594	0.686	0.727	0.767	0.803	0.840	0.875	0.907	0.970	1	1.02	1.06	1.08
330 / 411	0.236	0.334	0.409	0.472	0.527	0.578	0.667	0.707	0.747	0.782	0.817	0.852	0.883	0.944	0.973	1	1.03	1.06
[331]	0.229	0.324	[0.397]	[0.458]	0.512	0.561	[0.649]	0.687	0.725	[0.760]	[0.795]	0.827	0.858	[0.917]	0.945	0.971	[1]	[1.03]
[420]	0.224	0.316	[0.387]	[0.446]	0.500	0.548	[0.632]	0.670	0.707	[0.740]	[0.774]	0.807	0.837	[0.894]	0.922	0.947	0.975	[1]

* Boxed ratios are for an f.c.c. lattice.

206

ratio of the distances from the center to the spots with a table of such distances. Table 4–2 is for the cubic system. Recall (Figure 3–15) that by adjusting the lenses, we can either see an image, or the diffraction pattern.[10] If the intersection of two markings from known planes (such as slip traces) can be found, the orientation can be determined without the diffraction pattern. It is only necessary to ask what two lines on each of the planes can make the observed angle of intersection. The cross product of these lines gives the normal to the foil's surface. This procedure reduces the error in the method involving the diffraction pattern due to broad spots, and is useful if such marking *can* be found. If both edges of some known marking, such as a slip plane, can be seen in a transmission specimen, the thickness of the foil can be easily calculated once the orientation is known.

When the crystal is small, we can estimate its size in directions in the observed plane of the reciprocal lattice from the length of the spot in

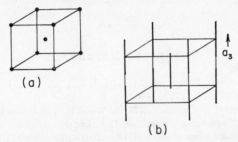

(a)

(b)

Figure 4–55. (a) Reciprocal lattice of f.c.c. material. Material large in all directions. (b) Same as in (a) but one unit cell thick in the $\bar{\mathbf{a}}_3$ direction.

these various directions, because the breadth is proportional to $1/N$. The crystal may also be quite thin in the direction of the beam, of the order of one unit cell. Although this is not generally true for metal crystals, it can be true for organic materials with large spacings. Then we have effectively two-dimensional diffraction—the spots in reciprocal space spread in a direction perpendicular to the specimen or parallel to the beam. (We can always think of the size of a crystal as applying pressure to the spot due to the terms

$$(\sin^2 \pi \mathbf{S}_i \cdot N_i \mathbf{a}_i)/(\sin^2 \pi \mathbf{S} \cdot \mathbf{a}_i);$$

[10] Because the lenses are electromagnetic, the image is rotated an amount which depends on the lenses and currents. This rotation is calibrated with a test specimen of known orientation or a small crystal whose edges are of known indices. This is important in comparing the image and the diffraction pattern, and has been corrected for, in the problems.

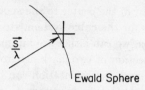

Ewald Sphere

Figure 4–56.

if the size goes down in any direction, the spot "oozes out" in that direction.) Extra reflections may appear as in Figure 4–55. Finally, because of this spreading, small crystals of regular dimensions can produce multiple intersections with the Ewald sphere. An example of this is given in Figure 4–56 for a small cubic crystal.

In the next chapter we turn our attention to the interaction of the different types of radiation with individual atoms.

Suggested References

1. *The International Tables for Crystallography*, Vol. II, III (Kynoch Press, Birmingham, England, 1959, 1962).

2. N. F. M. Henry, H. Lipson, and W. A. Wooster, *The Interpretation of X-Ray Diffraction Photographs* (Macmillan, Ltd., London, 1961).

3. C. S. Barrett, *Structure of Metals* (McGraw-Hill, New York, 1952).

4. M. J. Buerger, *X-Ray Crystallography* (John Wiley, New York, 1942).

5. A. Guinier, *La Radiocrystallographie* (Dunod, Paris, 1956).

6. E. A. Wood, *Crystal Orientation Manual* (Columbia University Press, New York, 1963).

7. L. V. Azároff and M. J. Buerger, *The Powder Method* (McGraw-Hill, New York, 1958).

8. H. P. Klug and L. E. Alexander, *X-Ray Diffraction Procedures* (John Wiley New York, 1954).

9. H. S. Peiser, H. P. Rooksby, and A. J. C. Wilson, *X-Ray Diffraction by Polycrystalline Materials* (Chapman and Hall, Ltd., London, 1960).

10. For lattice parameters, W. E. Pearson, *A Handbook of Lattice Spacings and Structures of Metals and Alloys* (Pergamon Press, New York, 1958).

11. R. W. G. Wykoff, *Crystal Structures* (Interscience Publications, New York, 1960).

12. *Tables for converting 2θ to d spacings*, PB13176K (Office of Technical Services, U.S. Department of Commerce, Washington 25, D.C.).

13. *For charts, graphs, etc.*
    (a) Polycrystal Book Service, P.O. Box 11567, Pittsburgh, Pa.15238.
    (b) N. P. Nies, 969 Skyline Drive, Laguna Beach, California.

PROBLEMS

1. Four back-reflection Laue patterns (3-cm distance) are given below. They have been taken along prominent axes of a crystal. Indicate the symmetry in each.

2. A striation was found in a germanium crystal as indicated in the diagram. Laue patterns were taken at (*a*) away from the striation

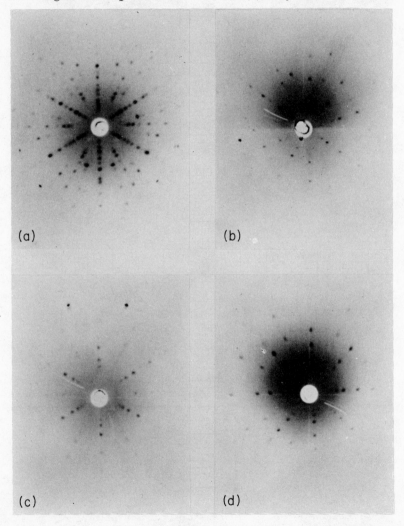

(a)

(b)

(c)

(d)

Problem 4-1.

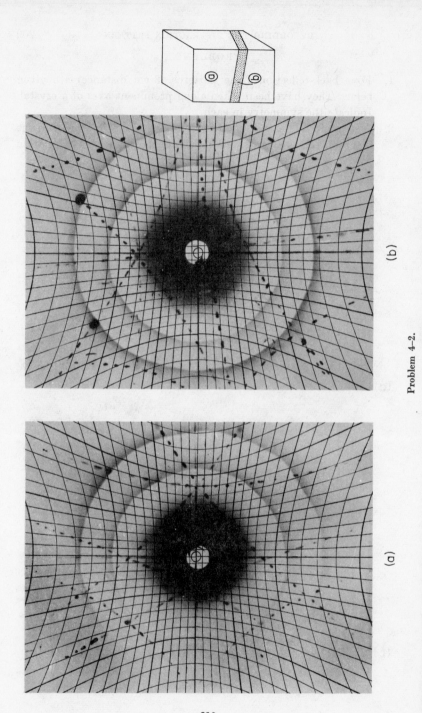

Problem 4-2.

and at (b) in the marking, and are given below. What can you say about the marking?

3. The two Laue back-reflection patterns below are from an aluminum-4 weight per cent copper single crystal; (a) is before deformation and (b) is after an elongation of 47.4 per cent. (They were taken by Professor J. G. Byrne of Stevens Institute of Technology.) The tensile axis was normal to the beam and vertical. The specimen cross section was rectangular and the long edge was horizontal and perpendicular to the beam. The slip planes are known to be {111}.

(a) Plot the pole figures before and after deformation.

(b) Determine the slip direction. (*Hint:* Plot the tensile axis before and after deformation in one standard (001) projection. Find the slip plane initially with the maximum resolved shear stress (see Reference 3, p. 345) and the direction in this plane to which the tensile axis rotates.)

(c) Just as slip started, what angles did the slip plane make with the faces of the crystal?

(d) What is the elongation you determine from the Laue patterns. [See E. Schmid and W. Boas, *Krystallplastizitat* (Springer, Berlin, 1935, p. 67).]

4. Silicon has a diamond cubic structure. An equator Weissenberg pattern is made using MoK_α and oscillating the crystal π about a cube edge (a_3).

(a) What fraction of the $hk0$ points in reciprocal space have zero structure factors?

(b) Making reasonable approximations, how many diffraction spots should be observed on either half of the pattern?

5. Show with the aid of sketches of reciprocal space how to distinguish between the primitive, face-centered, body-centered, or c-centered orthorhombic lattice with a rotation camera.

6. Below is an oscillating crystal photograph of a hexagonal crystal (taken by Professor E. J. Freise of Northwestern University). The oscillation axis was the a_1 axis, and the a_3 axis was initially along the direct beam. The oscillation angle was ± 15 degrees. $a_3 = 6.71$ Å. Index the intense reflections on the zero and first layers. Also identify the two weaker reflections near the

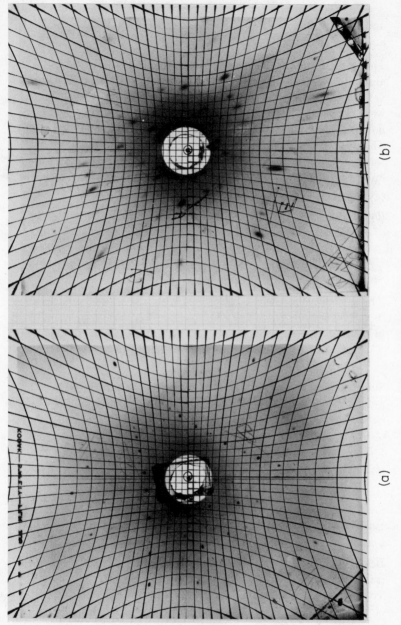

(a) (b)

Problem 4-3.

strong ones on the two layers. Filtered copper radiation was used.

7. A single crystal (f.c.c.) with identical atoms at each lattice point has a lattice parameter of 4 Å. A small portion of the crystal appears to be misoriented by a 90-degree rotation around [110], and the two pieces meet on {110}. With a 5-cm camera, an oscillation pattern (± 15 degrees) is taken with the [001] as the oscillation axis and filtered copper radiation. Initially the beam is along the [110]. The beam hits the entire crystal. Draw the pattern to scale.

8.* A new crystal, AB, has been grown. From chemical analysis and density it is known that there are 4 molecules in the unit cell. The crystal is a long plate as shown in the diagram. A Laue back-reflection pattern perpendicular to the large flat face (1) showed a twofold axis of symmetry. Laue's from the other faces were inconclusive, but all faces are at right angles to each other.

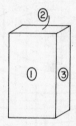

(a) What can you say now about the possible crystal systems?

(b) A rotation pattern was taken with the sample oriented with the long dimension horizontal and the large flat face vertical. The layer line spacing (call it a_3) was 4.40 Å. A pattern with the long dimension and the flat face horizontal gives $a_1 = 10.82$ Å. What is the system?

The rotation pattern shown below was taken with filtered copper radiation (4 hours, 40 kv, 15 ma). Determine a_2.

(c) What is the system?

(d) Make a reciprocal lattice plot of λ/a_1, λ/a_3, and index as many spots as you can. Note any uncertainties and any systematic absences. (This can best be done by placing the indexed spots

* This problem will be used in later discussions and should be solved now.

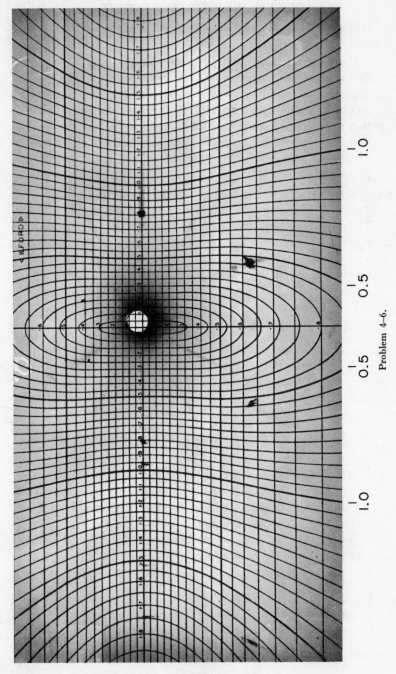

Problem 4-6.

in separate columns for $h00$, $hk0$, hkl, hhl, etc.) You are given that from rotations around other axes:

$$hk0 \quad h = 2n$$
$$h00 \quad h = 2n$$
$$0k0 \quad k = 2n$$

What is the diffraction symbol?

(In reading data from the film, average values to the left and right of center.)

(e) Certain of the conditions you have set up in (d) *from the film* are uncertain, aren't they? Pick one of these "problem areas" and sketch how you would check out some of the uncertainties with a diffractometer. Calculate the expected angles for the reflection(s) you are going to check.

9. The rotation patterns below were taken by Prof. R. De Angelis of the University of Kentucky, of a single crystal of copper shock-loaded to 435 kb. The rotation axis was [001]. In the following, (a) is a full 360-degree rotation, and (b) is a 15-degree oscillation to one side within 2–3 degrees of [100]. Filtered copper radiation was used.

(a) Index the spots. (Average readings from the film to the left and right of center.)

(b) Are there any extra spots? With the help of the oscillation patterns, what are the indices of these spots? What are they due to?

10. The powder pattern in Figure 4–43 is of a copper–gold alloy, taken with filtered copper radiation by Dr. P. Gehlen.

(a) What is the unit cell and its parameter?

(b) What is the composition?

11. A powder-diffraction pattern made on a diffractometer shows lines at $\theta = 70$ and 85 degrees. The radiation used was copper K_α and the $\alpha_1\alpha_2$ doublet is resolved on the pattern.

(a) Calculate the angular separation in degrees of the two components of the doublet for the two lines.

(b) If the same specimen was run in a Debye–Scherrer camera of 57.3 mm radius, how far apart in millimeters would the components of the two lines appear on the film?

(c) How far apart would they be with a symmetrical back reflection focusing camera of the same radius?

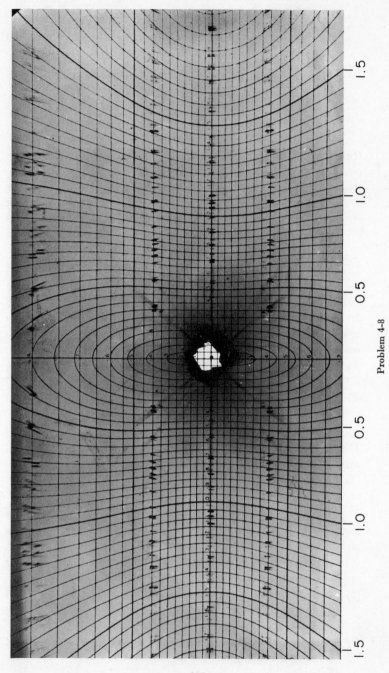

Problem 4-8

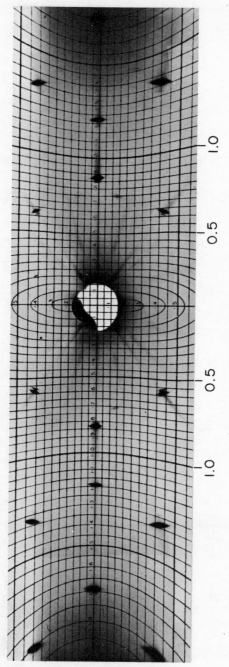

Problem 4-9(a)

217

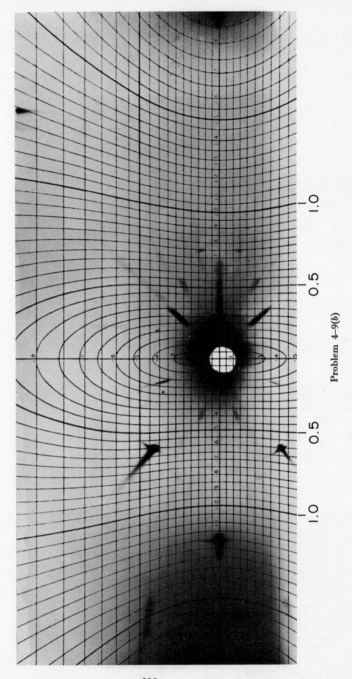

Problem 4-9(b)

(d) Qualitatively, how would the results in a, b, c be affected by changing to chromium radiation?

12. Metal A and B form an intermetallic compound γ. The following specimens were prepared and heat-treated by quenching powders from the temperatures indicated, and the lattice parameters of the body-centered cubic phase v were measured with the following results:

atomic

% B	450°C	400°C	350°C	300°C	250°C	200°C
30	3.2215 Å	3.2268	3.2305	3.2338	3.2365	3.2386
35	3.2229					
40	3.2284					
45	3.2334					
50	3.2386					
55	3.2432					
60	3.2479					
65	3.2519					
70	3.2536	3.2528	3.2515	3.2506	3.2500	3.2496

Determine the boundaries of γ phase for the temperature range studied (i.e., plot this region of phase diagram).

13. An alloy nominally of 50 per cent nickel–50 atomic per cent cobalt is a single-phase solid solution. A Debye–Scherrer film of this alloy made with copper K_α radiation gave the following $\sin^2 \theta$ values:

$\sin^2 \theta$	$\sin^2 \theta$
0.1420	0.5681
0.1894	0.7574
0.3787	0.8994
0.5207	

The measured density is 8.9 gm/cm³. Is this a defect structure?

14. The following data were obtained on an unknown white powder, using filtered copper radiation.

$2\theta°$	I above background/I max
28.2	1.00
35.6	0.078
46.9	0.672
55.6	0.193
60.0	0.036

68.5	0.054
75.8	0.046
87.3	0.118
94.2	0.029

Identify this material. Calculate its lattice parameter(s) and compare with the published data.

15. Using a Debye–Scherrer camera with fiducial markings every 10 degrees–2θ, the following data were obtained on an unknown specimen—a grey powder.

Position of Marking (cm)	Peak Position (cm)	2θ	Intensity
20.415		20°	
21.710		30°	
	22.630		M (medium)
	22.985		MW (medium weak)
23.010		40°	
	23.355		VW (very weak)
	23.520		S (strong)
24.310		50°	
	24.955		M
25.615		60°	
	26.065		VW
	26.745		VW
26.915		70°	
	27.025		S
	27.905		VW
28.210		80°	
	28.555		MS (medium strong)
	28.765		VW
	29.135		MS
29.480		90°	
	29.550		VW
	30.175		VW
30.755		100°	
	31.990		M
32.030		110°	
	32.885		M
33.285		120°	
	33.850		VW
	34.285		MS
	34.375		MS
34.550		130°	

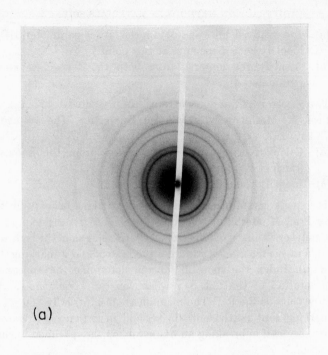

(a)

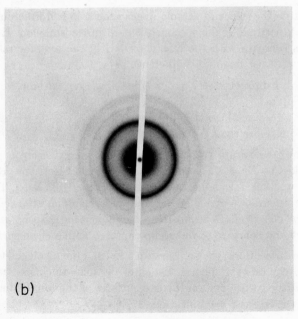

(b)

Problem 4–16.

(a) Index all the lines and obtain the lattice parameters. (Do *not* identify with d spacings at this point.)

(b) Identify the material from both the d spacings and the parameter(s).

16. Two electron diffraction patterns are presented below, taken by Prof. M. Meshii of Northwestern University. The voltage was 75 kv.

(a) Calculate the magnification factors from the known (b), *which is chromium*.

(b) Identify the unknown material in (a).

17. The single crystal electron diffraction patterns below were taken by Prof. M. Meshii of Northwestern University, inside a grain of a polycrystalline gold specimen by transmission through a foil, (c) is in the matrix, (b) straddles the matrix and a marking shown in (a). Index the spots in (b) and determine the approximate orientation of the foil. Say what you can about the marking. How thick is the foil? The magnification in (a) is 15,400 ×. (The marking runs north–south in (a) and in it there is a trace due to a dislocation breaking an oxide film on the specimen during its motion.)

18. Derive the effect of sample displacement in a diffractometer on peak position, if the specimen is used in transmission. How does this compare with the case described in the text for reflection? Of what use might this difference be?

19. With a diffractometer and a cubic *single crystal* how would you set up to:

(a) Measure along the $h_1 00$ line.

(b) Explore the $h_1 h_1 0$ plane.

20. Shown below are two-dimensional, low-energy electron patterns (taken by Dr. J. J. Lander, Head, Chemical Electronics Research Dept., Bell Telephone Laboratory, Murray Hill, N.J.). They are of two surfaces of a single crystal of germanium, after iodine has been adsorbed. Determine the two-dimensional space group for each and compare to the group expected with a clean surface.

21. The dislocations, shown below, in a foil of a (f.c.c.) nickel–titanium alloy lie on {111} planes. Estimate the foil's thickness, assuming the dislocations end on the two surfaces of the foil. (Films taken by Dr. S. Sass; magnification: 37,500 ×.)

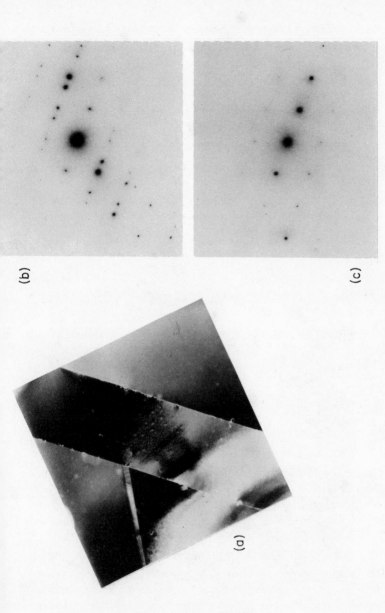

(b)

(c)

(a)

Problem 4-17.

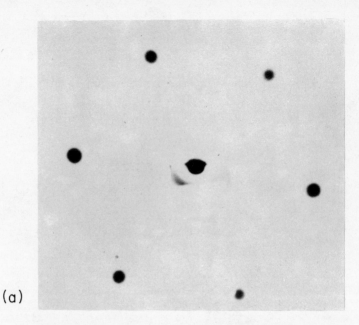

(a)

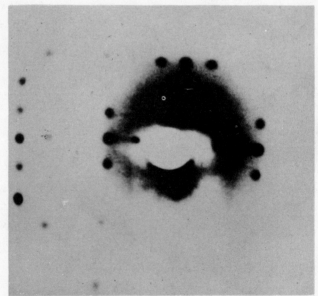

(b)

Problem 4–20.

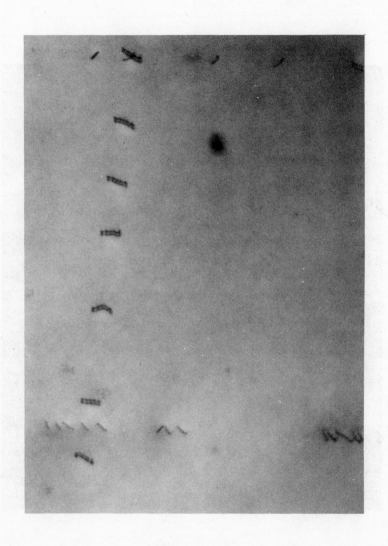

Problem 4–21(a)

225

Problem 4–21(*b*)

5 _The Interaction of X-Rays, Neutrons, and Electrons with Atoms_

In Chapter 2, we discussed the physics of diffraction; our results involved a scattering factor per atom. In this chapter we turn our attention to this scattering factor and also to absorption and refraction of the useful kinds of radiation. The matters we are to deal with here are associated with the interaction of the potential of the sum total of the atoms of the material and the radiation. This area can be dealt with in detail only with quantum theory and wave mechanics. We cannot hope to delve into these subjects in detail, to provide the necessary background, and, as a result, we shall be concerned mainly with qualitative physical arguments to understand the nature of the phenomena involved and to appreciate the quantitative relations presented.

The X-Ray Scattering Factor

When the electromagnetic field of an x-ray beam approaches an atom, it acts on the electrons; the potential of the atom, or more exactly, of the entire mass of atoms acts on this wave. As a result, the electrons of the atom oscillate. Because of the acceleration and deceleration associated with the oscillation, each electron gives off electromagnetic waves,[1] which at large distance (r) relative to the oscillation

---

[1] More correctly—quanta of radiation are given off.

is, as pointed out in Chapter 3:

$$|\boldsymbol{\epsilon}| = |\mathbf{h}| = \frac{|a(t')|e \sin \varphi}{rc^2}, \qquad (5-1)$$

$\boldsymbol{\epsilon}$ is the electric field, and $\mathbf{h}$ is the magnetic field at right angles to $\boldsymbol{\epsilon}$.

Note that the fields are proportional to $1/r$ not $1/r^2$; it is felt at a much larger distance than a stationary field. The reason this field is proportional to $1/r$ and not $1/r^2$ is easy to see; the total energy of the propagating wave is distributed over a sphere. As the surface of the sphere increases proportional to r^2, the energy at any point of observation on the sphere must fall off as $1/r^2$. The energy at any point depends on the square of the field, and therefore the field at any point falls off as $1/r$. The sine term, which we have discussed in Chapter 3, has a very simple meaning. The angle between the propagating field or observation point and the direction of oscillation is φ (Figure 5–1). Sin φ is a polariza-

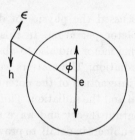

Figure 5–1. The fields around an oscillating charge.

tion term. At some point we "see" only the component of vibration parallel to the observer, or perpendicular to the direction of propagation. We can, as Barkla did in the nineteenth century, make a "polarizer" and an "analyzer" as in Figure 5–2(a) using blocks of, say amorphous carbon, to scatter the x-rays without diffraction.

From an x-ray tube, we can examine the polarization of the white and characteristic radiation as in Figure 5–2(b) and (c). The very short λ's in the white radiation *are* polarized as we might expect, as this radiation comes from almost a complete deceleration, in one step, of the electrons incident along the y axis, and not by a series of glancing collisions.

As we deal mainly with characteristic radiation in diffraction experiments, we are then dealing with an unpolarized beam. Let us explore for a moment what happens as such a beam scatters from a crystal. We shall consider the unpolarized instantaneous incident beam

$|\boldsymbol{\epsilon}_0|$ resolved into two components $|\boldsymbol{\epsilon}_{0\parallel}|$, $|\boldsymbol{\epsilon}_{0\perp}|$ as in Figure 5–3. Even though the initial beam is unpolarized, after scattering to some point A, it *is* partially polarized, because we are examining the scattering in a

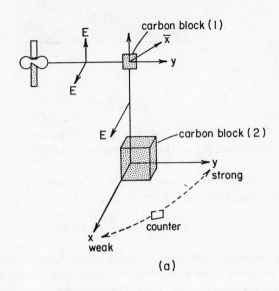

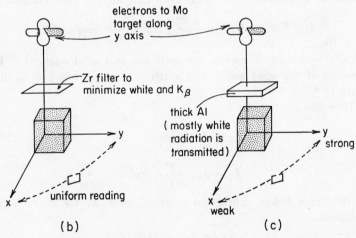

Figure 5–2.   Examining the polarization of the spectrum from an x-ray tube. The scattering from carbon blocks is examined in the *x-y* plane. In (c) Al absorbs more of the long λ's than the short; as we shall see this is the nature of absorption for all materials.

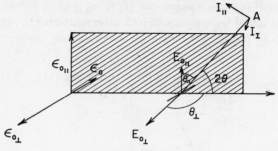

Figure 5–3.

specific direction. We wish then to express the polarization as a function of diffraction angle, as the polarization must affect the measured intensity.

In Eq. (5–1), we can replace a by $(|\epsilon_0|e)/m$ where $|\epsilon_0|$ is the magnitude of the incident field $(\epsilon_0 = \mathbf{E}_0 e^{iw(t)})$.

$$|\boldsymbol{\epsilon}| = |\mathbf{h}| = \frac{|\boldsymbol{\epsilon}_0|e^2}{mrc^2} \sin \varphi.$$

We can measure only average scattered intensity I, over some time, which, as we have seen, is related to the average of the square of the *maximum amplitude* of the field. Therefore, for any component,

$$I = KE^2 = KH^2 = \frac{KE_0^2 e^4}{m^2 r^2 c^4} \sin^2 \varphi = \frac{I_0 e^4}{m^2 r^2 c^4} \cos^2 2\theta$$

$(e^4/m^2 c^4 = 7.9 \cdot 10^{-26}$ cm^2 in cgs units per unit solid angle; $1/r^2$ is a measure of the solid angle. The scattering for one electron is quite small!)

Therefore at A,

$$I_\perp = I_{0\perp} \frac{e^4}{m^2 r^2 c^4},$$

$$I_\parallel = I_{0\parallel} \frac{e^4}{m^2 r^2 c^4} \cos^2 2\theta.$$

If the beam before diffraction is unpolarized, as for characteristic radiation,

$$I_{0\parallel} = I_{0\perp} = (1/2)I_0.$$

Thus,

$$I = \frac{I_0 e^4}{m^2 r^2 c^4} \left(\frac{1 + \cos^2 2\theta}{2} \right) = I_e. \tag{5–2}$$

This is known as the Thomson scattering per electron (J. J. Thomson first derived this).

If the beam is scattered first by, say, a monochromator crystal and then by a sample, the total polarization will of course be different (See Problem 10).

Now consider all the scattering around one electron; the total scattered power P is, as shown in Figure 5–4(a)

$$P = \int_0^\pi \frac{I_0 e^4}{m^2 c^4 r^2} \frac{1 + \cos^2 2\theta}{2} 2\pi r \sin 2\theta 2 r d\theta$$

$$= \frac{8\pi}{3} I_0 \frac{e^4}{m^2 c^4}. \tag{5–3}$$

The total scattering "cross section" P/I_0 is $6.7 \cdot 10^{-25}$ cm^2 (the scattering amplitude per electron has units of centimeters).

Considering one *atom*, we know that the scattering factor f is [Eq. (2–40)]:

$$f(\mathbf{S} - \mathbf{S}_o) = \int \rho'(\mathbf{r} - \mathbf{r}_n) \exp\left[2\pi i \left(\frac{\mathbf{S} - \mathbf{S}_o}{\lambda}\right) \cdot (\mathbf{r} - \mathbf{r}_n)\right] dV_{(\mathbf{r} - \mathbf{r}_n)}.$$

When $\mathbf{S}$ and $\mathbf{S}_O$ are parallel there is no phase factor between electrons, and f is the atomic number. The phase factor at other angles is important because $\mathbf{S} - \mathbf{S}_O$ and $\mathbf{r} - \mathbf{r}_n$ are of the same magnitude, so that there is a significant path difference for scattering at different points around an atom.

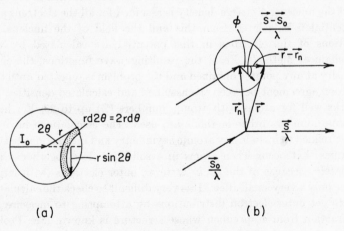

Figure 5–4. Scattering around an atom.

f is the scattering amplitude of an atom relative to that for a single electron; i.e., the total scattering is

$$f I_0^{1/2} \frac{e^2}{mc^2 r} \left(\frac{1 + \cos^2 2\theta}{2} \right)^{1/2} = \frac{I_0^{1/2}}{r} f_x \left(\frac{1 + \cos^2 2\theta}{2} \right)^{1/2}.$$

(Then $F(s)$ is the scattering of x-rays by a unit cell relative to the scattering by one electron.)

Assume that the electrons are distributed *spherically* around any one atom. Then $2\pi i(S - S_O)/\lambda \cdot (\mathbf{r} - \mathbf{r}_n) = 2\pi i(2 \sin \theta)/\lambda |\mathbf{r} - \mathbf{r}_n| \cos \phi$, as shown in Figure 5–4(b).

Let $k = (4\pi \sin \theta)/\lambda$. Then

$$f = \int_{|\mathbf{r}-\mathbf{r}_n|=0}^{|\mathbf{r}-\mathbf{r}_n|=\infty} \int_{\varphi=0}^{\pi} \exp[ik|\mathbf{r} - \mathbf{r}_n| \cos \phi](\rho' 2\pi |\mathbf{r} - \mathbf{r}_n| \sin \phi |\mathbf{r} - \mathbf{r}_n|)$$
$$\times \, d\phi d |\mathbf{r} - \mathbf{r}_n|,$$

and

$$f = \int_{|\mathbf{r}-\mathbf{r}_n|=0}^{\infty} \frac{\sin k|\mathbf{r} - \mathbf{r}_n|}{k|\mathbf{r} - \mathbf{r}_n|} 4\pi |\mathbf{r} - \mathbf{r}_n|^2 \rho' d |\mathbf{r} - \mathbf{r}_n|. \qquad (5\text{–}4)$$

Thus, f falls off with increasing k—i.e., as $\sin \theta/\lambda$ increases. The electron density ρ' at any one point is actually the product of the wave function (ψ) representing any electron times its complex conjugate—i.e., $\psi\psi^*$. The contribution is calculated for electrons in all shells, and added —i.e., $f = \sum f_e$, $f^2 = (\sum f_e)^2$. This can be evaluated in the following way, first devised by Hartree. Each electron is in the field of the others and the nucleus. A charge density is assumed for all the electrons and a potential is calculated from this and the field of the nucleus. The motions of the electrons in this potential are calculated by wave mechanical methods. From the resulting wave functions, the charge density at any point is obtained and the problem is repeated until there is good agreement between the assumed and calculated densities. This works well for atoms with atomic numbers (Z) up to 25. For higher atomic numbers other methods are used. The calculations have also been refined to include any atomic asymmetry and interactions between charges that occur when atoms in a solid are close together. Unfortunately, because of the $\sin kr/kr$ term, outer electrons (with large r) have only a very small affect. It is very difficult to check the calculations or to get outer-electron distributions by attempting to measure f by diffraction from a specimen whose structure is known. (See Problem 28, in Chapter 2, which indicates the effects of collecting only a limited amount of data—all we can ever measure!) Attempts to do this and refined calculations have been made, and although the accuracy of the calculations is quite good it is still questionable whether the contribution from outer shells can be determined, even in the most precise experiments.

With x-rays then, we always use calculated values of the f's in $F(\mathbf{s})$ and these *have* been checked sufficiently to indicate there are no large discrepancies (i.e., of more than a few per cent).

We can learn a great deal about the connection between various aspects of the interaction of radiation with matter if we look at this scattering in a simple way—as if each electron is a mass on a spring; and we shall adopt a treatment given by R. P. Feynman, R. B. Leighton, and M. Sands (*The Feynman Lectures on Physics*, Vol. I, Addison-Wesley, Inc., Reading, Mass., 1963). The attraction of the nucleus to which the electron is bound is the analogue to the spring's restoring force. The applied force is proportional to the incident field and to be reasonably general, we shall also include a "frictional" term. We can see why we need this if we first neglect such a term. Writing Newton's law:

$$m_{electron} \frac{d^2 x}{dt^2} = F - Kx.$$

Assume a general force of the form of a wave:

$$F e^{i(2\pi v t - 2\pi x/\lambda)} = F_0 e^{i\omega t}$$

($\omega = 2\pi v$, where v is the frequency.) (The force is not imaginary—we are again interested only in the real part—but we shall use the exponential form for ease in handling the equation.) The solution for this differential equation has the form $X = X_0 e^{i\omega t}$ and, substituting this solution,

$$X_0 = \frac{F_0/m}{(K/m) - \omega^2}.$$

If we did not apply any force,

$$\omega \equiv \omega_0 = \sqrt{K/m},$$

so that with a force,

$$X_0 = \frac{F_0/m}{\omega_0^2 - \omega^2}.$$

When $\omega = \omega_0$ there is an infinite displacement. This is not realistic because the electron is giving off the energy it absorbs from the field to put it in oscillation; thus we shall include a damping term proportional to the velocity. We already have a term proportional to the displacement, so this is the natural thing to try.

$$m \frac{d^2x}{dt^2} = -Kx - c \frac{dx}{dt} + F. \qquad (5\text{--}5a)$$

Let $c = m\delta$, $K = m\omega_0^2$. Then,

$$\frac{F}{m} = \frac{d^2x}{dt^2} + \delta \frac{dx}{dt} + \omega_0^2 x, \qquad (5\text{--}5b)$$

and with exponential forms for x, F:

$$x_0 = \frac{F_0/m}{(\omega_0^2 - \omega^2 + i\delta\omega)} = kF_0. \qquad (5\text{--}5c)$$

There is no infinite displacement now. This is the displacement we need to know to calculate the fields from an oscillating charge. Now:

$$\frac{1}{k} = \frac{1}{k_0 e^{i\theta}} = \frac{1}{k_0} e^{-i\theta},$$

and

$$\tan \theta = -\frac{\delta\omega}{(\omega_0^2 - \omega^2)}.$$

The displacement lags the applied field by as much as 180 degrees when $\omega \gg \omega_0$, because $\tan \theta$ goes to zero in the second quadrant. With x-rays, $\omega \gg \omega_0$, because the oscillation frequency for an emitting atom (ω_0) is estimated to be about 10^7 cps, whereas an x-ray has a frequency of about 10^{18} cps.

Suppose now that there are many atoms in a specimen being oscillated by the incoming field which has a different value at each electron in each atom. According to Eq. (5–5a), if we substitute $\sum_i X_i$ and $\sum_i F_i$, we get sums of differential equations, just like Eq. (5–5a), each with its own independent solution. This is why we can assume the scattered waves from the electrons in atoms to be additive. If the motion satisfies a *linear* differential equation (no powers of x or its derivatives), the solutions for each electron is independent. We should then write the solution in Eq. (5–5c) as a sum over all electrons in an atom and then over all atoms.

Let the incoming field for a wave traveling in the z direction be represented by $E_{\text{incident}} = E_0 e^{i\omega(t - z/c)}$. When it enters a material, it appears as if it is traveling with a speed c/n where n is the index of refraction of the material. Thus it will take an additional time increment to travel through a plate than through the same thickness outside the plate. If Δz is the thickness of a plate of the material, this increment is $(n - 1)\,\Delta z/c$. Therefore, after the wave has passed through the plate, relative to the field outside the material:

$$
\begin{aligned}
E_{\text{after}} &= E_0 e^{i\omega(t - \Delta t - z/c)} \\
&= E_0 e^{i\omega(t - (n-1)\Delta z/c - z/c)} \\
&= e^{-i\omega(n-1)\Delta z/c} E_0 e^{+ i\omega(t - z/c)}.
\end{aligned}
\tag{5--6a}
$$

If we assume the index will be only slightly different from unity, we can expand the first exponent and retain only the first two terms:

$$
\begin{aligned}
E_{\text{after}} &= E_0 e^{i\omega(t - z/c)}(1 - i\omega(n - 1)\,\Delta z/c) \\
&= E_0 e^{i\omega(t - z/c)} - i\omega(n - 1)\,(\Delta z/c)\,E_0 e^{i\omega(t - z/c)}.
\end{aligned}
\tag{5--6b}
$$

The first term is just the field of the source and thus the second must be the field produced by the oscillating charges in the plate (which of course depends on the size of the incoming field). The addition of the two can be made on the complex plane; the component due to the material is a small vector along the negative imaginary axis (it is tilted slightly counterclockwise from this axis, as can be seen by expanding the exponential term—i.e., it has a real part). We can ask ourselves now what the field due to the plate will be. The field due to a charge we know already [Eq. (5–1)]. All we need to do now is integrate this expression over the plate of material. Let b be the radius of a circle on the plane face of a plate of unit thickness and ρ be the electron density (per unit area). To get the acceleration of the electron we shall assume its motion is given by $x = x_0 e^{i\omega(t - r/c)}$ and differentiate twice. Then the field due to the electrons in the plate $\sum E$ is:

$$
\sum E = \int_{b=0}^{\infty} \frac{+|e|}{c^2 r}\, \omega^2 x_0 e^{i\omega(t - r/c)} \rho 2\pi b \; db.
$$

We shall neglect the trigonometric term, $\sin(\varphi)$ and any effects of diffraction. Now $r^2 = z^2 + b^2$, where r is the distance from a point b on the plane to the measuring point and z is the distance normal to the plate ($z = 0$ is the origin of the coordinates). $2r\,dr = 2b\,db$ as z is constant. Therefore,

$$
\sum E = \frac{|e|2\pi\omega^2 x_0 e^{i\omega t}}{c^2}\, \rho \int_{r=z}^{\infty} e^{-i\omega(r/c)}\, dr.
$$

The integral is $-(c/i\omega)e^{-i\omega(z/c)}$.

$$\sum E = \frac{+\rho|e|2\pi}{c} \, i\omega x_0 e^{i\omega(t-z/c)}$$

$$= \frac{+2\pi\rho|e|}{c} \times \text{(velocity of an electron)}. \qquad (5\text{--}7a)$$

The correct form for the motion of one electron is given by Eq. (5–5c) with $F = e \sum E$:

$$x = \frac{2\pi\rho|e|^2}{c} \frac{i\omega E_0 e^{i\omega(t-z/c)}}{m(\omega_0^2 - \omega^2 + i\,\delta\omega)},$$

or more generally for many atoms each with many electrons, rather than a uniform electron density, letting A_a be the atomic density in the plane face:

$$x \to \sum x = \frac{2\pi A_a|e|^2}{c} \sum_q \frac{i\omega N_q E_0 e^{i\omega(t-z/c)}}{m(\omega_{0q}^2 - \omega^2 + i\,\delta\omega)}, \qquad (5\text{--}7b)$$

where $\sum_q$ is the sum over the electrons in one atom and N_q is the number of electrons of each type q.

Putting Eq. (5–7b) in (5–7a) and comparing with Eq. (5–6b):

$$(n - 1)\,\Delta z = \sum_q^2 \frac{2\pi A_a|e|^2 N_q}{m(\omega_{0q}^2 - \omega^2 + i\,\delta\omega)}.$$

If ρ_a is the number of atoms per unit volume, $\rho_a\,\Delta z = A_a$ and

$$n = 1 + \frac{\rho_a|e|^2 2\pi}{m} \sum_q \frac{N_q}{(\omega_{0q}^2 - \omega^2 + i\,\delta\omega)}. \qquad (5\text{--}7c)$$

When ω approaches ω_{0q} the index rises and then falls as ω exceeds ω_{0q}. For the case of x-rays, $\omega \gg \omega_{0q}$ for most of the electrons in each atom, and n is smaller than unity. How much smaller? Let $\omega \, (= 2\pi\,c/\lambda)$ be $\gg \omega_0$—i.e., neglect ω_0 and also the imaginary term. If N_0 is Avogadro's number, A is the atomic weight, Z the atomic number, ρ the mass density, then assuming all electrons the same, so that

$$\rho_a \sum N_q = \frac{N_0 Z\rho}{A}$$

then,

$$n \cong 1 - \frac{e^2\lambda^2 N_0 Z\rho}{m2\pi c^2 A}.$$

If we substitute numerical values (cgs and esu units are called for), n is less than 1 by a few parts per million for all materials.

But how can a wave travel with more than the speed of light, which is what an index less than unity means? X-rays are quanta-pulses of energy made up of many waves. If we add, say, two waves together we obtain

$$e^{i[\omega_1 t - (2\pi x/\lambda_1)]} + e^{i[\omega_2 t - (2\pi x/\lambda_2)]}$$
$$= e^{1/2\, i[(\omega_1 + \omega_2)t - 2\pi x(1/\lambda_1 + 1/\lambda_2)]}$$
$$\times \{e^{1/2\, i(\omega_1 - \omega_2)t - 2\pi x(1/\lambda_1 - 1/\lambda_2)]} + e^{-1/2\, i[(\omega_1 - \omega_2)t - 2\pi x(1/\lambda_1 - 1/\lambda_2)]}\}$$
$$= 2e^{1/2\, i[(\omega_1 + \omega_2)t - 2\pi x(1/\lambda_1 + 1/\lambda_2)]}$$
$$\cos\left(1/2\,[(\omega_1 - \omega_2)t - 2\pi x(1/\lambda_1 - 1/\lambda_2)]\right).$$

We have a resultant wave or group that travels with an average frequency and average wave number, and this wave is modulated by the differences in these two quantities for the two waves. This *modulation* or group has a velocity V_m:

$$V_m = \frac{\omega_1 - \omega_2}{2\pi(1/\lambda_1 - 1/\lambda_2)},$$

whereas each wave has a velocity $\omega_i/(2\pi/\lambda_i)$. It is the modulation that is of interest—we want the velocity of the group, because it is the square of the amplitude of the group that is proportional to the energy of the group, and it is the group velocity that is carrying the energy through the material. According to our formula for the index of refraction, assuming $n \cong 1$, we can write

$$1 \cong 1 - \frac{K}{\omega^2} = 1 - \frac{K}{(\omega 2\pi c/\lambda)},$$
$$\frac{2\pi}{\lambda} = \frac{2\pi}{\lambda} - \frac{K}{\omega c} = \frac{w}{c} - \frac{K}{\omega c},$$
$$\frac{d(2\pi/\lambda)}{d\omega} = \frac{\omega^2 + K}{\omega^2 c}; \qquad \frac{d\omega}{2\pi d(1/\lambda)} = \frac{c}{(1 + K^2)/\omega^2}.$$

The group velocity of a packet *is* in fact *less* than the speed of light.

Without carrying out the calculations any further, it is clear now that the scattered amplitude and intensity could be calculated for an atom (by using the field of an oscillating charge and the displacement, Eq. (5–5c), to get the acceleration in the equation for the field); it is also clear that the scattered amplitude may be complex!

When the wavelength of the radiation used in diffraction approaches that of one of the absorption edges of a material, we can see from the above equations that the electrons associated with the absorption differ in phase (θ) from the others, see Figure 5-5. These "corrections" to the calculated f values are important. In materials science we are usually dealing with radiation close to $\lambda_{kabs.}$ for our specimen (e.g., copper radiation and a zinc specimen). It also turns out, as we can see in our equations for E or x_0, that it is in the vicinity of this "dispersion" that the imaginary terms in the atomic scattering factor will be significant—i.e., $f = f_0 + \Delta f' + i\,\Delta f''$. Let us look at some of the consequences of these corrections. (Tabulated values for these terms, often referred to as the Hönl correction, can be found in an Appendix to Reference 1 for dispersion of K electrons, or for more

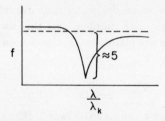

Figure 5-5.   The change in scattering factor near $\lambda/\lambda_K = 1.0$ (f is the order of the atomic number).

accurate values, in The International Tables, Vol. III, pp. 213–216. The values for the f's are on page 201.)

Let us take β-brass, a CsCl structure with a copper atom at the corner of the cubic cell and a zinc at the center. Its lattice parameter is 2.45 Å. Certain peaks such as 200 have $F = f_{Cu} + f_{Zn}$, others such as the 100 have $F = f_{Cu} - f_{Zn}$. A table of f and Δf for the 100 and 200 peaks for MoK_α and CuK_β is given below; for the moment we shall ignore $\Delta f''$.

| | MoK_α | | CuK_β | |
	100	200	100	200
f_{Cu}	25.5	18.0	18.0	11.4
$\Delta f'_{Cu}$	+0.3	+0.3	−5.2	−5.2
f_{Zn}	26.1	19.0	19.0	12.2
$\Delta f'_{Zn}$	+0.3	+0.3	−2.8	−2.8

$F_{100}^2/F_{200}^2 = 0.02$ per cent with molybdenum radiation, but if we use $CuK_\beta, \lambda/\lambda_{kabs}$ for copper is 1.0085, and for zinc is 1.08. The corrections will be large. $\Delta f'_{Cu} = -5.2$, $\Delta f'_{Zn} = -2.8$. Then, f_{Cu} is 12.6, f_{Zn} is 15.4, $F^2_{100}/F^2_{200} \cong 4$ per cent, and the 100 can be detected!

Now let us look at the imaginary terms. If $f = fo + \Delta f' + i\,\Delta f''$ we can see that we can write f in the form $f = |f|e^{i\varphi}$ for calculations of $F(\mathbf{s})$, where

$$|f| = \sqrt{(fo + \Delta f')^2 + |\Delta f''|^2}, \tag{5-8}$$

and

$$\varphi = \tan^{-1}\frac{\Delta f''}{fo + \Delta f'}.$$

When we add the vectors from atoms in a unit cell for $F(\mathbf{s})$, those that have electrons with energies close to the λ being used have a small term at 90 degrees to the real terms. (Actually, all the f values have such a term, but it is most important for λ close to λ_k.) The result for an hkl and $\bar{h}\bar{k}\bar{l}$ reflection from a crystal that does not have a center of symmetry in it is shown in Figure 5–6. The magnitudes of the F's are

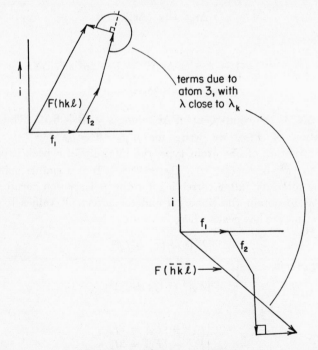

Figure 5–6. The structure factors $F(hkl)$ and $F(\overline{hkl})$. The imaginary terms for atom 3 (the vector at right angles to the first vectors for atom 3) are generally small and are exaggerated in the drawing.

different! (If the crystal had a center of symmetry there would be two identical atoms with imaginary terms on either side of the center, and these would cancel the effect.) It thus becomes possible, if the contribution of the atom involved to a given reflection is large enough, to know, from diffraction, if a center of symmetry is missing.

Finally, it is necessary in using f values to take into account the fact that the atoms in a structure are vibrating with an rms displacement $(\langle u^2 \rangle^{1/2})$, 5–10 per cent of the interatomic separation at room temperature. The tabulated f values assume no vibration. This introduces an additional phase factor. For any term $fe^{-2\pi i s \cdot r_n}$ we can write at some instant $fe^{-2\pi i s \cdot (r_n + \Delta r_n)} = fe^{2\pi i s \cdot r_n} e^{(+2\pi i s \cdot \Delta r_n)}$. Expanding the second term:

$$e^{+2\pi i \cdot s \cdot \Delta r_n} = 1 + 2\pi i s \cdot \Delta r_n - 2\pi^2 (s \cdot \Delta r_n)^2.$$

But, averaging over time and the volume irradiated:

$$\langle s \cdot \Delta r_n \rangle = s \cdot \langle \Delta r_n \rangle = 0.$$

Therefore,

$$e^{+2\pi i s \cdot \Delta r_n} = 1 - 2\pi^2 \langle (s \cdot \Delta r_n)^2 \rangle = 1 - 2\pi^2 |s|^2 \langle |\Delta X_n|^2 \rangle$$
$$= e^{(-8\pi^2 \sin^2 \theta)/\lambda^2 \langle |\Delta X_n|^2 \rangle} = e^{-M}, \qquad (5\text{-}9)$$

where ΔX_n is the component of Δr_n along $s = (S - S_0)/\lambda$. Thus, in a calculation of $F(s)$, we write for f, $f_0 e^{-M} = f_0 e^{-B \sin^2 \theta / \lambda^2}$. For a simple structure of one atom type, the intensity of a peak is proportional to $|F^2|$ or to $f_0^2 e^{-2M} = f_0^2 e^{-2B \sin^2 \theta / \lambda^2}$. It is a simple matter to plot log intensity (after correcting for the polarization term) versus $\sin^2 \theta / \lambda^2$ to obtain the slope $2B$ and to correct all values to $|F_0|^2$. If the structure has peaks where for some indices,

$$|F_1|^2 = (f_A - f_B)^2,$$

and for others

$$|F_2|^2 = (f_A + f_B)^2;$$

then

$$|F_1| + |F_2| = 2f_A,$$
$$|F_1| - |F_2| = 2f_B.$$

It is therefore possible to separate out the individual terms due to each atom and plot the $\ln f_A$ versus $\sin^2 \theta / \lambda^2$ to get the correction term for each atom. For more complex structures, this cannot be done. However, if we look at FF^* in this case, we can see what we can do:

$$FF^*(hkl) = \left(\sum_i f_i e^{-2\pi i(hu + kv + lw)}\right)\left(\sum_j f_j e^{+2\pi i(hu' + kv' + l\omega')}\right)$$

$$= \sum_i \sum_j f_i f_j e^{2\pi i[(h(u'-u) + k(v'-v) + l(w'-w)]}$$

$$= \sum f_j^2 + \sum_{\substack{i \\ i \neq j}} \sum_j f_i f_j e^{2\pi i[h(u'-u) + k(v'-v) + l(w'-w)]}.$$

If we take many $|F|^2$ (hkl) values at about the same 2θ and *average*, the second term will tend to zero. Then

$$F^2 \to \sum_j f_j^2 = \sum_j f_{j_0} e^{-2M_j},$$

assuming that all the atoms have the same e^{-2M} and that the vibrations are the same in all directions. Then

$$\ln\left(\frac{F^2}{\sum f_0^2}\right) = -2M. \tag{5–10}$$

This very approximate correction is about the best that can be done; it is better than nothing! (We could allow for anisotropy and take into account each atom type in very detailed studies—see Vol. III of The International Tables.) Temperature reduces many peaks at room temperature to only a half or a third of their intensity at, say, liquid nitrogen. (This can easily be seen by taking $\langle\Delta X_n^2\rangle^{1/2}$ 5 per cent of interatomic distance in Eq. (5–9).) If at all feasible, it would be good to do the measurements at low temperatures—at liquid nitrogen temperature, e.g. Not only will this minimize the vibrational effect,[2] but weak peaks will be easier to detect and measure, and the approximations discussed above will be less important.

A useful and interesting set of data on the temperature depression can be found in The International Tables, Vol. III, pp. 232–245.

The correction term calculated in this manner may include a static displacement because in close packed structures, differences in atomic sizes of the species may force atoms off lattice points. This static displacement $\langle u_{\text{static}}^2\rangle^{1/2}$ can be determined by evaluating $2M$ at two

[2] It is not possible to *eliminate* the effect of vibrations as there is some even at absolute zero; this term accounts for about 20 per cent of the total at room temperature.

temperatures and separating the two parts, as $2M = 2M_{\text{static}} + 2M_{\text{dynamic}} \times T + 2M_{\text{zero point vibration}}$. The last term can be calculated (see Reference 1 at the end of the chapter.)

The dynamic displacement is related to the Debye temperatures and to elastic constants and can be a useful tool in itself. However this topic is beyond the scope of this text and the reader is referred to the literature (see Reference 1).

We have so far been assuming that the interaction of x-rays with electrons is completely elastic. This is actually generally satisfactory. The vibrational modes of an atom in a solid are of about 0.01–0.1 ev, whereas an x-ray has an energy of about 10 Kev; there will be little change of energy of the x-ray beam. However, it is still possible that the electrons "recoil" when the incident beam is incident upon it. A. H. Compton realized this in 1923 and also realized that there should be a larger effect with elements of low atomic number where the binding energy for the electrons would be lower. He performed the experiment illustrated in Figure 5–7.

A second broad peak was observed, centered about $\lambda = 0.73$ Å, after scattering from the carbon block. [Figure 5.7(b).]

Consider the scattering process illustrated in Figure 5–8. For conservation of energy:

$$h\nu_0 = h\nu + \left(\frac{1}{2}\, \text{m}v^2\right) \text{electron.}$$

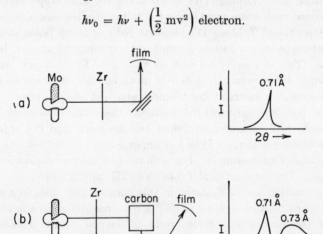

Figure 5–7.   Scattering by loosely bound electrons in carbon.

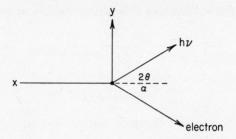

Figure 5–8.   A quantum of energy $h\nu_0$ is incident on an electron along the x-axis.

For a photon's energy E:

$$E = h\nu = mc^2,$$

$$m = \frac{h\nu}{c^2}, \qquad mv = \frac{h\nu}{c}.$$

For conservation of momentum in the x direction:

$$\frac{h\nu_0}{c} = \frac{h\nu}{c} \cos 2\theta + mv \cos \alpha,$$

and in the y direction is

$$0 = \frac{h\nu}{c} \sin 2\theta + mv \sin \alpha.$$

Now α and v are eliminated in the equations, as it is the scattered radiation that is of interest. The result is that

$$(\lambda - \lambda_0) = \frac{h}{m_0 c} (1 - \cos 2\theta), \qquad (5\text{–}11a)$$

or

$$\Delta\lambda = 0.0243(1 - \cos 2\theta). \qquad (5\text{–}11b)$$

The higher 2θ the greater the separation in λ. The separation $\Delta\lambda$ is *independent* of the initial λ; this beam of changed λ is, of course, incoherent. It does not contribute to diffraction but appears as background, which is difficult to avoid. It can be eliminated though, as indicated in Problem 3, and it is sufficiently large in scattering from glasses or polymers (the atomic numbers of the elements are small) to be annoying. Its intensity, as it is incoherent, depends on N, the number of scattering atoms, not N^2 as for diffracted beams.

More detailed calculations show that for the total scattering for one bound electron

$$I_{coherent} + I_{incoherent} = I_e \quad \text{(the Thomson scattering)},$$
$$I_{incoherent} = I_e - I_e f^2$$
$$= I_e(1 - f^2).$$

(For a free electron only Compton-scattering occurs.)

For many electrons

$$I_{incoherent} = I_e\left[\sum_1^Z 1 - (f_j{}^2)\right] = I_e\left(Z - \sum_j f_j{}^2\right),$$

$$i_{incoherent} \text{ (in "electron units")} = \frac{I}{I_e} = Z - \sum f_j{}^2. \quad (5\text{--}12)$$

Consider the lithium atom which has 2 K-electrons and 1 L-electron.

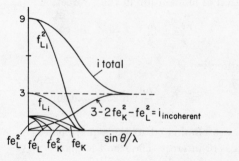

Figure 5–9. Schematic of the contribution of the electrons to the x-ray scattering from Li.

The various terms are shown schematically in Figure 5–9. The heavier the element, the larger the ratio of coherent to Compton incoherent scattering. Values for incoherent scattering can be found in The International Tables, Vol. III, pp. 247–253. There it will be seen that there is an additional term due to the Pauli exclusion principle which excludes two electrons from occupying the same state. Also there is a small correction due to the difference in wavelength of the incident radiation and the Compton scattering.

This scattering can be calculated and subtracted to obtain the coherent scattering in the most precise experiments, but this is not worthwhile unless a monochromator has been used and air

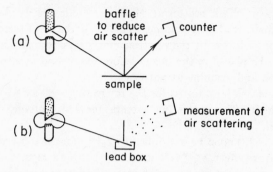

Figure 5–10. Measuring air scattering.

scattering is measured (as in Figure 5–10), or eliminated by evacuating the entire path from tube to counter. In Chapters 7 and 8 we will see how to measure I_0 for this calculation.

Electron Scattering Factor

In considering the scattering of an electron by an atom we have much the same theoretical problem as for x-rays, except that there is scattering by the nucleus as well as by the electron cloud, and the two have opposite signs (with x-rays only the electrons scatter).

$$f_e = 2 \frac{me^2}{h^2} \times \left(\frac{(Z - f)}{|s|^2} \right) \simeq \frac{me^2\lambda^2}{2h^2\theta^2} (Z - f),$$

as θ is small,

$$f_e(\text{Å}) = 0.0239 \frac{(Z - f)\lambda^2}{\theta^2}. \tag{5–13}$$

In this equation, $(Z - f)/\theta^2$ is the scattering factor of an atom for electrons, in electron units (like f). f is simply the x-ray scattering factor in electron units; m is the mass of the electron. (Values of f_e are tabulated in The International Tables, Vol. III, pp. 217–227.) This equation is not valid at small angles near 0 degrees 2θ (i.e., when $Z \to f$); extrapolation from higher angles can be used.

There are several important features of this formula. Note that the constant in front of the term $(Z - f)/|s|^2$ is much larger than the scattering of one electron for x-rays. The term $(Z - f)/|s|^2$ is larger than f up to about $\sin \theta/\lambda = 0.3$–$0.4$ but then is lower than f. However, because of the constant, the electron scattering is always greater than that for x-rays. Weak scattering effects are more easily detected—e.g., from small irradiated volumes. This is the basis of selected area diffraction procedures. In the electron microscope a small adjustable aperture can be placed in the image before the second lens to define a specific region and examine its pattern.

The formula has been tested for the range 15 kv–80 kv with reasonable agreement. The scattering factors for low voltages are still questionable.

Equation (5–13) must be multiplied by $I_0^{1/2}/r$ for the total scattering. The temperature effect, e^{-2M} is identical to that for x-rays.

Electrons can exist in two spin states and therefore in principle electrons can be "polarized." However, in practice, the fields of a structure are not large enough to do this to the incoming electrons. Some slight polarization has been detected but it is not yet well understood.

Neutron Scattering Factor

The interaction of a neutron with an atom is essentially an interaction with the nucleus. There is an interaction of the magnetic moment associated with the spin of the neutron and the moments of the atoms. This additional term occurs mainly for elements with unfilled outer shells, such as the transition elements. We shall not discuss this point here, but the student can find information on this in Reference 3. Suffice it to say that this interaction leads to the ability to detect the orientation of spins of atoms in the cell—i.e., not just the location of atoms, but the direction of their magnetic moment. This actually also leads to an extension of the space groups as mentioned in Chapter 1; we can now tell whether an atom is "black or white."

When a neutron approaches the nucleus, scattering is essentially related to two phenomena. First there is a potential scattering, for which the intensity is that for an impenetrable sphere, $4\pi R^2$.[3] R is the radius of the nucleus, $1.5 \times 10^{-13} A^{1/3}$, where A is the mass *number* ($A^{1/3}$ because nuclear matter has constant density). Second, when the neutron is close to the nucleus, its energy becomes distributed throughout the entire

---

[3] This is the analog to the term we would have obtained with x-rays for the *intensity* from a single electron, if the polarization term was missing, upon integrating to get the total power.

system—neutron and nucleus. We can think then of a "compound" nucleus containing the neutron. A metastable state forms, which decays, re-emitting the neutron. The total scattering factor (or amplitude) can be written as

$$b \text{ (cm)} = R - \frac{\gamma_n^{(R)}}{2\kappa E_R}. \tag{5-14}$$

Here, $\kappa = 2\pi/\lambda$, E_R is a resonance energy the neutron must have to form the compound nucleus and γ_n^R is the spread in energy during re-emission. Values of b are given on pp. 228–232 of Vol. III of the International Tables. Again we see that these are two terms out of phase, for essentially the same reason as for x-rays near the absorption edge. Because the nucleus is so small ($\simeq 10^{-13}$ cm) compared to the wavelength of thermal neutrons, there is no variation in b with $(\sin \theta)/\lambda$. Also there is no polarization, except in special cases involving the magnetic scattering from transition elements because this involves the outer electrons. Furthermore $\gamma_n^{(R)}$ is proportional to κ so that b is independent of λ, as well as θ. Experimental values of b are available, which is a big advantage over electrons or x-rays where we have only theoretical values. One is using values that have been measured, not only calculated.

Table 5–1

	$b \times 10^{+12}$ cm		$f_e \times 10^{+12}$ cm*		$f_x \times 10^{+12}$ cm	
$\dfrac{\sin \theta}{\lambda} = 0.1$		$= 0.5$	0.1	0.5	0.1	0.5
H	−0.378	−0.378	4,530	890	0.23	0.02
Cu^{63}	0.67	0.67	51,100	14,700	7.65	3.85
W	0.466	0.466	118,000	29,900	19.4	12.0

* Multiply by $(1 - V^2/c^2)^{1/2}$ where V is electron velocity

For the sake of comparison, we give in Table 5–1 scattering factors for x-rays, neutrons, and electrons for hydrogen, copper, and tungsten. All the constants have been included except $I_0^{1/2}/r$.

Neighboring atoms in the periodic table often have sufficient difference in their neutron scattering factor to aid in detecting weak peaks; e.g., the weak x-ray peaks in β brass discussed above are easily detected. Light elements are more easily detected in electron diffraction than in x-ray diffraction, and even more readily with neutrons.

For atomic nuclei with even mass number and even charge, there is no interaction of the spin of the nucleus and the neutron because there is no net spin for the nucleus. But, if the angular momentum of the atoms' nucleus is I, the compound state with an incident neutron will have a spin of $I + 1/2$ or $I - 1/2$. The total spin can have $2I + 1$ possible orientations in space, so that the compound nucleus can have $(2(I + 1/2) + 1)$ or $(2(I - 1/2) + 1)$ states, or an average of $2I + 1$. The scattering factor is somewhat different for the different states. All possibilities can occur with a mass of atoms so that the weight of the state associated with the plus sign for the neutron's spin in the compound state is on the average $w_+ = (I + 1)/(2I + 1)$ and that of the minus spin state $w_+ = (I)/2(I + 1)$. Let us see the effect of this and at the same time include the fact that most samples, even of pure elements, contain several isotopes of the element. We can write for the diffracted intensity from material with one atom at each lattice point:[4]

$$I(\mathbf{s}) = K \sum_{n} \sum_{n'} b_n b_{n'} e^{2\pi i \mathbf{s} \cdot (\mathbf{r}_{n'} - \mathbf{r}_n)}$$

$$= \sum_{0}^{N-1} b_n^2 + \sum_{\substack{n \\ n \neq n'}} \sum_{\substack{n' \\ }} b_n b_{n'} e^{2\pi i \mathbf{s} \cdot (\mathbf{r}_{n'} - \mathbf{r}_n)}.$$

We can observe the average of $I(\mathbf{s})$:

$$\langle I(\mathbf{s}) \rangle = N \langle b_n^2 \rangle + \sum_{\substack{n \\ n \neq n'}} \sum_{\substack{n \\ }} \langle b_n b_{n'} e^{2\pi i \mathbf{s} \cdot (\mathbf{r}_n - \mathbf{r}_n)} \rangle.$$

The occupation of the various lattice sites does not depend on the value of the exponential term; the lattice is defined by one function—the occupancy by another. Assuming random occupation, the occupancy of one site *does not affect* any other; thus,

$$\langle I(\mathbf{s}) \rangle = N \langle b_n^2 \rangle + \sum_{n \neq n'} \sum_{} \langle b_n b_{n'} \rangle e^{2\pi i \mathbf{s} \cdot (\mathbf{r}_{n'} - \mathbf{r}_n)},$$

and adding and subtracting the term missing in the sum:

$$\langle I(\mathbf{s}) \rangle = N(\langle b_n^2 \rangle - \langle b_n \rangle^2) + \sum_{n} \sum_{n'} \langle b_n \rangle^2 e^{2\pi i \mathbf{s} \cdot (\mathbf{r}_{n'} - \mathbf{r}_n)}. \quad (5-15)$$

---

[4] If there is more than one atom at each lattice point, b_n can be replaced by F_n in the expressions that follow.

That is, the scattering factor to be used for the *coherent* scattering (in the sum) is an average scattering factor based on the atomic fraction (not the weight fraction).

With neutrons, we must weigh first the various spin states of each isotope of each element, then weigh the various isotopes, and finally, if necessary, the different elements present. Because some of the b's are negative, b in an alloy or compound can even be reduced to zero; an interesting example is shown in Figure 5–11.

With x-rays or electrons, to calculate the structure factor for an alloy (not a compound), we must replace b_n with f_n in Eq. (5–15) and use a weighted f value at each atomic position—i.e., f_n is the atomic fraction times the appropriate scattering factor.

There is a continuous background, $N(\langle f_n^2 \rangle - \langle f_n \rangle^2)$, say, from an alloy with x-rays (called the Laue monotonic or $N(\langle b_n^2 \rangle - \langle b_n \rangle^2)$ from a pure element for neutrons—even for a single isotope, if the scattering nucleus has an odd mass number or odd nuclear charge (spin incoherent scattering)). If the occupation of sites is not random, this continuous background will be modulated—i.e., it will show broad bumps indicating a tendency to ordering where peaks from an ordered cell might show up. We will discuss this in more detail in Chapter 8.

Neglecting the structure—i.e., assuming independent atoms, as in a gas—the *total* scattering *cross section* per average atom for neutrons is

$$\sigma = 4\pi(w_+ b_+^2 + w_- b_-^2).$$

We can break this scattering into two parts:

$$= \underbrace{4\pi(w_+ b_+ + w_- b_-)^2}_{l} + \underbrace{4\pi(w_+ b_+^2 + w_- b_-^2) - 4\pi(w_+ b_+ + w_- b_-)^2}_{P},$$

or

$$\sigma = l + P.$$

The P term in the scattering cross section is the incoherent scattering. The other term l is the coherent scattering.

For H^1, $\sigma = 81.5 \times 10^{-24}$ cm^2 (or 81.5 barns) while l is 1.79 barns. For deuterium, H^2, $l = 5.4$ barns, $\sigma = 7.6$ barns. The background due to spin incoherent scattering is much lower in a diffraction pattern if H^2 rather than H^1 is involved.

Because of the mass of neutrons, its energy is the order of 0.1 ev, and there is energy exchange with the thermal energy of the atom. This leads to an inelastic scattering both coherent and incoherent; some

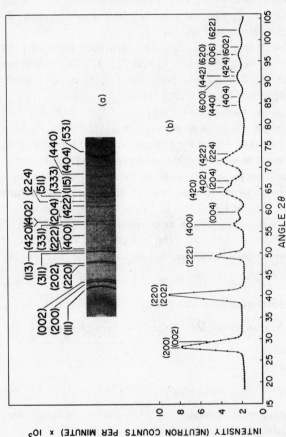

Figure 5–11. Diffraction patterns of $MD_{1.99}$ [M = 62 at pct Ti − 38 pct Zr, D = H^2] (a) filtered Cu; camera radius 114.6 mm. (b) neutrons λ = 1.09 Å. Structure is similar to that for CaF_2 with M at the corner and face positions of a slightly distorted cubic cell and D at all tetrahedral sites, so that for hkl all even or all odd, $F_{hkl} = 4[\overline{b}_M + Cb_D \cos\{(\pi/2) \times (h + k + l)\}]$ and C is the mole fraction of D (1.99). For the Ti-Zr composition chosen, $\overline{b}_M$ is zero so that the neutron scattering is from the second term only, the structure formed by the interstitial deuterium which is a slightly distorted simple cubic cell. (Reprinted with permission from a paper by S. S. Sidhu, LeRoy Heaton, and M. H. Mueller, Jrnl. Appl. Phys., 30, 1959.) The indexing of the neutron diffraction pattern is the same as that for the x-ray pattern, i.e., 200 instead of 100, etc.

of the neutrons undergo a change in wavelength due to this as well as to recoils. We shall discuss this further in Chapter 8.

In calculating the diffracted intensity, we shall have to calculate the number N of atoms scattering. This will require knowing the depth to which the beam penetrates and how its intensity varies with depth. We need then to examine the sum total of interactions with material and the resultant effect, absorption.

Absorption

Of X-Rays

When an x-ray beam is incident on a material, it passes through a certain depth and is absorbed by a variety of processes, all of which we have already discussed. These are summarized in Figure 5–12.

We have seen that the index of refraction is complex and we can write it in the form:

$$n = n_R - in_i.$$

Then from Eq. (5–6a), after a beam has passed through a material,

$$E_{\text{after}} = e^{-\omega n_i \Delta z/c} e^{-i\omega(n_R-1)\Delta z/c} E_0 e^{i\omega(t-z/c)}.$$

The first term is an exponential term—an *absorption* in the plate. Thus the imaginary terms for the scattering, which are related to those for

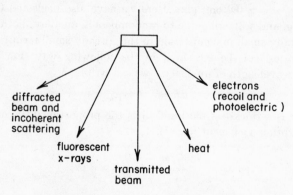

Figure 5–12. Contributions to Absorption. (After N. F. M. Henry, H. Lipson, and W. A. Wooster, *The Interpretation of X-Ray Diffraction Photographs*, Macmillan Co., London, 1951.)

the index, are also terms that lead to absorption. All of these phenomena are linked together.

If the sample is thick enough, no transmitted beam may come through.

The effect of scattering coherent and incoherent on absorption can be calculated as soon as we complete our calculation of the total intensity in a peak (not just the maximum value) in the next chapter. It would be necessary then for a powder specimen, to calculate the intensity for all the possible diffracted cones for $\lambda/2d < 1$—i.e., we would have to calculate the total intensity in all the cones inside the sphere of reflection of radius $2/\lambda$. We can take another approach and calculate the scattering per electron and sum for all the electrons in the material. This would be the situation for a gas, e.g., or a single crystal not diffracting. Now $\sigma_e = P/I_0$, the coherent scattering cross section per electron, has a value of 6.7×10^{-25} cm^2. We can write our absorption due to scattering as

$$\frac{\sigma}{\rho} = \frac{cm^2}{gm} = \sigma_e \times \left(\frac{\text{no. of electrons}}{gm}\right).$$

By dividing by ρ, we have an absorption term that is independent of the state of the material but depends only on the number of atoms scattering; and for solid samples, quantities are involved (the surface area and weight) which are relatively easy to measure.

Now,

$$\frac{\sigma}{\rho} = \sigma_e \frac{N_0 Z}{A} \quad \text{and} \quad \frac{Z}{A} \approx \frac{1}{2}.$$

Therefore, $\sigma/\rho \cong 0.2$ cm^2/gm. (Here we have also neglected Compton scattering, and scattering due to randomness in an alloy; both of these are generally small in comparison to this already small term.)

Absorption can be measured in the following way. For a single incident wavelength of intensity I we can write

$$dI = -I\,dx\mu_L,$$

where dx is a thickness (cm) and μ_L is the proportionality constant—the absorption coefficient (cm^{-1}).

$$\ln\frac{I}{I_0} = -\mu_L x,$$
$$I = I_0 e^{-\mu_L x}$$
$$= I_0 e^{-(\mu_L/\rho)\rho x}.$$

It is then possible to measure I and I_0 and determine μ/ρ. If we did this we would find that *for x-rays* absorption is generally two to three orders of magnitude greater than $0.2\ cm^2$; scattering is a minor factor and the most important term is fluorescence.

If there are several atom types present in a sample, because absorption depends only on the number of atoms present, we can imagine each atom type in one section of the sample, as in Figure 5–13.

Let w_i = weight fraction of the ith element.

$\quad t_i$ = its thickness.

$\quad \rho_i t_i = \dfrac{\text{gms}}{\text{cm}^2}$ of the ith element.

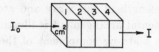

Figure 5–13.   Absorption from a material with four elements.

Then, the intensity passing through the sample in Figure 5–13 is absorbed by each layer:

$$I = I_0 e^{-(\mu/\rho)_1 \rho_1 t_1} e^{-(\mu/\rho)_2 \rho_2 t_2} e^{-(\mu/\rho)_3 \rho_3 t_3} \cdots,$$

$$I = I_0 e^{-\sum_i (\mu/\rho)_i \rho_i t_i},$$

$\rho_i t_i = M w_i$ where M is the total mass per unit area. Therefore,

$$I = I_0 e^{-\sum_i [(\mu/\rho)_i] w_i M},$$

but $M = \rho t$ of the entire specimen. Therefore,

$$I = I_0 e^{(-\sum_i [(\mu_i/\rho)_i w_i \rho t])}. \qquad (5\text{–}16)$$

As an example of absorption calculations, let us calculate the absorption of 100 cm of air for $CrK\alpha$ radiation. Absorption coefficients for x-ray are listed in The International Tables, Vol. III, starting on p. 157.

$(\mu/\rho)_{\text{oxygen}}$ for $CrK\alpha = 35,$ $\qquad (\mu/\rho)_{\text{nitrogen}}$ for $CrK\alpha = 22,$

$$\frac{I}{I_0} = e^{-[(1/5(35) + 4/5(22)]\frac{29\ \text{grams}}{22,400\text{cc}} \times 100}$$

$$\cong \frac{1}{10}.$$

A simple calculation will also show that $I/I_0 = 1/100$ in 0.001 in. of most solids samples so that diffraction is generally from a thin layer.

Barkla, the man who demonstrated polarization of x-rays, was also one of the pioneers in the study of absorption of x-rays. In the

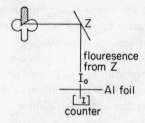

Figure 5–14.   Measuring the absorption of an Al foil for fluorescent x-rays from a specimen of atomic number Z.

nineteenth century he showed the fundamentals of the variation of absorption with wavelength of the x-ray and atomic number of the absorber. His experimental arrangement is illustrated in Figure 5–14. (Fortunately, $K\alpha$ was a strong component of the radiation from the tube—a fact which was assumed in the work!) Some of his results are shown in Figure 5–15. (He arbitrarily called one curve the K curve, the other the L curve, for the nature of the spectrum was then not understood. These letters are still associated with the atomic shells from which electrons are ejected in producing fluorescence.) In each curve, $(\mu/\rho)_{Al} \propto Z^{-6}$. Moseley later demonstrated that

$$\sqrt{v} \propto Z; \quad \text{therefore,} \quad \lambda \propto \frac{1}{Z^2}.$$

Hence, $\mu/\rho \propto \lambda^3$. Also, $\mu/\rho \propto Z^4$ where Z is the atomic number of the absorber. Thus

$$\mu/\rho \cong (KZ^4_{\text{absorber}})\lambda^3_{\text{of radiation}}. \tag{5–17}$$

For any given element μ/ρ appears as in Figure 5–16. The three edges of the L spectra arise because, as indicated in Chapter 3, there are three energy levels in the L shell. The jump at the K edge (when the

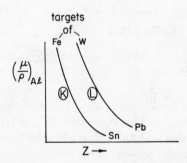

Figure 5-15. $(\mu/\rho)_{Al}$ vs. Atomic Number Z.

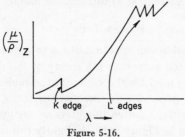

Figure 5-16.

wavelength is short enough) increases in relative magnitude as Z decreases. We can make use of this drop in a very simple way to "clean up" the spectrum, as an element of $Z - 1$ has a K edge between K_β and K_α of a target with atomic number Z. This is illustrated in Figure 5–17. We can even do a better job than this. If we take foils of $Z - 1$, $Z - 2$, the one of $Z - 2$ will have a sharp rise in absorption on the long wavelength side of the K_α. This situation is illustrated in Figure 5–18. If we can adjust the absorption of the two foils to be equal outside the range $\Delta\lambda$, around K_α from the tube, then the difference in readings with first one filter, then the other, will eliminate all radiation but that in the middle.

$$\text{Power } (P) \text{ transmitted} = (I_0 e^{-\mu_L t_{z-2}} - I_0 e^{-\mu_s t_{z-2}}) \, \Delta\lambda,$$

where t is thickness. Maximizing this, i.e., setting

$$\frac{d \text{ Power}}{dt} = 0,$$

$$\frac{\log \mu_s/\mu_L}{\mu_s - \mu_L} = t_{z-2} \tag{5–18a}$$

for maximum power through filter 2.

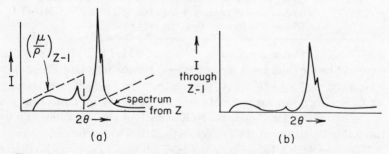

Figure 5-17. (a) The X-ray spectrum from Z and the absorption of element $Z - 1$. (b) The X-ray spectrum from Z through a foil of $Z - 1$.

The thickness of filter $(z - 1)$ can then be found:

$$\mu_C t_{(z-2)} = \mu_D t_{(z-1)}. \tag{5-18b}$$

For very precise balancing it is important to use measured values for the μ's, not tabulated values, as the purity of the foils may be vastly different than those used for the values in the tables.

The drop in μ/ρ goes up as Z goes down, and a match of the two filters at point D will not match the filters on the long wavelength side of the K_α, as shown in Figure 5-19. A slightly thinner piece of element

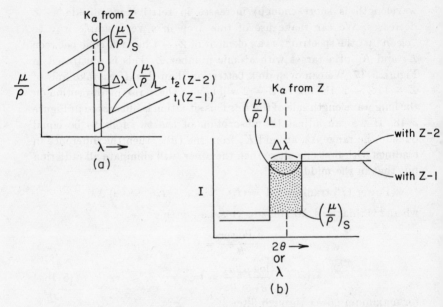

Figure 5-18.   (a) μ/ρ for thickness t_2 of element $Z - 2$ and t_1 of element $Z - 1$ (b) Schematic of intensity through foils of $Z - 2$, $Z - 1$. (After P. Kirkpatrick, *Rev. Sci. Instr.*, 10, 1939.)

$Z - 1$ can be used and a piece of aluminum added to it; its absorption edge will be far from the λ for any target. Its μ/ρ, following Eq. (5-17), is larger on the long λ-side of K_α than on the short λ side. (The balancing, for CuKα, e.g., can easily be checked at all stages by measuring μ/ρ of the two filters for CoKα and MoKα. Each of the two filters can be tilted slightly to adjust their effective thickness to the beam.)

How does such a balancing procedure compare to a monochromator or to a pulse height analyzer? (This is an electronic device which has

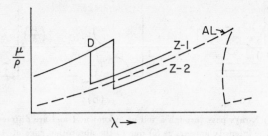

Figure 5-19

adjustable voltage "windows" for a counter and can therefore be set to distinguish the energy (E) of a pulse and hence its wavelength. There is a range of voltages for any λ so a plot of I versus E for any λ is a broad peak.) With a monochromator, $\Delta\lambda$ due to dispersion is $\approx 10^{-3}$ Å and for 90 per cent acceptance of the desired radiation with a pulse-height analyzer, an appreciable contribution of λ's closer than $\lambda/2$ is included. Let us look at the balanced filters. From Moseley's law,

$$Z^2\lambda = \text{constant.}$$

Differentiating, $2Z\,dZ\lambda + Z^2\,d\lambda = 0$. Letting $dZ = -1$ for balanced filters,

$$\frac{d\lambda}{\lambda} = \frac{2}{Z}.$$

The greater the Z of the target, the smaller the interval. Some typical intervals are given below:

Radiation	Filter	$\Delta\lambda$
AgKα	Rh–Ra	0.03 Å
CuKα	Co–Ni	0.12 Å
CrKα	Va–Ti	0.23 Å

Balanced filters are better than a pulse-height analyzer but not as good as a monochromator.

Absorption can be very useful in a practical way. In steel mills the roll separation is often automated to provide very uniform thickness in thin sheet by adjusting automatically to I/I_0. Platings on cans are checked by measuring the total fluorescence from tin or the diffraction intensity of a peak from the iron under the tin—this depends on the amount of tin above it. We can also use absorption for quantitative

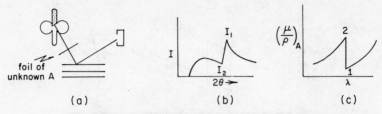

5-20. (a) X-rays pass through a foil of unknown A and are diffracted from a crystal. The intensity appears as (b) due to the absorption edge of A (as shown in (c)).

analysis. As shown in Figure 5–20, the sharp edge in a spectrum can be used to identify an element.

For element A:

$$I_1 = I_0 e^{-[(\mu/\rho)_{A_1} w_A + (\mu/\rho)_B w_B + \cdots]\rho t},$$

$$I_2 = I_0 e^{-[(\mu/\rho)_{A_2} w_A + (\mu/\rho)_B w_B + \cdots]\rho t},$$

$$\ln \frac{I_1}{I_2} = [(\mu/\rho)_{A_2} - (\mu/\rho)_{A_1}] w_A \rho t,$$

$$\frac{\ln I_1/I_2}{(\mu/\rho)_{A_1} - (\mu/\rho)_{A_2}} = w_A \rho t = \frac{\text{mass}}{\text{cm}^2} \quad \text{of } A. \tag{5-19}$$

This technique is not as general for chemical analysis as fluorescence because of the fact that one must go through the specimen and thus the specimen must be quite thin. Also the μ/ρ's for the element must be *extrapolated* from the tables to the edge according to Eq. (5–17), which is only approximate.

There is another way of using absorption for analysis. Suppose there are two elements A and B; $w_A + w_B = 1$. Using one λ from a monochromator and measuring ρ as a function of (w_A) and measuring thickness, we can determine w_A from $I = I_0 e^{-[(\mu/\rho_A)w_A + (\mu/\rho)_B w_B]\rho t}$. Thus it becomes a simple matter to analyze a diffusion couple, e.g., automatically, by moving a slab of the couple slowly past a beam and counting or recording I, as illustrated in Figure 5–21. Phase boundaries can be found this way.

If we use *two* λ's, we can avoid determining ρ as a function of (w_A) and the thickness of the specimen at each point.

$$I_1 = I_0 e^{-[(\mu/\rho)_{A_1} w_A + (\mu/\rho)_{B_2} w_B]\rho t},$$

$$I_2 = I_0 e^{-[(\mu/\rho)_{A_2} w_A + (\mu/\rho)_{B_2} w_2]\rho t},$$

$$\frac{l_n(I_1/I_0)}{l_n(I_2/I_0)} = \frac{(\mu/\rho)_{A_1} w_A + (\mu/\rho)_{B_1}(1 - w_A)}{(\mu/\rho)_{A_2} w_A + (\mu/\rho)_{B_2}(1 - w_A)}. \tag{5-20}$$

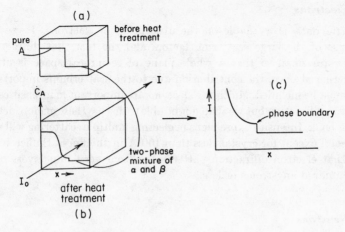

Figure 5–21. The diffusion couple in (a) is heat treated to give the composition profile in (b); the transmitted intensity appears as in (c).

In order to do this, the two λ's should be chosen so that one is on one side of an absorption edge of at least one element and the other is on the other side, as shown in Figure 5–22. Because of the sharp drop for $(\mu/\rho)_A$ the equations for λ_1 and λ_2 are not related. If we did not do this, then $(\mu/\rho)_A$ and $(\mu/\rho)_B$ in the numerator and denominator of Eq. (5–20) would be related by λ_1^3/λ_2^3 and a solution would not be possible. Two different targets can be used (with a monochromator to get each λ independently of other λ's from the target) or the K_α and K_β from one target may provide the necessary condition. Fluorescent radiation can also be used.

Fine details in the absorption edges can also be used to learn something about the energies of the outer electron shells, where the excited electrons go.

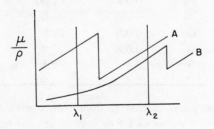

Figure 5–22.

Of Electrons

Little data is available on the absorption of electrons. However, because of the large scattering factors and the fact that diffraction angles are small so that a whole plane of reciprocal space is often scattering at once, the contribution due to the scattering is important and must be included. Multiple reflections are important in intensities of electron diffraction but we shall not be able to discuss these in more detail in this book. Intensity expressions neglecting multiple scattering will not be useful except for crystals less than 100 Å in thickness. Suffice it to say that electron diffraction patterns are from very thin layers of a few hundred angstroms or less.

Of Neutrons

With neutrons, the scattering contribution to absorption is more important than for x-rays. The scattering factors are smaller than those for x-rays; however, since true absorption is much smaller, there is more penetration and hence scattering is more important. True absorption coefficients for neutrons are listed in Table 5–2 along with some data for the total absorption for x-rays.

Table 5–2

True Absorption Coefficients for Neutrons and Total Absorption Coefficients for X-Rays

	cm^2/gm 1.08 Å *Neutrons*	cm^2/gm 1.54 Å *X-Ray*
Be	0.0003	1.50
Al	0.003	48.6
Cu	0.021	52.9
W	0.036	17.2
B	2.4	2.4

This true absorption, similar to fluorescence with x-rays, is due to neutron capture. It varies as $1/v$ or is proportional to λ (as $\lambda = h/mv$), compared to λ^3 for x-rays. For a very few elements such as boron, the absorption is very large at the usual λ's because we are near the resonant peak, and the absorption may be as large or larger than that for x-rays. (Values are tabulated in The International Tables, Vol. III, pp. 197–199.)

To these *true absorption* factors for neutrons we must add the calculated scattering, ordered and disordered elastic, and inelastic. We have already seen how to calculate the disordered elastic. We shall see how to calculate the ordered elastic contribution in the next chapter. As an example of the type of plot expected we show results for powdered nickel in Figure 5–23. At very long λ's diffraction is not

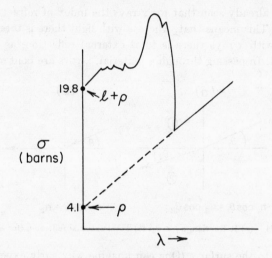

Figure 5–23.   Neutron cross section for Nickel. (After G. E. Bacon, *Neutron Diffraction*, Clarendon Press, Oxford, 1962.)

occurring and at very short's λ's the diffraction effects average out. As λ increases, the discontinuities correspond to changes in the number of diffraction peaks from the powder. In practice, the easiest way to determine the *total* absorption coefficient for neutrons is simply to measure it for the given specimen under the given experimental conditions. (It is important to remember *with all radiations* that if the diffracting particles are very small, the diffraction peak will be spread out (as will all peaks, of course), and if fine slits are used in a transmission experiment to get I/I_0, some of the scattering will be missed.) Because of the deeper penetration of neutrons, a typical specimen has dimensions of several millimeters—an order of magnitude larger than for x-rays. One must check to be sure intensities are proportional to F^2; because of the deeper penetration, multiple scattering can be troublesome. As we have seen that each reflection causes a 180 degree phase shift, a twice diffracted beam is out of phase with the main beam, reducing its intensity below the value assuming $I\ F^2$.

Refraction

We have already seen that for x-rays the index of refraction is less than unity. This means that, whereas with light there is total internal reflection, with x-rays there is total external reflection, as shown in Figure 5–24. In passing through a material, x-rays are bent *away* from

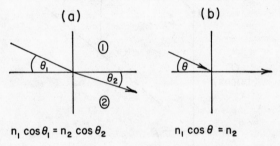

(a)   **(b)**

$$n_1 \cos\theta_1 = n_2 \cos\theta_2 \qquad\qquad n_1 \cos\theta = n_2$$

Figure 5–24.   (a) Refraction, $n_2 < n_1$; (b) Total external reflection (for $n_2 < n_1$).

the normal to the surface. (One can imagine why early experimenters might have had trouble in proving that x-rays were radiation like light!) More important, however, is the fact that the wavelength is different inside the material, and the observed diffraction angle may be slightly different than the true one. (In other words, Bragg's law is valid *inside* the crystal.) The d spacings will be in error in the fourth or fifth decimal place. For highest accuracy, a correction is required. Examples of how to correct for this are given in the Problem section. In reflection, the *apparent* angle of a peak is too large.

For electrons, the field inside the specimen due to the ions and electrons retards the electrons, and

$$n = \frac{\sqrt{V + V \text{ specimen}}}{\sqrt{V}}.$$

Thus n is greater than 1. The specimen diffracts at a lower apparent angle, as if the λ in the specimen was less than the value outside—i.e.,

$$n = \frac{\lambda_{\text{vacuum}}}{\lambda_{\text{in specimen}}}.$$

For neutrons,

$$n = 1 - \frac{\lambda^2 \sum\limits_i N_i b_i}{2\pi}.$$

Where N_i is the number of i nuclei/cm^3; n can be greater or less than 1 because b can be positive or negative. The index differs from unity in any case by 1 part per million or less. It is clear that total internal or external reflection will occur if b is negative or positive, and also that a value for b can be obtained by measuring the angle for which total reflection just starts.

Suggested Readings

1. R. W. James, *The Optical Principles of the Diffraction of X-Rays* (G. Bell and Sons, London, 1950).
2. Z. G. Pinsker, *Electron Diffraction* (Butterworth's, London, 1953).
3. G. E. Bacon, *Neutron Diffraction* (Clarendon Press, Oxford, 1962).

Problems

1. A steel containing 1.5 wt-per cent carbon and 13 wt-per cent manganese can be retained in the austenitic state on quenching. Consider the structure factor and show whether or not it is possible to tell whether the carbon atoms are randomly distributed in tetrahedral or octahedral sites, using:

   (a) X-ray diffraction.
   (b) Neutron diffraction.

2. 5 mole per cent of FeO is dissolved in MgO. MgO has the same structure as NaCl.

(a) Can the Fe^{+2} ions fit in the octahedral positions? If the iron ions had the valence $+3$ would they fit any better in the tetrahedral positions?

(b) Consider the structure factors of the 111, 200, 220 peaks of (Fe, Mg)O. Can you tell whether the iron is in octahedral or tetrahedral sites, or arranged in a spinel-like region (the spinel Fe_2MgO_4 precipitates after some time at high temperatures). Consider (1) x-rays, (2) neutrons.

3. Suppose you wish to eliminate Compton scattering from a measurement, experimentally, not by calculation.

(a) Consider placing a monochromator before the specimen or after it. Can either arrangement accomplish this? How?

(b) Is there any other way you can think of doing this? Give a detailed example.

4. A monochromatic beam of antimony K_{α_1} is scattered by a block of paraffin. On a concentric film (AgBr in gelatin) arranged to catch the scattered radiation, an absorption edge appears due to the change in sensitivity of the film at the wavelength $\lambda_{Kabs.}$ of silver. At what scattering angle does this edge appear and which side is darker, the high-angle or low-angle side?

5. Tungsten L_{α_1} is scattered by a block of paraffin. The intensity of scattered radiation (modified and unmodified) is measured by a counter in front of which is a nickel foil. On varying 2θ (the angle the counter makes with the direct beam) a discontinuous jump occurs in the intensity.

(a) At what 2θ angle does this occur?

(b) On which side of this 2θ is the reading greater?

(c) The counter is set just on the high-angle side at this 2θ and the intensity (I) is read. With the nickel filter in the incident beam the intensity is reduced to $I/64$. With the filter in the scattered beam, the intensity is $33I/128$. What fraction of the intensity is due to unmodified scattering?

6. You are building a device to hold a sample under an atmosphere for use with CuK_α. How thick can a beryllium window be to reduce the radiation by $1/2$? (Remember the beam goes through the window to the sample and then out again as scattered radiation.) How thick would pyrex have to be? Mylar?

7. An x-ray beam from a copper target is monochromated by a LiF monochromator. This crystal, which has an NaCl structure, is

being used, cut to a (100) plane. The first reflection for λ (1.54 Å) is the 200 peak. But there is a component of $\lambda/2$; the fourth order—i.e., the reflection from 400 occurs at the same position. If the diffracted beam is sent through an aluminum sheet 0.1 mm thick it is reduced to 57 per cent of its value without the sheet.

(a) What fraction of the intensity from the LiF comes from $\lambda/2$?

(b) To what percentage of its value with one foil of aluminum would the beam be reduced if a second sheet was placed in the beam from the LiF?

8. Two f.c.c. metals have exactly the same atomic size, but $f_B = 3f_A$. A powder sample contains $N_A = 3N/4$ of A and $N_B = N/4B$ atoms. (N is the total number of atoms.) Consider three cases:

(a) A powder sample is a mechanical mixture of A and B.

(b) A powder sample is made up of f.c.c. crystals of a completely random solid solution.

(c) A powder sample is made up of a completely ordered arrangement of A and B (A at faces, B at corners of the unit cell). Compute the values of F^2 for the 200 reflection for all three cases. In (b) compute the Laue monotonic scattering and compare to the 200 peak.

9. A powder sample of copper contains vacancies randomly distributed. Assume you are using unpolarized CuK_α radiation with $I_0 = 10^9$ cps, and a diffractometer with a radius of 5.73 in. What concentration of vacancies is required to detect the diffuse scattering if 1 cps is the lowest level you can detect? Would you do any better by attempting to measure a decrease in peak intensity? Suppose you could detect a 1 per cent change.

10. Derive the polarization expression for double scattering, as shown in the diagram. Express the intensity I_2 in terms of I_1. This is the geometric expression for scattering from a monochromator. Compare its angular dependence with that for filtered radiation.

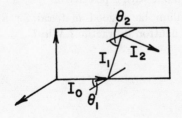

11. Assume there is double scattering within the crystal, as in the figure for Problem 10. Express I_2 as a function of I_0 and explain how you might be able to tell if there was double scattering.

12. Derive the refraction correction to Bragg's law for the transmission case, shown below.

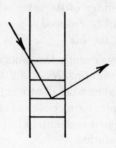

(Remember $n = \dfrac{\lambda_{\text{outside}}}{\lambda_{\text{inside}}}$, and Snell's law!)

13. Derive the refraction correction to Bragg's law for reflection, as shown below.

Consider that the sample is nickel. Calculate the correction for the 200 and 400 peaks, for neutron and x-ray diffraction.

14. Derive an equation for determining the value of b using total reflection. Estimate the angle involved for one material with a negative b and one with a positive b.

15. Would vanadium be a good material for a sample holder or container for neutron diffraction? Why?

6 The Integrated Intensity

The peak intensities are not very useful for examining the details of the structure—i.e., for obtaining information about FF^*. The breadth of the peak is markedly dependent on the perfection of the crystal. If the incident beam is not collimated perfectly, different regions will diffract at slightly different angles. Small mosaic regions will diffract at different angles even if the beam is well collimated. The maximum would correspond to the overlapping patterns from all regions. We would also need a very narrow slit to truly measure the maximum intensity. Instead, it is easier to work with a divergent beam and the total (integrated) intensity under a diffraction peak, ignoring its shape (but see Chapter 8). In this chapter we shall consider the formulae for this integrated value for various techniques.[1]

For Single Crystals

Consider first a single crystal, diffracting a roughly collimated beam from the hkl planes, and rotating through the diffracting position with an angular velocity ω about an axis parallel to (hkl) and perpendicular to S_0. This situation is shown in Figure 6-1.

At some receiving plane described by coordinates Z', Y', is placed a film or counter with a slit opened to get all the diffracted radiation during the rotation. During this rotation, all points of the crystal under the beam form the Bragg angle with each and every direction of the primary beam. (This rotation corresponds to the formation of a spot on the equator of a rotation pattern.) We shall assume our crystal is a

---

[1] We shall follow a treatment first taught to the author by Professor B. E. Warren. This treatment is independent of the type of radiation used.

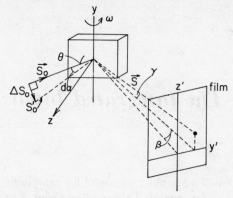

Figure 6–1.   (After B. E. Warren in *X-Rays in Theory and Experiment* by A. H. Compton and S. K. Allison, D. Van Nostrand Co., Princeton, N.J., 1963.)

parallelepiped with N_1 repeating units along $\mathbf{a}_1$, N_2 along $\mathbf{a}_2$, N_3 along $\mathbf{a}_3$.

Now the intensity (I) is the energy per unit area of film, per unit time, but what we want is energy, E:

$$E = \int I \, dt \, dA.$$

Instead of the crystal rotating, we shall consider $\mathbf{S}_0$ rotating. The time S_0 spends between θ and $\theta + d\alpha$ is

$$dt = \frac{d\alpha}{\omega},$$

$$dA = dy' \, dz' = R^2 d\beta \, d\gamma,$$

where R is the distance from the crystal to the measuring plane. Thus,

$$E = \int \int \int I \, \frac{R^2}{\omega} \, d\alpha \, d\beta \, d\gamma.$$

Our expression for I has a term depending on the scattering per unit ... I_u. For example, for filtered x-rays,

$$I_u = \frac{I_0 e^4}{m^2 c^4 R^2} \frac{1 + \cos^2 2\theta}{2},$$

for one electron. I also includes FF^* and three terms like

$$\frac{\sin^2 (\pi/\lambda)(\mathbf{S} - \mathbf{S}_0) \cdot N_1 \mathbf{a}_1}{\sin^2 (\pi/\lambda)(\mathbf{S} - \mathbf{S}_0) \cdot \mathbf{a}_1}.$$

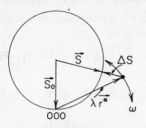

Figure 6-2.

Now at any instant of time during the rotation, $(\mathbf{S} - \mathbf{S}_0)' = \lambda \mathbf{r}^* + \Delta \mathbf{S}$, as shown in Figure 6-2. Therefore,

$$\frac{\sin^2 (\pi/\lambda)(\mathbf{S} - \mathbf{S}_0) \cdot N_1 \mathbf{a}_1}{\sin^2 (\pi/\lambda)(\mathbf{S} - \mathbf{S}_0) \cdot \mathbf{a}_1} = \frac{\sin^2 (\pi/\lambda) \, \Delta S \cdot N_1 \mathbf{a}_1}{\sin^2 (\pi/\lambda) \, \Delta S \cdot \mathbf{a}_1}.$$

This is so because whenever $(\mathbf{S} - \mathbf{S}_0) = \lambda \mathbf{r}^*$, the phase angle between scattering elements changes by 2π; the magnitude of the $\sin^2 Nx / \sin^2 x$ term does not change. Thus,

$$E = I_u \frac{R^2}{\omega} F F^* \int \int \int \frac{\sin^2 (\pi/\lambda) \, \Delta S \cdot N_1 \mathbf{a}_1}{\sin^2 (\pi/\lambda) \, \Delta S \cdot \mathbf{a}_1} \frac{\sin^2 (\pi/\lambda) \, \Delta S \cdot N_2 \mathbf{a}_2}{\sin^2 (\pi/\lambda) \, \Delta S \cdot \mathbf{a}_2}$$

$$\times \frac{\sin^2 (\pi/\lambda) \, \Delta S \cdot N_3 \mathbf{a}_3}{\sin^2 (\pi/\lambda) \, \Delta S \cdot \mathbf{a}_3} \, d\alpha \, d\beta \, d\gamma.$$

We can remove $F F^*$ and I_u from the integral because they vary very slowly compared to the interference terms. To remove the vectors from the equation: let $\Delta \mathbf{S} = \lambda(h_1 \mathbf{b}_1 + h_2 \mathbf{b}_2 + h_3 \mathbf{b}_3)$. Then,

$$E = I_u \frac{R^2}{\omega} F F^* \int \int \int \frac{\sin^2 \pi N_1 h_1}{\sin^2 \pi h_1} \frac{\sin^2 \pi N_2 h_2}{\sin^2 \pi h_2} \frac{\sin^2 \pi N_3 h_3}{\sin^2 \pi h_3} \, d\alpha \, d\beta \, d\gamma.$$

Now note, in Figure 6-3, that the terminal point of the vector $\mathbf{S}$ sweeps out a parallelepiped during the rotation. $\Delta \mathbf{S}_0$ is approximately

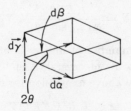

Figure 6-3.

perpendicular to S_0; the volume associated with the motion of the tip of S is drawn in Figure 6–3.

$$d\boldsymbol{\alpha} \cdot d\boldsymbol{\beta} \times d\boldsymbol{\gamma} = \Delta V = |d\boldsymbol{\beta}|\,|d\boldsymbol{\gamma}|\,|d\boldsymbol{\alpha}| \sin 2\theta.$$

In addition,

$$\Delta V = \lambda\, dh_1 \mathbf{b}_1 \cdot dh_2 \mathbf{b}_2 \times dh_3 \mathbf{b}_3$$

$$= \frac{\lambda^3}{V_{\text{cell}}}\, dh_1\, dh_2\, dh_3.$$

Equating the two expressions for ΔV:

$$d\alpha\, d\beta\, d\gamma = \frac{\lambda^3}{V_{\text{cell}} \sin 2\theta}\, dh_1\, dh_2\, dh_3.$$

We have now obtained the right variables for the integration:

$$E = \frac{I_u R^2}{\omega} \frac{F F^* \lambda^3}{V_{\text{cell}} \sin 2\theta} \int_{-\infty}^{+\infty} \frac{\sin^2 \pi N_1 h_1}{\sin^2 \pi h_1}\, dh_1$$

$$\times \int_{-\infty}^{+\infty} \frac{\sin^2 \pi N_2 h_2}{\sin^2 \pi h_2}\, dh_2 \int_{-\infty}^{+\infty} \frac{\sin^2 \pi N_3 h_3}{\sin^2 \pi h_3}\, dh_1\, dh_2\, dh_3.$$

These terms cannot be integrated from $-\infty$ to $+\infty$. There are an infinite number of peaks in this range. However, for any significant value for the N's, the terms have appreciable values only for very small values of $h\pi$. $\sin^2 h\pi$ can be replaced by $(h\pi)^2$—i.e.,

$$\frac{\sin^2 \pi N_1 h_1}{\sin^2 \pi h_1} \cong \frac{\sin^2 \pi N_1 h_1}{(\pi h_1)^2}.$$

This new function has only one maximum, rather than the infinite number of the original function, but then we are only interested at the moment in one of the peaks. Now,

$$\int_{-\infty}^{+\infty} \frac{\sin^2 \pi N_1 h_1}{(\pi h_1)^2}\, dh_1 = N_1.$$

Therefore,

$$E = \frac{I_u R^2 \lambda^3}{\omega V_{\text{cell}} \sin 2\theta}\, N_1 N_2 N_3,$$

$N_1 N_2 N_3$ is the total number of unit cells in the crystal, say N, and $N(V_{\text{cell}})$ is the volume of the crystal (ΔV). Therefore, multiplying the top and bottom of the above expression for total energy by V_{cell},

$$E = \frac{I_u R^2 \lambda^3 F F^* \Delta V}{\omega V^2_{\text{cell}} \sin 2\theta}. \tag{6–1}$$

We now do not need to consider the crystal as a parallelepiped, for our equation involves only the volume. The total energy is independent of R because in I_u there is the term $1/R^2$.

If we are continually rotating the crystal, as in a rotation pattern, after n rotations in time t,

$$\omega = \frac{2\pi n}{t}.$$

The total energy after n rotations is obtained from Eq. (6–1) by substituting for ω. If we are oscillating the crystal N radians per oscillation (i.e., rocking the crystal),

$$\frac{\omega}{N} = \text{oscillations/sec.}$$

The total energy will be Eq. (6–1) $\cdot \omega/N \times t$. $E\omega/I_0$ is often reported as the value for the integrated reflection as it is independent of the incident intensity and ω. Its units are

$$\frac{\text{energy radians time area}}{\text{time energy}} = \text{radians} \cdot (\text{area}).$$

Usually I_0 times the cross-sectional area of the incident beam is what is measured, rather than I_0, so that $E\omega/P_0$ (radians) is often given (see Chapter 7).

We have, of course, to evaluate ΔV; it is the *effective* volume of the crystal, not the total volume, because the incident beam is reduced in intensity as it penetrates. As an example of this evaluation, assume the diffracting planes are parallel to the surface of the crystal platelet as in Figure 6–1. This is illustrated in Figure 6–4. The total volume irradiated in a region ΔZ thick at a depth Z is $A_0/\sin\theta\, dZ$. The incident intensity at this depth is $I_0 e^{-(\mu/\rho)\rho(Z/\sin\theta)}$. The diffracted intensity is absorbed as it leaves the depth Z, the exponential term also being $e^{-(\mu/\rho)\rho(Z/\sin\theta)}$. Thus,

$$I_0\,\Delta V = I_0 \int_0^\infty e^{-(2u/\rho)\rho(Z/\sin\theta)}dZ \cdot \left(\frac{A_0}{\sin\theta}\right) = \frac{A_0 I_0}{2\rho(\mu/\rho)}.$$

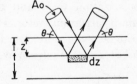

Figure 6–4.

In this case the absorption is independent of θ—but only because the diffracting planes are parallel to the surface. At small angles the path is large, but so is $A_0/\sin\theta$. Including this term,

$$\frac{E\omega}{I_0} = \underbrace{\frac{I_u}{I_0} \frac{R^2\lambda^3}{V_{\text{cell}}} FF^* \frac{1}{\sin 2\theta}}_{Q} \frac{A_0}{2(u/\rho)\rho},$$

or

$$\frac{E\omega}{I_0} = Q\,\Delta V.$$

The effective volumes are also easy to calculate for a cylindrical or a spherical crystal (these can be found in Vol. II of the International Tables starting on page 291). For an odd-shaped crystal, the effective volume can be evaluated graphically as shown in Figure 6–5. This can

$$dV = \text{beam height} \times \frac{\sum e^{-\mu(t_1+t_2)}\Delta A}{n\Delta A}$$

(n is the number of parallelograms
of area ΔA)

Figure 6–5.   (After M. J. Buerger, *Crystal Structure Analysis*, John Wiley, New York, 1960.)

be done most easily by ruling two pieces of transparent paper and laying them over a scaled drawing of the crystal at the correct angles of incidence and 2θ.

The term $1/\sin 2\theta$, that arose in the integration, is known as the Lorentz factor—the polarization term and this term often being referred to as the Lorentz-polarization factor. The physical meaning of this Lorentz factor (L) can be made more clear following the treatment by M. J. Buerger (*Crystal Structure Analysis*, Wiley, New York, 1960).

$$L = \frac{1}{\sin 2\theta} = \frac{1}{2\sin\theta\cos\theta}.$$

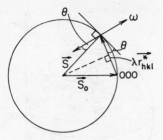

Figure 6–6.

Consider Figure 6–6

$$|\mathbf{S} - \mathbf{S}_0| = 2 \sin \theta;$$

therefore,

$$\sin 2\theta = 2 \sin \theta \cos \theta = |\mathbf{S} - \mathbf{S}_0| \cos \theta,$$

and

$$L = \frac{1}{|\mathbf{S} - \mathbf{S}_0| \cos \theta}.$$

If the crystal is rotating at angular velocity ω about (000), the velocity of a diffracting point is $\omega/\lambda|\mathbf{S} - \mathbf{S}_0|$, and the component of velocity normal to the sphere $(V_\perp)$, is $\omega/\lambda|\mathbf{S} - \mathbf{S}_0| \cos \theta$. The time (t) for a point to pass through the reflecting position is proportional to $1/V_\perp$

$$t = K \frac{1}{V_\perp} = \frac{K\lambda}{\omega|\mathbf{S} - \mathbf{S}_0| \cos \theta},$$

$$\frac{\omega}{V_\perp} = \frac{K\lambda}{|\mathbf{S} - \mathbf{S}_0| \cos \theta},$$

$$L = \frac{\omega}{V_\perp K\lambda}.$$

Thus the Lorentz factor is simply related to the time it takes a point in the reciprocal lattice to move through the Ewald sphere.

For the more general case of a nonzero point P moving in the direction shown in Figure 6–7,

$$V_\perp = \omega \cos \alpha,$$

$$L = \frac{1}{K' \cos \alpha}.$$

For highest accuracy, care must be taken in the integration to use a

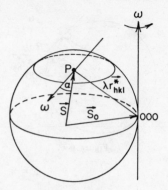

Figure 6–7.   (After M. J. Buerger, *Proc. Nat. Acad. Sci. U.S.*, **26**, 637, 1940.)

monochromator and to eliminate multiple reflections from the mono-chromator. (A simple energy scan of a diffraction peak with a *PHA* will reveal such effects.) Usually, however, work is done with filtered radiation; let us look more closely at this practice.[2]

An ω scan or rock with a stationary counter is not really quite good enough with filtered radiation. In addition to multiple reflections, the crystal has finite dimensions (Figure 6–8a), a mosaic spread will broaden the peak, the incident beam is not perfectly collimated, and there is a wavelength spread. (The angular terms due to these can be calculated in detail.) Thus r^*, in effect, exists over a range of angles.

Consider Figure 6–8(b). The shading represents the λ distribution from an x-ray tube with filtered radiation; the darkest region corre-sponds to K_α. As a result of the spread in r^*_{hkl}, the spot will intersect the sphere over a wide range, as shown in the figure. The stationary receiving slit must be open to receive the entire range for K_α. (The spread due to mosaic is covered in the ω scan and is not included as part of the angular spread of λr^*_{hkl}.)

Note that during an ω rock the crystal literally falls off the wave-length distribution depicted in Figure 6–8. During the rock, the receiving slit sees nothing, then some white, then K_α, white, and nothing again. It is not possible to really decide where the true background is around the K_α, due to this sharp drop. In a θ–2θ scan, in principle, we are moving along a specific direction in reciprocal space, as shown in Figure 6–9. This is because in this scan, the normal to the diffracting

[2] This discussion is based on L. E. Alexander and G. S. Smith, *Acta Crystallo-graphica*, **15** (1962), 983.

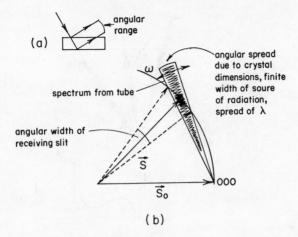

Figure 6–8. (After L. E. Alexander and G. S. Smith, *Acta Cryst.*, **15**, 983, 1962.)

planes always remains as the bisector of **S** and **S₀**. Including the divergences due to mosaic, etc., the situation in reciprocal space is as shown in Figure 6–10(*a*). We must include the mosaic now, as when the counter moves to a new position, some region may be diffracting to the previous position. We are then looking along the distribution of λ's and peaks will look, with filtered radiation, like those shown in Figure 6–10(*b*). It is much easier to find the true background, and multiple λ's need not be eliminated—they contribute very similarly in the background on either side of the peak and under the peak. They are effectively removed by drawing a base line from one side of the peak to the other, or by measuring the background on either side of the peak, averaging, multiplying by the angular range of the peak, and subtracting.

As was mentioned before, in the ω scan the range of the crystal mosaic is covered in the rocking action, and the slit need only be wide enough to account for the other three factors, but in a θ–2θ scan it must be wide enough to also include the range due to any mosaic. A good rule is to keep opening the slits until, in a scan, the integrated intensity

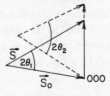

Figure 6–9.

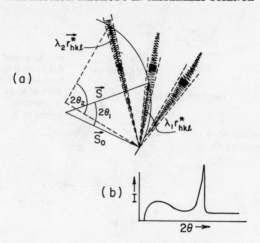

Figure 6–10. (After L. E. Alexander and G. S. Smith, *Acta Cryst.*, **15**, 983, 1962.)

(above background) does not change. As a counter window is only 5–6 degrees in 2θ, in certain situations with a highly mosaic crystal it may be necessary to use a monochromator and an ω scan.

For a Peak in a Powder Pattern

Consider next a powder of n small crystals each of volume dV and a parallelepiped in shape. For a given hkl diffraction cone, the incident (we shall assume monochromatic) beam makes an angle θ with the $\{hkl\}$ planes. Note that this means that the incident beam literally chooses only those crystals properly oriented to diffract. For two different hkl peaks, different grains in the powder are involved. In the diffractometer, due to the focusing condition, an hkl peak comes only from those grains with $\{hkl\}$ parallel to the surface of the sample.

Let us represent the orientation of all the crystals by poles to their $\{hkl\}$ planes—i.e., their termini are on the surface of a vast sphere. If the crystals (whose number is n) are randomly arranged, the fraction of crystals whose $\mathbf{r}_{hkl}^*$'s are oriented so that the incoming beam is between θ and $\theta + d\alpha$ is dn/n. As shown in Figure 6–11, dn/n is then the surface area of the sphere enclosed by $\mathbf{r'}_{hkl}^*$s, in a range $d\alpha$:

$$\frac{dn}{n} = \frac{2\pi R \sin (90° - \theta)}{4\pi R^2} \cdot R \, d\alpha = \frac{1}{2} \cos \theta \, d\alpha.$$

There are several {hkl} planes reflecting at the same angular position because of the multiplicity of any form {hkl} (200, 020, 002, $\bar{2}$00, 0$\bar{2}$0, 00$\bar{2}$ with a cubic material, e.g.). Therefore, all of those grains with any *one* of the possible planes in the form properly oriented will diffract at the same 2θ. We shall call this the multiplicity (m):

$$\frac{dn}{n} = \frac{1}{2} m \cos \theta \, d\alpha.$$

The intensity from any one crystal is the usual expression:

$$I = I_u F F^* \frac{\sin^2 \pi[(\mathbf{S} - \mathbf{S}_0)/\lambda] \cdot N_1 \mathbf{a}_1}{\sin^2 \pi[(\mathbf{S} - \mathbf{S}_0)/\lambda] \cdot \mathbf{a}_1}.$$

In order to evaluate the total energy, we would have to calculate the effective rotational velocity of each group of *hkl* planes to estimate the

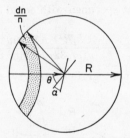

Figure 6–11. (After B. E. Warren in *X-Rays in Theory and Experiment* by A. H. Compton and S. K. Allison, D. Van Nostrand Co., Princeton, N.J., 1963.)

time they spent in passing through the diffraction sphere. We can avoid this simply by calculating the diffracted *power* (P_{hkl}), energy per unit time for any *hkl* cone. In fact, for a powder pattern, the sample need not rotate at all, and what we would really want in this case would not be any integration with time, but the total energy per unit time for a scan through the peak. Thus,

$$P_{hkl} = \int \int I \, dn \, dy' \, dz',$$

where y' and z' are again the axes in our measuring plane:

$$P_{hkl} = I_u F F^* \frac{mn \cos \theta}{2} \int \int \int \sin^2 \cdots R^2 \, d\alpha \, d\beta \, d\gamma.$$

This is the same integral as before; thus, with dV the volume of a small grain:

$$P_{hkl} = I_u R^2 F F^* \frac{m}{2} \frac{n \cos \theta}{\sin 2\theta} \frac{\lambda^3 \, dV}{V_{cell}^2},$$

$$= I_u R^2 F F^* \frac{m}{2} \frac{1}{2 \sin \theta} \frac{\lambda^3}{V_{cell}^2} \Delta V.$$

As the circumference of a diffracting cone is $2\pi R \sin 2\theta$, along a diffracting cone (see Figure 6–12), the power per unit length of this cone (P'_{hkl}) is

$$\frac{P_{hkl}}{2\pi R \sin 2\theta} = P'_{hkl} = I_u R^2 F F^* \frac{\lambda^3 m}{V_{cell}^2} \frac{\Delta V}{\sin \theta \, 8\pi R \sin 2\theta}. \quad (6\text{–}2a)$$

For a powder specimen, the total energy received in a counter rotating ω radians per second $[d(2\theta)/dt]$ is $E = \int P \, dt = 1/\omega \int P \, d2\theta$; with n the number of cells per unit volume, A the area of the receiving slits, $P_0 = I_0 A_0$ and for a flat specimen with equal angles of incidence and diffraction:

$$\frac{\omega E_{hkl}}{P_0} = \frac{I_u R^2 F F^* \lambda^3 m n^2 A}{I_0 \, (\mu(\rho)\rho 32\pi R^2 \sin^2 \theta \cos \theta} \quad (6\text{–}2b)$$

In the expressions for integrated intensity, for both single crystals

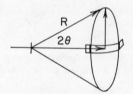

Figure 6–12.

and powder specimens, the trigonometric terms are to be calculated for the center of a peak. If the peak is fairly broad, this is not quite right as they have quite different values from one side of the peak to another. A more appropriate form can be obtained by not carrying out the third integration—i.e., with respect to dh_3. We can think of any hkl reflection as a $00l$ reflection from another unit cell (i.e., we could pick a cell such that this is true). Then,

$$h_3 |\mathbf{b}_3| = \frac{2 \sin \theta}{\lambda},$$

$$dh_3 = \frac{a_3 \cos \theta \, d2\theta}{\lambda},$$

and $(P'_{hkl})_{2\theta}$, the power per unit length of diffracting cone as a function of 2θ for a powder, is

$$(P'_{hkl})_{2\theta} = \frac{a_3 \cos \theta}{N_3 \lambda} I(h_3) = \frac{I_u R^2 F F^* \lambda^2 \, \Delta V m}{16\pi R V_{\text{cell}}^2 N_3 \sin^2 \theta} \frac{\sin^2 \pi \mathbf{s} \cdot N_3 \mathbf{a}_3}{\sin^2 \pi \mathbf{s} \cdot \mathbf{a}_3}. \tag{6-3}$$

We multiply the numerator and denominator by N_3 to get the final expression in terms of ΔV.

Including the polarization term in I_u, the trigonometric term is

$$\frac{1 + \cos^2 2\theta}{\sin^2 \theta}.$$

The peak can now be corrected point by point for this term and then the integration carried out. The integral would then be

$$P_{hkl} = I_u R^2 F F^* \frac{\lambda^3}{V_{\text{cell}}^2} \, \Delta V \frac{m}{6\pi R} (1 + \cos^2 2\theta) \tag{6-4}$$

The diffracted intensity as a function of 2θ is also useful in examining the effects of various phenomena on the shape of a peak. These effects are often readily calculated in reciprocal space; the integration of the expression with respect to $dh_1 \, dh_2$ but not dh_3 projects the effect on the h_3 axis and leaves one with a function of 2θ to be compared to an experiment. We shall make use of this in Chapter 8.

We will consider the use of integrated intensities in determining simple structures. We wish to indicate first, however, that the expression for powders is especially useful in determining the relative volumes of phases. For example, if there are two phases α and β present and a pattern is taken, say of a flat powder sample in a diffractometer,

$$V_\alpha = c_\alpha \frac{A_0}{2(u/\rho)_m \rho_m},$$

where c_α is the volume fraction and $((u/\rho)_m \rho_m)$, is the absorption for the mixture. Then,

$$\frac{P_{hkl-\alpha}}{P'_{h'k'l'-\beta}} = \frac{F_\alpha F_\alpha^* (m_{hkl})_\alpha c_\alpha (V_{\text{cell}}^2)_\beta \left(\dfrac{1 + \cos^2 2\theta}{\sin \theta \sin 2\theta}\right)_\alpha}{F_\beta F_\beta^* (m'_{h'k'l'})_\beta c_\beta (V_{\text{cell}}^2)_\alpha \left(\dfrac{1 + \cos^2 2\theta}{\sin \theta \sin 2\theta}\right)_\beta}.$$

All other terms such as R^2, λ^3, I_u cancel, provided the same slits are used for both peaks. As $c_\alpha + c_\beta = 1$ the expression can be solved for c_α or c_β. Note that the expression is most sensitive when V_β, V_α, and $F_\alpha F_\alpha^* / F_\beta F_\beta^*$ are similar. Thus, for example, as little as 0.2 per cent retained austenite can be detected in a martensitic steel, if a mono-chromator is used to minimize the background (but the limit is about 5 per cent with filtered radiation). The technique can of course be extended to many phases by using a peak from each phase. If neces-sary, the volume fraction of one or more of these phases can be estimated with a microscope. Two precautions must be mentioned. When using powders, care must be taken to minimize texture; never press a powder into a holder—sprinkle it. Also, because of porosity, and surface rough-ness, there may be an angularly dependent absorption factor. In some cases, this can produce errors of 30 per cent or more. Suppose there is an element in the specimen of about the same atomic number as the radiation, it can be caused to fluoresce with some other radiation. If there was no surface roughness, this fluorescite would not vary with 2θ. The variation in the background is then a measure of this correction term. It vanishes at $\theta = 90°$ (with a pulse-height analyzer one can pick out the fluorescense from the normal diffraction with this other radia-tion; see Chapter 7).

Determining an Atom's Location in a Structure

From the extinctions, size considerations, and the number of atoms in a unit cell we have seen that it is possible to obtain the space group and, even in most cases, to eliminate many of the possible equi-points. The final step in our analysis is to select the equipoints for each atom type and to find the actual coordinates of each atom. From the integrated intensities for single crystals we can get $|F|^2$.

For simplicity, let us consider a centrosymmetric structure using the origin for the structure factor at this symmetry position. The structure factor is then a cosine function in terms of h, k, l and x, y, z for each atom type. (Recall that for a given atom at all positions in an equipoint, the structure factor simplifies to a cosine function times a constant times the atomic scattering factor for that atom.) Plots can be made for the various possible equipoints of, say, $|F|^2_{hoo}$ versus x of one atom type, or for various fixed values of x of one atom versus x of the other atom, if both have unknown x values; y and z are not involved as k, $l = 0$. After correcting the *observed* intensities for absorption, temperature, and the L.P. factor, the point on the graphs can be sought that gives the *observed* relative F^2_{hoo}. The same procedure can be followed for y using F^2_{oko} or as x is now known, F^2_{hko}. As the cosine curves are all symmetric about o and π, other peaks will be needed to decide if x, y, z are each plus or minus. If there are not too many atoms (20 or so) and too many unknown sets of x, y, z (2 or less), then we can proceed to evaluate the structure. Finally we can judge correctness by comparing all observed and calculated F^2. The R factor is useful for this:

$$R = \frac{\sum (F_{obs} - F_{cak})}{\sum F_{obs}}.$$

If R is of the order of 0.2 or less, this is a good indication of a satisfactory structure determination; values of 0.05 or less are becoming more and more frequent.

Much more complex crystals can, however, be handled these days involving literally thousands of atoms—such as penicillin, vitamin A, hemoglobin, etc. Some of the recent Nobel prizes have been for just such complex structures. We can give here only a sketch of some of the ways to proceed in complex cases. A structure determination is systematic but not routine, and each one tests the ingenuity of the experimenter.[3]

The most direct approach, if it were not for the phase problem, would be to plot the electron density at various levels in the unit cell. In Problem 27 in Chapter 2, we saw that this was a Fourier series with the structure factors as coefficients. This equation is merely a statement of what an optical or electron microscope does—mix the diffracted intensities to form the image. But what we do not have in a diffraction experiment is the phase of $|F|$, or its sign if the structure is centrosymmetric. It is not "lost," we just cannot measure it with intensity! A variety of special techniques have been developed to get this information, but no fully satisfactory general method has been reported as yet. We have seen one way—with anomalous dispersion. Graphical sums on the complex plane can be drawn for F_{hkl}, $F_{\bar{h}\bar{k}\bar{l}}$ to compare to measured values of $|F|$. The correct values then yield $|F|e^{i\varphi}$ to use in the equation for electron density. Another very useful technique is the heavy or replaceable atom method. Suppose we have a centrosymmetric structure and there is an atom of high atomic number (relative to the others). Then,

$$F_{hkl} = F_{\text{heavy atom}} + F_{\text{remainder}}.$$

[3] The reader will find an excellent detailed account of this area in Professor M. J. Buerger's book, *Crystal Structure Analysis* (John Wiley, New York, 1960).

Clearly the sign of the cosine term, if $F_{remainder}$ is less than $F_{heavy\ atom}$ (because the f's are sufficiently small in the former), is that of F_{heavy}. It turns out that it *is* sometimes possible to synthesize structures in which a heavy atom replaces a lighter one, and a comparison of the structure factors for the two cases will fix the signs of the F's for the original structure. The heavy atom is located perhaps because it can fit in only one equipoint, because of the number per unit cell, or perhaps by examining the Patterson function to deduce its location (Problem 28, Chapter 2). Such a plot will emphasize the location of heavy atoms; by trial and error we can decide which arrangement of them could give rise to the observed Patterson plot. This may not be unique; more than one arrangement may be possible, but this will still be helpful in eliminating several possibilities.

With the use of modern computers to evaluate the sums and such clever ideas as these, electron-density plotting has become a powerful tool for revealing the structure of even the most complex systems.

SUGGESTED READING

1. M. J. Buerger, *Crystal Structure Analysis* (John Wiley, New York, 1960).

PROBLEMS

1. Ruby is a dilute solution of Cr_2O_3 in Al_2O_3 (space group $R\bar{3}c$) and is a good maser. In order to understand the fundamental behavior, it is desirable to know the positions of the ions to see the effect of the field of aluminum and oxygen ions on the chromium energy levels. You have obtained intensity data with MoK_α from an Al_2O_3 and a ruby crystal (4 mole per cent Cr_2O_3). After correcting for absorption and the L.P. factor:

hkl	Al_2O_3	Ruby
00.6	4,410	2,476
00.12	37,048	42,562
00.18	33,936	34,582
00.24	558	722
00.30	15,086	17,136

(a) Evaluate B_O, B_{Al}, ω_{Al} from the data on Al_2O_3 ($f = foe - B \sin^2 \theta / \lambda^2$ and w is the atomic position along the $\mathbf{a}_3$ axis).

It is known that for Al_2O_3, and for Cr_2O_3, that the oxygen atoms are at $\pm$ $(0.36, 0, \frac{1}{4}; 0, 0.36, \frac{1}{4}; -.36, -.36, \frac{1}{4})$ and therefore these positions are the same for all solid solutions.

(b) Evaluate w_{Cr}, B_{Cr} from the data for the ruby crystal. (See S. C. Moss and R. E. Newnham, *Z. für Krystallographie*, **120** (1964), 359 for any further details you may wish to have.)

2. As you have seen in Problem 1 in Chapter 1 and Problem 8 in Chapter 2, GeSe is orthorhombic, its space group is *Pnma*, and there are four "molecules" per cell with the 4 atoms of germanium and 4 of selenium on the $4c$ equipoint. You have measured the integrated intensity with CuK_α, corrected it for absorption and the L.P. factor, and taken its square root. Determine the atomic coordinates. Ignore any effects of temperature and use the data in Chapter 2 Problem 8, if needed.

hkl	$(Relative\ Intensity)^{1/2}$
202	26
200	196
400	54
600	20
004	13
113	25

3. It sometimes happens that similar atoms can exchange positions from unit cell to unit cell—i.e., there is an "average" atom at each position, as we discussed in Chapter 5. This can make solution of a structure more difficult, but in simple structures the "degree of order" can be easily evaluated and is a useful measure of the atomic arrangement. An alloy of 50 atomic per cent A and 50 atomic per cent B forms a simple CsCl structure at low temperatures, with A at the corners of the cubic cell and B at the centers. At higher temperatures, atoms interchange and some A atoms appear on centered positions (β sites) and some B's are in A positions (α sites). Let

v_α = the fraction of α sites occupied by A atoms (i.e., rightly occupied).

w_α = the fraction of α sites wrongly occupied (i.e., by B atoms).

v_β = fraction of β sites occupied rightly by B atoms.

w_β = fraction of β sites wrongly occupied by A atoms.

In this alloy, because of the equal compositions of A and B,

$$w_\alpha = w_\beta \qquad\qquad w_\beta = 1 - v_\alpha$$

$$v_\alpha = v_\beta \qquad\qquad w_\alpha = 1 - v_\beta$$

Define a long range order parameter $S = a + bv_\alpha$ where

$S = 1$ when $v_\alpha = 1$, and

$S = 0$ when $v_\alpha = x_A$ (the atomic fraction).

(a) Show that

$S = 2v_\alpha - 1$, and also that:

$S = v_\alpha - w_\beta$.

(b) Derive an expression for the structure factor, using the terms v_α, v_β, w_α, w_β. Simplify this, if possible, with one of the definitions of S in (a).

(c) Discuss the diffraction pattern and how it will change with increasing temperature up to $S = 0$. Keep in mind that f_A and f_B are really $f_{A_{0^\circ K}}e^{-M}$ and $f_{B_{0^\circ K}}e^{-M}$. How could you actually obtain a value for S?

4. Consider a diffraction experiment in transmission as in the figure with Problem 12 in Chapter 5. Evaluate the effective volume ΔV. What thickness would give the maximum diffracted intensity?

5. Derive an expression for $(P'_{hkl})_{2\theta}$ the intensity per unit 2θ, for a *single crystal* being examined along the $\mathbf{b}_3$ direction in reciprocal space.

7 *Equipment for Measuring Intensities*

In electron, neutron, and x-ray diffraction, intensities can be measured with films or with counters. We shall discuss the equipment in detail for x-rays, as this is the area which is most thoroughly developed, and then indicate any unique features with other sources of radiation.

Films

X-Rays

Most films (AgBr in gelatin) have a linear range of density ($D = \log_{10} I_0/I$) versus exposure (intensity times time), as shown in Figure 7–1. This range extends over four orders of magnitude of I. The user should specify to the manufacturer that he wants film for x-ray work, in order to get one with a good linear range and steep slope. This linearity occurs because one quanta of x-rays is enough to create a nucleus that will form metallic silver on developing. At very high exposures, an already sensitized region is being hit over and over again, and the curve "bends over." The curve depends on the film and developing procedure (time, developer). To measure I, it is only necessary then to prepare a calibration by causing a diffraction spot from a specimen to hit the film for different times. If the development procedures are kept fixed, then by comparing spots on a film with this calibration set, a relative scale of "intensity" can be set up for all the spots in a pattern. It is best, for this comparison, to use a spot from the

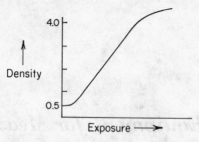

Figure 7–1.   Response of film to X-Rays.

specimen being studied, so that the shape of the spot will be the same in the calibration and in the actual pattern; in this way the viewer is not "fooled" by the shape of the spot. With considerable practice, precisions of the order of ±5–10 per cent can be achieved by eye. The linear range can be extended by using multiple films in the calibration, recording a medium strength spot on several films to estimate the true intensity on say, the second film with respect to that on the first. Then the use of multiple films in taking the actual pattern will allow accurate measurement of very strong peaks.

More precise measurements of the spot "blackness" can be made with photometers; several types of these are available commercially.

With electrons, the linearity range is greatly reduced to one order of magnitude or less, but the principle of calibration is the same. With neutrons, as was mentioned before, the low intensities require broad slits and the angular resolution is not too good; films are generally used only for rough qualitative work, using a substance such as B^{10} or Li^6 in a ZnS film over the film so that the α particles emitted, when these isotopes absorb neutrons, cause light flashes in the ZnS. No attempts at quantitative measurements have been reported as yet, but because light is exposing the film, linearity will be poor and more detailed calibration will be required.

Counters and Associated Electronic Components

For X-Rays

There are two types of counters in use with x-rays. One of these is a gas-filled tube with a potential drop, Figure 7–2(a). In Figure 7–2(b) some of the associated electronics are shown. Ionization is produced by

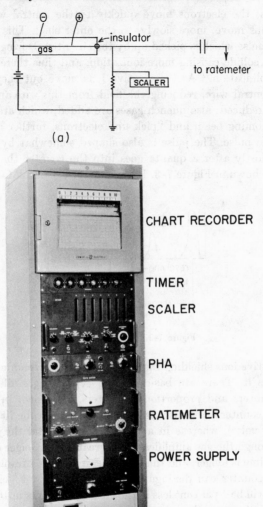

CHART RECORDER

TIMER

SCALER

PHA

RATEMETER

POWER SUPPLY

PRINTER

(b)

Figure 7-2. (a) Gas filled counter. (b) Associated electronics.

the x-rays; the electrons move quickly to the central wire and the positive ions move, more slowly, to the outer shell. This discharge is a current pulse which is picked up by the circuitry. During the motion, gas atoms collide causing more ionization, and thus there is considerable "amplification." As the positive ions move out they shield the positive central wire, reducing the field from this wire and hence the current is reduced; also quench gases are added, which are dissociated by the incoming beam and "pick up" electrons, further reducing the time of the pulse. The pulse is also shaped somewhat by a capacitor circuit. Shortly after a quanta goes into the counter the pulses look like those shown in Figure 7–3. Pulses cannot be "seen" for a time due

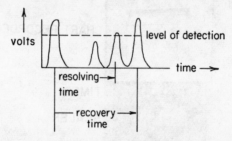

Figure 7–3.   Counter response.

to the positive ions shielding the wire, producing a volume that has no field across it. There are basically two types of gas-filled counters, Geiger counters and proportional counters. As shown in Table 7–1, the Geiger counter has a discharge throughout the tube (it operates at 1700–1800 volts), whereas in a proportional counter the discharge is local. Although the gas amplification is greater in a Geiger counter, the resolving time is longer, and this is important. With a resolving time of 1 μsec, a counter can distinguish 10^6 counts without "choking up," and there will be 1 per cent loss in the measured counts in 10,000 counts per second (because the counts are arriving in a random way, and some may be "bunched up" in time). A proportional counter may then be quite linear—up to 50,000 cps. Most scalers, which total the pulses by using the pulses in the counter to trigger lights, will have a resolving time of only 1 μsec, so that the overall electronic system is linear to, at best, about 10,000 cps. With a Geiger counter, however, linearity is lost at about 200 cps or less.

All counters have "plateaus." That is, there is a flat portion in a plot of counts per second versus voltage to the counter (see Figure

Table 7-1

Characteristics of Counters

Counter	Current (amperes)	Voltage (amplified in Two Stages to 10–100 v)	Amplification	Discharge	Proportional	Approximate Resolving Time
Ionization	10^{-12}	1–2 mv	1	local	No	20 µsec
Proportional	10^{-10}	1–2 mv	10^5–10^6	local	Yes	0.2 µsec
Geiger-Muller	10^{-10}	2–50 mv	10^8	throughout tube	No	50–200 µsec
Scintillation		1–2 mv	10^7		Yes	0.2 µsec

289

(a)   (b)

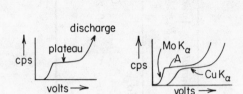

Figure 7-4. Proportional counter plateaus.

7–4(a)), between the initial voltage sufficient to provide a measurable pulse and complete discharge. This plateau occurs because, with a certain gas pressure and gas in the tube, the amplification is limited for a finite range of voltage (of the order of 150–250 volts). The slope is the order of 0.05 per cent per volt, so that to keep the error in intensity to ± 0.2 per cent, the voltage to the counter need only be stabilized to ± 6 volts, when the plateau is in the vicinity of 1500 volts (a typical value).

The proportional counter has another interesting feature, which led to its name. The voltage of the pulse is proportional to the incident energy so that, as shown in Figure 7–4(b), the plateau is shifted for different wavelengths. If you set the voltage at A for MoK_α, the counter will not see CuK_α. In addition, with the help of an adjustable voltage "window" (called a pulse-height analyzer), which can be made to accept only pulses of a voltage in a certain adjustable range ($E + \Delta E - E$), we can closely "select" the wavelength being examined.

After establishing a counter's plateau, the pulse-height analyzer is adjusted in the following way:

1.   Use a narrow voltage window, a counter voltage on the plateau, and a K_α diffraction peak from a sample that does not fluoresce. Increase E and record the intensity. A curve like that in Figure 7–5(a) results. (The pulse-height analyzer usually allows us to set a window, and when E is changed the window is moved with it.) Alternately, the window can be left out and E raised, resulting in the curve of Figure 7–5(b). Then E and ΔE are chosen to include some percentage of the desired K_α. If only the white radiation is being excluded, 90 per cent is a good figure. If fluorescence from the sample to be used, caused by the white radiation, is the principal problem, a lower value can be chosen. It should be remembered, however, that the breadth in Figure 7–5(a) is sufficiently large that with 90 per cent of λ accepted, only about

90 per cent of a wavelength $\lambda/2$ or 2λ will be eliminated; it will be very difficult to do much with fluorescence from elements of atomic numbers within two of that of the x-ray tube's target. (The PHA is thus a good device for eliminating the $\lambda/2$ that may diffract from a monochromator in second order in the same position as the first order.) As the (E) setting is proportional to the energy (E) of the pulse, it can be written $E = K/\lambda$ and the position of a curve for a different λ can be estimated (Figure 7–5(a)). Actually, the curve sharpens somewhat as λ decreases, but this is not too important in the range of λ's commonly employed.

2.   With these settings, and the x-rays off, the electronic noise and cosmic background are checked; they should be close to zero. (A lower

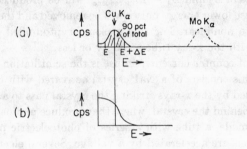

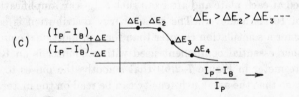

Figure 7–5.   (a) Pulse distribution with narrow window (differential curve) (b) integral curve (no window) (c) effect of window size on peak intensity, I_P (I_B is background intensity).

window E is generally used, even without ΔE to keep the noise down, so that the background is of the order of 0.5 cps.) If the noise is high (1–2 cps) the gain (amplification of the counter pulses) is reduced and the procedure started over. If we half the gain, the intensity is not reduced to half. The pulses have a voltage distribution, and thus the *intensity* will not be directly proportional to gain.

3.   Finally, a plot is made of peak intensity (I_P) minus background (I_B) with a window, over the same difference without any window, versus the peak to background ratio, for different windows. A typical

plot is shown in Figure 7–5(c). On this curve we wish to operate on a flat portion, so that minor drifts in the electronics do not affect precision—the window chosen in (1) should be on the flat portion of this curve.

There are a variety of counters, filled with argon or krypton, using different pressures, shapes, etc.—primarily because the sensitivity of the tube can be adjusted so that, e.g., the counter may be highly sensitive to CuK_α but not $\lambda/2$. This too can be helpful in "cleaning up" the spectrum, and obviously such a counter will not yield high intensities with MoK_α. With certain counters, if the x-ray tube's voltage is high enough, some of the white radiation entering the tube will fluoresce the gas and pulses of E_λ and $E_\lambda - E_{\text{fluorescence}}$ will be produced. When using a PHA, these lower energy pulses will be removed and the counter may appear quite nonlinear. For this reason, krypton-filled counters should be used with the x-ray tube at 35 kv or less.

Another type of counter currently in use is the scintillation counter. One version of this consists of a NaI crystal activated with thallium. Light pulses caused by the x-rays striking the crystal pass to a film of a CsSb compound behind the crystal, where they produce photoelectrons. They enter a dynode, a tube with a series of photoelectric plates, to which the electrons are accelerated by a voltage. Several electrons are produced at each plate and after ten such stages an amplification of the order of 10^7 is achieved. The pulse-energy distribution is somewhat broader for a scintillation counter than for a proportional counter.

Another essential component used with a counter is an RC circuit (the rate meter in Figure 7–2(b)) that smooths the pulses to a steady current, so that the average intensity can be read on the meter or fed to a chart recorder for continuous scanning of a pattern. The time constant, or rate of decay of this RC circuit can be adjusted so that we can be sure that the pen on a chart recorder is responding to the counts without an unnecessary time delay. A good rule of thumb is to be sure that the pen is oscillating as it passes through a sharp peak. The rate meter and chart should occasionally be calibrated against the scaler.

Because the counts are arriving in a random manner, the fractional error in N counts is $(0.67\sqrt{N})/N$ for 50 per cent confidence limits, and for 96 per cent confidence limits, it is three times this. If there is a large difference in peak and background intensities, it may be better to count for fixed counts and use the inverse of the time as a measure of the intensity, rather than count for fixed time. In this way the statistical error in peak and background will be the same. (The error in taking a difference is the square root of the sums of the squares of the individual errors.)

If the slits on the counter are going to be quite wide, as they must be in examining a peak from a single crystal, then it is necessary to be sure the counter has a uniform response across its opening. This can be checked by scanning the direct beam with no receiving slit and a narrow divergence slit. (Occasionally intense peaks will appear at the edges of such a scan—i.e., near the edges of the window. These are due to fluorescence from the metal container caused by the direct beam.) If the central wire is too thick, it may cause a dead spot in the center and the slits should be placed to avoid this or the counter tilted. In order to insure good precision, we want to be sure that we operate in the linear range; this should always be checked, with a given counter and electronics. There are two simple ways of doing this, illustrated in Figure 7–6. With a series (n) of foils of the same thickness (t_1) we can

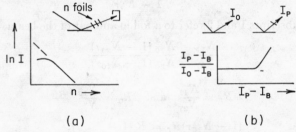

Figure 7–6. Methods of checking linearity.

use the absorption law, $I = I_0 e^{-ut_1 n}$. A plot of $\ln I$ (corrected for background) versus n can be made using a crystal such as Si cut to (111) to get only the K_α reflection and not $\lambda/2$ ($F_{222} = 0$). The plot should be linear as long as the system is linear. The foils should be as similar in absorption as possible to avoid scatter in the plot. This can be arranged by placing the foils on rings in front of the counter and rotating each one until I is the same within say ± 0.6 per cent, which is the stability of the unit.[1] Remember to take long counts in doing this, so that the *statistical* error is 0.1 per cent or less. Another way is to plot the ratio of the intensity from a crystal with and without one foil in the beam's path versus the intensity without the foil. As shown in Figure 7–6(b), this ratio should be constant until the counting rate,

[1] Thin metal foils for this purpose and for filters can be obtained from A. D. Mackay, Inc., 198 Broadway, New York 38, N.Y.

which can be adjusted by varying the tube's current, exceeds the range of linearity. With this method, only one foil is used and its exact thickness is not too important, as long as it is reasonably uniform. Again, this should be checked with x-rays—not a micrometer—by surveying the absorption of the foil with a small beam (a movable pinhole near the foil will help).

In these ways we can choose operating conditions to achieve a conservative counting rate and be certain of linearity, at least within a few per cent. If more precise information is required, or if more exact linearity is required, it will be necessary to measure the linearity more carefully. This can be done in the following way, suggested to me by Dr. D. Chipman.

If N_T is the true count, N_0 the observed count, and τ the system's time constant, then it can be shown that for small deviations from linearity,

$$N_T = \frac{N_0}{1 - N_0 \tau}. \tag{7-1a}$$

Let the subscripts 1 and 2 refer to a foil in and out of the beam. Then,

$$\frac{N_{1T}}{N_{2T}} = \frac{N_{10}}{N_{20}} \frac{(1 - N_{20}\tau)}{(1 - N_{10}\tau)}. \tag{7-1b}$$

If

$$R_T = \frac{N_{1T}}{N_{2T}} \quad \text{and} \quad R_0 = \frac{N_{10}}{N_{20}}.$$

$$(1 - N_{10}\tau)R_T = R_0(1 - N_{20}\tau);$$

using the definition of R_0;

$$R_0 = R_T + \tau N_{10}(1 - R_T). \tag{7-1c}$$

As N_{10} goes to zero, R_0 approaches R_T. Plotting R_0 versus N_{10} should yield a straight line whose intercept is R_T and whose slope is $\tau(1 - R_T)$. A typical result is given in Figure 7-7 for a modern scintillation counter system. Here, τ was 5.4 ± 10^{-6} sec for 90 per cent confidence limits. One per cent losses occurred at 1800 cps. As we have seen, one might have estimated that with a scintillation counter, 1 per cent losses would not occur until 5000–10,000 cps, so we can see the necessity for actual checking out the linearity of the entire system some way!

With this value of τ, observed readings can be corrected; as the correction is not generally larger than 20 per cent or so, the error in τ contributes an error of 1 per cent or less in the correction.

Equation (7-1a) with τ, and a plot of ln I versus number of foils can

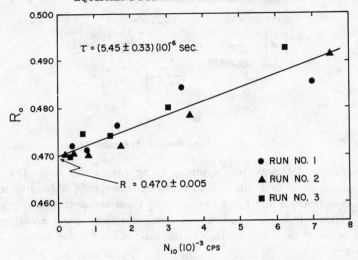

Figure 7–7. Determining the time constant of a counter and its electronics using Eq. (7c). (From L. Schwartz Ph.D. thesis, Northwestern University, 1964.)

then be used to get a measure of the direct beam, and if this is done carefully an accuracy and reproducibility of 1–2 per cent (or less) is possible. Because long counts may be necessary in this process if an accuracy of less than 1 per cent is required, a monitor counter should be used to eliminate the effects of instability in x-ray generation, ± 0.6–3 per cent for long times. This can be done by placing a thin foil of an element of $Z - 2$ in the beam from target Z and using the counts from the fluorescence as a timer. That is, those counts are fed to another scalar and counting is stopped for a fixed number of counts to this monitor. The foil should only reduce the beam 10 per cent or so.

For Neutrons

As we have mentioned before, neutron counters are generally filled with BF_3 gas, enriched in B^{10}. The rest of the circuitry is quite similar to that for x-rays. Because of the low and variable intensities, a monitor and step scanning are commonly employed with long counts at each position. The equipment is made automatic with a printer to record the data after each count and the entire system, positioning of a crystal, recording data, and analyzing it can be tied to a computer, increasing the efficiency of the process—and its cost!

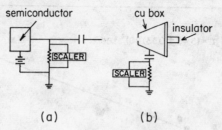

Figure 7–8.   (a) Solid state detector; (b) Faraday Cage.

Solid-state detectors are beginning to appear in this field. The α particles from a Li^6F film on a semiconductor produce conducting charges—electrons and holes—by exciting them across the band gap. An electric field applied to the semi-conductor then causes a current pulse before these charges return to the valence band. Such a device is shown in Figure 7–8(a).

For Electrons

Hardly any work is now done in electron diffraction with counters. However, the "Faraday Cage" is used to measure electron current in electron generators and will probably be used when these measurements begin. It is essentially an insulated metal cup into which the electrons pass and, as shown in Figure 7–6(b), the charge build-up causes pulses through a capacitor. Solid state counters may also be useful in this field.

SUGGESTED READINGS

1. H. P. Klug and L. E. Alexander, *X-Ray Diffraction Procedures* (John Wiley, New York, 1954).
2. M. J. Buerger, *Crystal Structure Analysis* (John Wiley, New York, 1960).

PROBLEM

1. You wish to build a counter for neutrons with $\lambda = 1$ Å using BF_3 gas with the isotope B^{10}. What isotope enrichment is required to make the counter 90 per cent efficient in a counter one foot long filled with the gas at 1 atmosphere, and 20°C?

8 Imperfections

So far we have been centering our consideration on the characterization of crystal structures. This is an important aspect of diffraction studies and it has enabled us to learn most of the fundamental concepts. We have in fact found a great many uses for diffraction, as the following list indicates:

1. Crystal structure.
2. Chemical analysis (in selected regions with the electron microscope).
   (a) From the pattern from a substance.
   (b) From the lattice parameter.
   (c) From absorption.
   (d) From fluorescence.
3. Phase boundaries.
   (a) From lattice parameters.
   (b) From integrated intensities.
4. Volume fraction of a phase.
5. Residual stresses.
6. Theoretical densities.
7. Coefficients of expansion.
8. Twin elements.
9. Texture.

In the last twenty years it has been found that perturbations in the structure can also be detected and described in some detail using diffraction, and in this chapter we shall look at this area. We shall be concerned mainly with qualitative understanding, but in a few cases a detailed treatment will be given to indicate the methods that are used to get quantitative information.

We shall, as we go along, discuss some of the applications of the electron microscope to this area, as this has become a powerful tool for the study of imperfections. At the outset, it is necessary to realize that although imperfections may play a primary role in the behavior of a material, they do not involve a large fraction of the atoms. Severely distorted crystals may contain 10^{12} dislocations/cm^2 and even if the core of each dislocation contains ten atoms, less than one atom in ten is involved. The lower long-range strain fields may, however, affect all atoms. Thus, only a small fraction of the atoms are strongly involved, and this is bothersome in x-ray diffraction, because when we average over all the atoms under the beam, most of them are only affected in a minor way. On the other hand, the small range of effects from an imperfection is the very reason we can see individual ones in the electron microscope.

Thermal-Diffuse Scattering

There is one "imperfection" that involves all the atoms; they are all vibrating. This vibration can be thought of at any instant as due to a great many displacement waves traveling through the solid. The displacement of each atom is the sum total of the effects of all these waves.

We saw in Chapter 5, that thermal vibrations reduced the intensity of the diffraction peaks, but because there is conservation of energy, there must be other scattering somewhere. When we looked at this before, we considered each atom individually. This time let us look at the intensity from *all* the atoms. We shall again consider only one atom per lattice point and that all atoms are identical:

$$I_{\text{eu}} = \sum_n \sum_m f_n f_m e^{2\pi i \mathbf{s} \cdot (\mathbf{r}_n - \mathbf{r}_m)}.$$

Let $\mathbf{r}_n = \mathbf{r}_n^\circ + \Delta \mathbf{x}_n$, where $\mathbf{r}_n^\circ$ is vector of the average structure, and $\Delta \mathbf{x}_n$ is the instantaneous thermal displacement. Then,

$$I_{\text{eu}} = \sum_n \sum_m f_n f_m e^{2\pi i \mathbf{s} \cdot (\mathbf{r}_n^\circ - \mathbf{r}_m^\circ)} e^{2\pi i \mathbf{s} \cdot (\Delta \mathbf{x}_n - \Delta \mathbf{x}_m)}.$$

Assuming the thermal displacements are small, the last term can be expanded (as we did before in Chapter 5):

$$\langle e^{2\pi i \mathbf{s} \cdot (\Delta \mathbf{x}_n - \Delta \mathbf{x}_m)} \rangle = 1 - 2\pi^2 \langle \{ \mathbf{s} \cdot (\Delta \mathbf{x}_n - \Delta \mathbf{x}_m) \}^2 \rangle. \tag{8-1}$$

The carets indicate a time and space average. The cross-product terms average to zero only if the vibrations of the atoms are independent.

Because the atoms are "bound" together and because the displacements are of the order of a few per cent of the interatomic distances, this is not really to be expected. It was our assumption before, but we shall not use it here.

Let us consider the displacements as the result of many plane waves, transverse and logitudinal, with wave vectors $\mathbf{K}$ and frequencies f_K:

$$\Delta \mathbf{x}_n = \sum_K \mathbf{A}_K \cos (2\pi f_K t - (\mathbf{K} \cdot \mathbf{r}_n) - \delta_K). \qquad (8\text{--}2)$$

The term involving $\mathbf{K} \cdot \mathbf{r}_n$ represents the displacement of the atom at $\mathbf{r}_n$ along the direction of propagation of the wave, represented by the vector $\mathbf{K} = (2\pi/\lambda)$. The other part of the phase angle, δ_K, changes often during our observation; the waves may start and damp out rapidly during this time. We can add the waves, if we assume that the atoms are moving according to a linear differential equation, and there is a restoring force proportional to displacement.

Using Eq. (8–2) in (8–1), squaring and taking the time average, cross products in the sums vanish as the waves are independent and only the squares of terms with the same $\mathbf{K}$ for the nth and mth atom remain.

$$1 - 2\pi^2 \Big\langle \Big\{ \sum_K \mathbf{s} \cdot \mathbf{A_K} \left[\cos (2\pi f_K t - \mathbf{K} \cdot \mathbf{r}_n - \delta_K) \right. $$
$$\left. - \cos (2\pi f_K t - \mathbf{K} \cdot \mathbf{r}_m - \delta_K) \right] \Big\}^2 \Big\rangle$$

The two cosine-squared terms average to one-half, and

$$-\langle 2 \cos (2\pi f_K t - \mathbf{K} \cdot \mathbf{r}_n - \delta_K) \cos (2\pi f_K t - \mathbf{K} \cdot \mathbf{r}_m - \delta_K) \rangle$$
$$= -2 \langle \cos A \cos B \rangle = -\langle \{ \cos (A + B) + \cos (A - B) \} \rangle.$$

The term that involves (t), $\cos (A + B)$, averages to zero over the time of measurement, so that we are left only with the term in $(A - B)$. Thus,

$$1 - 2\pi^2 \langle \{ \mathbf{s} \cdot (\Delta \mathbf{x}_n - \Delta \mathbf{x}_m) \}^2 \rangle$$
$$= 1 - 2\pi^2 \Big\langle \sum_K (\mathbf{s} \cdot \mathbf{A}_K)^2 (1 - \cos (\mathbf{K} \cdot (\mathbf{r}_m - \mathbf{r}_n))) \Big\rangle$$
$$= e^{-[2\pi^2 \langle \Sigma_K (\mathbf{s} \cdot A_\mathbf{K})^2 (1 - \cos(\mathbf{K} \cdot (\mathbf{r}_m - \mathbf{r}_n))) \rangle]}$$
$$\cong e^{-2M\{1 + \langle \Sigma_K (\mathbf{s} \cdot A_\mathbf{K})^2 \cos (\mathbf{K} \cdot (\mathbf{r}_m - \mathbf{r}_n)) \rangle\}}.[1]$$

---

[1] $2M = 2\pi^2 \langle \sum_K (\mathbf{s} \cdot A_K)^2 \rangle$ is analogous to $\dfrac{16\pi^2 \sin 2\theta}{\lambda^2} \langle \Delta x^2 \rangle$ as $|\mathbf{s}| = 2 \sin \theta/\lambda$ and $\langle \Delta x^2 \rangle$—the mean square displacement along $\mathbf{s}$ due to a wave is half the wave's mean square amplitude. We can easily prove this, for it involves essentially the average value of $\cos^2 \alpha$ where α is the angle between $\mathbf{s}$, Δx_n.

When we put this back into Eq. (8–1) we see that there are the usual sharp peaks with f^2 reduced by e^{-2M} and also a term

$$\sum_k \sum_m \sum_n f^2 e^{-2M} e^{2\pi i s \cdot (\mathbf{r}_n - \mathbf{r}_m)} \langle \Sigma_K (\mathbf{s} \cdot \mathbf{A}_K)^2 \cos(\mathbf{K} \cdot (\mathbf{r}_m - \mathbf{r}_n)) \rangle. \qquad (8\text{–}3)$$

Each cosine term can be written:

$$\frac{e^{2\pi i \mathbf{K} \cdot (\mathbf{r}_m - \mathbf{r}_n)} + e^{-2\pi i \mathbf{K} \cdot (\mathbf{r}_m - \mathbf{r}_n)}}{2},$$

Thus, Eq. (8–3) will have peaks for $\mathbf{s} + 1/\lambda = \mathbf{r}^*$, $\mathbf{s} - 1/\lambda = \mathbf{r}^*$. There will be a set of satellites for each $\mathbf{K}$.[2]

There is a limit to the number of waves in the sum over K. The shortest wavelength is twice the interatomic distance because, as shown in Figure 8–1 for a transverse wave, any shorter wavelength is really

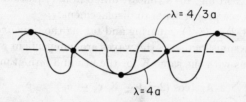

Figure 8–1.   The same atomic displacement represented by two waves.

represented by a longer one. There are then a great many waves of different wave lengths, but a minimum wavelength $2a$, so that the satellite farthest from the main diffraction peak is halfway between two points in reciprocal space. If we differentiate Eq. (8–2) to get the velocity of an atom during vibration, we can see that the average kinetic energy (which is about kt) will be proportional to the sum of the frequencies and also that the amplitude of each satellite will be inversely proportional to the satellite's frequency. At each point in this temperature-diffuse scattering ("TDS") we know the position $1/\lambda$, so that from the intensity we can get frequency and from the two we can get the velocity of an elastic wave (and hence linear elastic constants) at frequencies up to 10^{13} cps—a much higher frequency than is possible with any mechanical device! We can explore the entire vibrational spectrum to compare to theory. More complete discussions can be found in References 1 to 3 but velocity can vary with λ in this frequency range.

[2] The more advanced reader will note that a few steps earlier the term cos $[\mathbf{K} \cdot (\mathbf{r}_m - \mathbf{r}_n)]$ appeared in the exponent and a sum of Bessel functions will then arise for each wavelength.

Neutrons, with their larger mass, can exchange energy with the structure; from the change in energy in some of the neutrons at some position around a Bragg peak, the frequency of the wave with the λ corresponding to that position can be obtained without measuring the intensity of the weak TDS, as one has to do with x-rays. The neutrons' energy can be measured with two slotted rotating discs at the end of a tube; neutrons with a certain velocity will get through the discs at each speed of rotation of one of them relative to the other. Most work on the vibrational spectrum is now proceeding with neutrons.

Because the intensity of a wave is smaller for the shorter wavelengths (that is, for the thermal scattering far from a peak), there is a collection of this diffuse scattering under each Bragg peak. For integrated intensities to be accurate to better than 5–10 per cent, a correction is required (see References 4 and 5). If the peaks are at very large values of $|s|$, then the error in neglecting this can be large. This correction involves some knowledge of the Debye temperature or elastic constants, and some approximate estimate of these will be needed to make use of these corrections.

The static displacement due to atoms of different sizes will give rise to exactly analogous effects—a peak depression and diffuse scattering under the Bragg peak. From these, information can be obtained on the atomic volume of the species in an alloy to compare to the pure elements (see References 6 to 8).

Distortion and Mosaic Size

A great many interesting effects fall into this category; dislocations formed in cells will produce a mosaic structure. Even the regions between individual dislocations can be considered as small "particles." The dislocations produce strain fields. So also do atoms of a different size than the host atom, vacancies around which the lattice collapses, and clusters of solute atoms.

With x-ray or neutron diffraction, we shall want expressions that include averaging over the sample irradiated, but with the electron microscope we are interested only in the effects near one defect and the averages are not necessary (on the other hand, it is harder to be quantitative with the microscope because of multiple scattering). Recall from Chapter 3 that the diffraction pattern forms near the

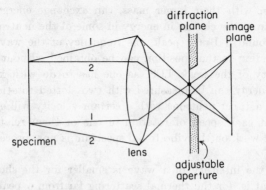

Figure 8–2.   Bright field or dark field in the electron microscope is chosen by placing the adjustable aperture over the transmitted beam (not shown) or the diffraction spots. 1 and 2 are two different diffraction peaks. (The aperture can be moved or changed in size.)

objective lens, as shown schematically in Figure 8–2. With an aperture nearby, we can look either at the image produced by the direct beam (bright field), excluding diffracted spots, or the image produced by one of the diffraction spots (dark field) excluding the direct beam. Either way, changes in diffracted intensity will affect the image; this image will not be a "good" one because this requires all the diffraction beams to add at the image plane, but it will reveal the distortion.

We have seen that the electron density can be written (Chapter 2, Problem 27), if every unit cell is the same, and the structure is periodic,

$$\rho_{uvw} = \frac{1}{V_{\text{cell}}} \sum_h \sum_k \sum_l F_{hkl} e^{-2\pi i (hu + kv + lw)}.$$

Suppose in the microscope we are looking along the [00l] in the real crystal, then what we see at the image plane is the projection of this density along [00l]—i.e.,

$$\int_0^{+n} \rho_{uvw} c \, dw,$$

$$\rho_{uv} = \frac{c}{V_{\text{cell}}} \sum_h \sum_k \sum_l F_{hkl} e^{-2\pi i (hu + kv)} \int_0^n e^{-2\pi i l w} \, dw.$$

The integral for large n is zero unless $l = 0$ and then it is unity, so that the result is the projection of the electron density along c,

$$\rho_{uv} = \frac{c}{V}_{\text{cell}} \sum_h \sum_k F_{hko} e^{-2\pi i (hu + kv)}. \tag{8–4}$$

This is what we see. (It is also the form often used in diffraction studies rather than evaluating a three-dimensional plot of ρ_{xy_2}.) If terms are cut out by an aperture, the image cannot be perfect—no matter how good the lenses.

We can make certain qualitative observations in advance of a more detailed treatment. First, the broadening of a diffraction spot due to small "particle" size will be the same for all diffracting points in the reciprocal lattice and proportional to $1/N$. Thus, on a precession film or electron diffraction pattern, all spots are changed in the same manner. In a record such as a diffractometer trace, the broadening will be greater at higher angles. Suppose we consider a $00l$ reflection. If it is broadened by the amount Δh_3, then as

$$h_3|\mathbf{b}_3| = \frac{2 \sin \theta}{\lambda}.$$

$$\frac{\Delta h_3|\mathbf{b}_3|\lambda}{\cos \theta} = \Delta 2\theta,$$

and as $\Delta h_3 b_3$ is $1/N|\mathbf{a}_3|$, where $N\mathbf{a}_3$ is the average dimension of the particles normal to the diffracting planes

$$\Delta 2\theta = \frac{\lambda}{N|\mathbf{a}_3| \cos \theta}.$$

The broadening will vary as $1/\cos \theta$.

If there is distortion, i.e., if $\mathbf{r}_n = \mathbf{r}_n^\circ + \Delta \mathbf{x}_n$. then the broadening will be greater the greater the distance from the origin of reciprocal space, because this term appears in the form

$$e^{2\pi i \mathbf{s} \cdot (\mathbf{r}_n^\circ + \Delta \mathbf{x}_n)}.$$

In a θ–2θ scan the broadening will vary more rapidly with θ than $1/\cos \theta$. Generally, both effects are present and in a quantitative treatment, we want to avoid any assumptions about the nature of the broadening. If we just use the breadth, we must assume some form for the instrumental broadening to correct for it with the shape of a peak from a well-annealed specimen, or use Fourier analysis as in Chapter 2. (In the latter case we shall shortly find that there is no reason to replot the peak to get the breadth!)

We are interested in the diffracted amplitude $A(\mathbf{s})_{\text{eu}}$ in the electron microscope's image, as from Eq. (8–4) the image is formed from summing diffracted amplitudes—F_{hkl}'s. When there are imperfections, F will depend on the position of the unit cell in the specimen, and

$$A(\mathbf{s})_{\text{eu}} = \sum F_n e^{-2\pi i \mathbf{s} \cdot \mathbf{r}_n}.$$

Figure 8–3. Ni-10+ Ti. 100,000X, 100 Kv. Fringes near the edge of a foil.
(Photo by S. Sass.)

Recall from our study of the interference function that if we are not
exactly on a diffraction spot (i.e., $s = r^* + \Delta s$), the sum A_{eu} on the
complex plane is a circle whose radius depends inversely on Δs (for
small Δs) and which opens and closes as the number of terms in the
sum increases. Thus near the edge of a thin piece of material in the
electron microscope, there will be fringes due to the thickness variation
(Figure 8–3). Near an imperfection, r_n is not the vector of the perfect
lattice; due to some distortion we can write as before $r_n = r_n^\circ + \Delta x_n$.
Assuming that both Δx_n and Δs are small, Eq. (8–4) can be written as

$$A_{eu} = \sum F_n e^{-2\pi i \Delta x_n \cdot r^*} e^{-2\pi i r_n^\circ \cdot \Delta s} e^{2\pi i r^* \cdot r_n^\circ} e^{2\pi i \Delta s \cdot \Delta x_n}. \qquad (8\text{–}5)$$

The last exponent is essentially unity because Δx_n and Δs are assumed
small. The next to last is just unity.

The first exponential term represents an additional phase factor over that which would be present without the distortion. We shall prove that the material can be considered as individual columns of unit cells, so that Eq. (8–5), instead of being a three-dimensional sum, can be evaluated for a given Δs in columns around the imperfection. The imperfection may increase or decrease the resulting diffracted amplitude, depending on where in the column the imperfection is. If it extends over some large region, there may be fringes. In bright field, the pattern will be dark where the diffracted amplitude (blocked by the aperture) is large, and light where it is small; this is illustrated in Figure 8–4.

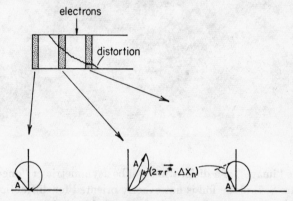

Figure 8–4. The effect of a distortion on the scattered amplitude A. The phase amplitude diagrams indicated by the arrows show how the total amplitude scattered by the foil is affected by a fault or distortion. As this diffracted amplitude oscillates with the position of the distortion, so does that of the transmitted beam. The image will then contain fringes which reverse contrast in bright and dark field.

This first exponential will have no effect if $\mathbf{r^*} \cdot \Delta\mathbf{x}_n = 0$. Thus, we can tell the direction of maximum distortion, such as the Burger's vector of a dislocation, by examining dark field images and looking for the one diffraction spot for which the contrast vanishes. For a spherical distortion ($\Delta\mathbf{x}_n$ the same in all directions) there will always be a "plane of no contrast" perpendicular to the strongest operating diffraction spot, as shown in Figure 8–5.

Consider the second exponential. If a region of the foil is bent to reduce Δs, the diffraction will increase and a black band or "extinction contour" will appear in bright field, Figure 8–6. On one side of an edge dislocation, the planes are bent one way, on the other side the other way,

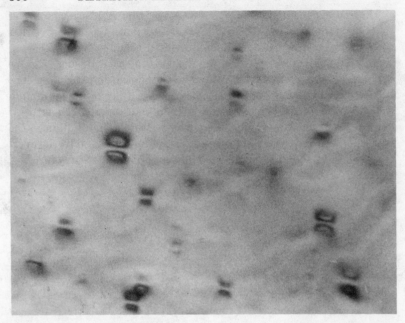

so that the "image" of a dislocation will be asymmetric or "one-sided," as in Figure 8–7, if the foil is not exactly oriented for diffraction.

The same $r^* \cdot \Delta x_n$ condition can be applied to an x-ray "picture." If a film is placed near the sample (1 mm away with 40 cm from focus to a crystal set for diffraction or near diffraction) the variation in diffracted intensity will be recorded (the Berg–Barrett method). Keep in mind, that although any x-ray photograph can be enlarged, say 200 ×, this is low magnification, so that the density of distortion sites must be low, or highly nonrandom to use x-rays.

When there is multiple (or dynamic) scattering, the total diffracted intensity is much less, and this is important in electron scattering, or in perfect regions, with an x-ray "picture." The intensity is less because the multiple scattered waves interfere destructively with the direct beam as it moves through the specimen, reducing its intensity and hence reducing diffraction from subsequent planes. We can make *use* of this though with x-rays, by making two pictures—one with white radiation at low voltage showing only the variation in diffracting power or state of perfection (a tilted region will just cause that region to choose a different λ), and one with characteristic radiation, by setting for

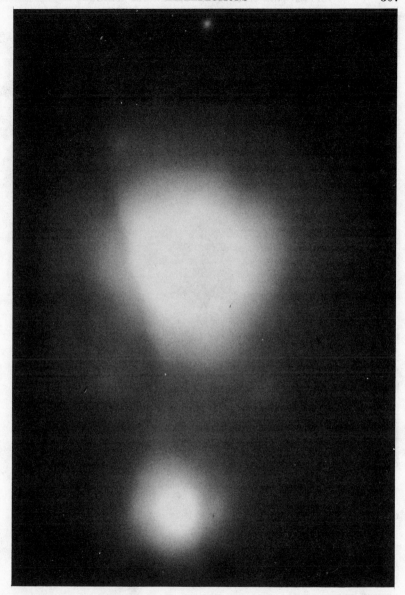

Figure 8–5.   Ni-10% Ti. Solution treated at 1150°C for 1/2 hour. Aged at 800°C
for 5 minutes. 200,000X. Diffraction pattern is (110) with $2\bar{2}0$ operating reflection. Note Plane of no contrast perpendicular to $2\bar{2}0$.
(Photos by S. Sass.)

Figure 8–6.   Bend contours in Ni-10% Ti. 75,000X, 100 Kv. (Photo by S. Sass.)

diffraction and using higher voltages; tilts as well as regions of varying perfection will show up.

[If a crystal is too perfect we shall have trouble in a structure determination with x-rays due to multiple scattering. Abrading a sample or quenching it may be required if intensities, especially strong peaks, appear low.]

Now let us consider in detail the problem of the effect of imperfections on x-ray or neutron diffraction intensities. Here we must remember that we have many distortions in the bulk specimen under the beam and

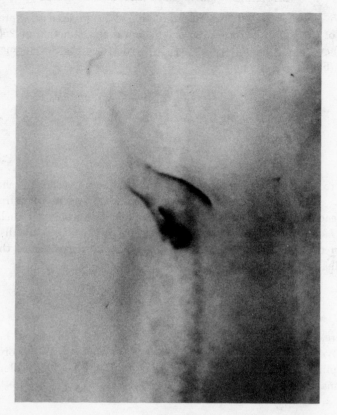

Figure 8–7. Ni-10% Ti solution treated at 1150°C for 1/2 hour. 150,000X, 100 Kv. Asymmetric image of a dislocation. (Photo by S. Sass.)

we see an "average" effect. We will follow the treatment by Warren and Averbach (see Reference 2). The material will be considered to be cubic with a cell edge a_0. The intensity can be written:

$$I_{\mathrm{eu}} = \sum_{n_1} \sum_{n_2} \sum_{n_3} \sum_{m_1} \sum_{m_2} \sum_{m_3} F^2 e^{2\pi i \mathbf{s} \cdot (\mathbf{r}_n - \mathbf{r}_m)}$$

$$= \sum_n \sum_m F^2 e^{2\pi i \{h_1(n_1 - m_1) + h_2(n_2 - m_2) + h_3(n_3 - m_3) + \mathbf{s} \cdot (\Delta \mathbf{x}_{n_i} - \Delta \mathbf{x}_{m_i})\}}. [3]$$

The Δ's are displacements of unit cells from the average.

[3] We write the intensity in electron units, i.e., per electron. The actual intensity is this times $\dfrac{e^4}{m^2 c^4 R^2} \left(\dfrac{1 + \cos^2 2\theta}{2} \right)$ for unpolarized (filtered) radiation.

We generally record power as a function of 2θ; we need an expression not of the total integrated power but power as a function of $2\theta(P_{2\theta})$.

Then, from Chapter 6 for, say, a powder (see the development of Eq. (6–2)):

$$(P_{\text{total}})_{\text{eu}} = \frac{mnR^2\lambda^3}{4V_{\text{cell}}} \int\int\int \frac{I_{\text{eu}}}{\sin\theta} \, dh_1 \, dh_2 \, dh_3.$$

and

$$(P')_{\text{eu}} = \frac{P_{\text{eu}}}{2\pi R \, \sin 2\theta},$$

where P'_{eu} is the power per unit length of diffracting cone. We shall let $M = mn$ represent the number of domains or regions of diffraction instead of crystals or particles. We can always find a unit cell, such that the hkl diffraction peak is a $00l$ peak from this new cell; the distance from the origin in reciprocal space is the same regardless of the co-ordinate system so that

$$\frac{l}{|\mathbf{a}_3|} = \frac{(h^2 + k^2 + l^2)^{1/2}}{a_0} \equiv \frac{h_0}{a_0}. \tag{8–6}$$

(Here, $\mathbf{a}_3$ may be the "fictitious" parameter used in the actual Fourier analysis, see Chapter 2.) We now work with this new cell in order to simplify the mathematics; the variable is now only h_3 which is along the normal to the diffracting planes. Thus with $dh_3 = (\cos\theta \, d2\theta)/|\mathbf{b}_3|\lambda$ and $I_{\text{eu}'} = I_{\text{eu}}/F^2$:

$$(P'_{2\theta})_{\text{eu}} = \frac{MR\lambda^2F^2}{16\pi V_c|\mathbf{b}_3|\sin^2\theta} \int\int I'_{\text{eu}} \, dh_1 \, dh_2$$

$$= K(\theta) \int\int I'_{\text{eu}} \, dh_1 \, dh_2.$$

The terms in θ and F^2 are removed from the integral because they vary slowly compared to the inteference function. Considering only one peak at a time, the integrals are from $h_1, h_2 = -1/2$ to $h_1, h_2 = +1/2$. Also

$$\Delta\mathbf{x}_n = x_n\mathbf{a}_1 + y_n\mathbf{a}_2 + z_n\mathbf{a}_3.$$

With:

$$\mathbf{s} \cong l\mathbf{b}_3$$

then,

$$\mathbf{s}\cdot(\Delta\mathbf{x}_n - \Delta\mathbf{x}_m) = l(z_n - z_m).$$

Therefore,

$$(P'_{2\theta})_{eu} = K(\theta) \sum_{n_1} \sum_{n_2} \sum_{n_3} \sum_{m_1} \sum_{m_2} \sum_{m_3} \frac{\sin \pi(n_1 - m_1)}{\pi(n_1 - m_1)}$$

$$\times \frac{\sin \pi(n_2 - m_2)}{\pi(n_2 - m_2)} \, dh_1 \, dh_2 \, e^{2\pi i l(z_n - z_m)} e^{2\pi i l h_3 (n_3 - m_3)}.$$

The sine terms are each zero unless $m_1 = n_1$, $m_2 = n_2$ and then are unity, so that the sum over $m_1 \, m_2$, $n_1 \, n_2$ becomes $N_1 \, N_2$ where the N's are the total number of columns in a mosaic region. This is why we can think of the crystal in terms of columns or cells perpendicular to the diffracting planes. The remaining terms $\sum_{m_3} \sum_{n_3}$ are sums between pairs of cells $n_3 - m_3$ apart in a column. Let $n = n_3 - m_3$ and N_n be the average number of cells with an nth neighbor in a column, the average being over all columns in all mosaic regions. Take the average value of the term involving z over all these pairs of cells n cells apart in all the columns in all the mosaic regions. Then,

$$(P'_{2\theta})_{eu} = K(\theta) N_1 N_2 \sum_n N_n \langle e^{2\pi i l z_n} \rangle e^{2\pi i n h_3}.$$

Multiplying and dividing by N_3, the *average number* of cells in a column gives

$$(P'_{2\theta})_{eu} = K(\theta) = K(\theta) N_1 N_2 N_3 \left\{ \sum_{-\infty}^{+\infty} \frac{N_n}{N_3} \langle \cos 2\pi l z_n \rangle \cos 2\pi n h_3 \right.$$

$$\left. - \frac{N_n}{N_3} \langle \sin 2\pi l z_n \rangle \sin 2\pi n h_3 \right\}. \quad (8\text{--}7)$$

Equation (8–7) is in a form suitable for Fourier analysis, as it is a Fourier series: $A_n = N_n/N_3 \langle \cos 2\pi l z_n \rangle$, $B_n = -N_n/N_3 \langle \sin 2\pi l z_n \rangle$. The coefficients A_n, B_n are those after correction for instrumental effects; this correction is described in Chapter 2.

Let us look at the various terms in the equations. Those involving displacement depend on l as we predicted, and also as we expect, N_n, the particle size term does *not* depend on l. The peak will be asymmetric if there is a net displacement, i.e., if the sine term involving z_n does not average to zero; the peak will tail to high angles for a negative net strain, and in the opposite direction for a positive net z_n. If there are many sine terms, i.e., if the strain exists over a large distance, the peak will actually shift. The effects of mosaic size and strain can be separated (because the former does not depend on l) by analyzing several orders of a peak—e.g., $hkl = 200, 400, 600$, plotting A_n versus l and extrapolating to $l = 0$. (Unless the material is elastically isotropic, the displacements will vary with crystallographic direction; thus we cannot use peaks representing different directions.) However, with a powder or a poly-crystalline material the third order often overlaps with another peak. For example, with an f.c.c. material the 600 occurs at the same position as the 442. The strains are small however, so the cosine term can be expanded ($\cos x = 1 - x^2/2 + x^4/24 \ldots$). Including only the first two terms and taking the logarithm of the expansion:

$$\ln \left(\langle \cos 2\pi l z_n \rangle\right) = -2\pi^2 l^2 \langle z_n^2 \rangle.$$

Now, $z_n a_3$ is the change in length of a column of length na_3, so that the strain ε_n is

$$\varepsilon_n = \frac{z_n a_3}{na_3} = \frac{z_n}{n},$$

or

$$n\varepsilon_n = z_n.$$

Inserting this value for z_n in Eq. (8–7) and using Eq. (8–6):

$$\ln A_n = \ln \frac{N_n}{N_3} - 2\pi^2 \frac{h_0^2 a_3^2}{a_0^2} n^2 \langle \varepsilon_n^2 \rangle, \qquad (8\text{–}8a)$$

or

$$\ln A_L = \ln \frac{N_n}{N_3} - 2\pi^2 h_0^2 \frac{L^2}{a_0^2} \langle \varepsilon_L^2 \rangle, \qquad (8\text{–}8b)$$

where $L = na_3$ is the true distance between cells in a column normal to the diffracting planes. If there are no strains, just small particles, $\ln A_L$ versus h_0^2 for each L will be a horizontal line. If there is no particle size broadening but just strains, all the lines for various L's intersect at $L = 0$, $\ln A_L = 0$.

According to Eq. (8–8b) only two orders of a peak are needed to separate the effects of particle size and strain and obtain N_L/N_3 and $\langle \varepsilon_L^2 \rangle$ versus L. This is because $\ln A_L$ versus h_0^2 is a straight line (with a slope yielding $\langle \varepsilon_L^2 \rangle$): it *is* possible to do the analysis with a powder or polycrystalline specimen. This result occurs because we have left off higher terms than the second in the expansion of the cosine. How valid is this? a_3/a_0 is typically about 5, $\langle \varepsilon_L^2 \rangle^{1/2}$ unelastic strain is at most about 0.005. Substituting these values in the expansion of $\cos 2\pi l z_n = \cos 2\pi (h_0 a_3/a_0) n\varepsilon_n$, nh_0 can be about 6 with the third term in the expansion still only 6 per cent of the second. Thus, for the first few harmonics, $\ln A_L$ versus h_0^2 is practically quite linear.

If there are net strains over large distances, the peak will shift. If the origin for the analysis is chosen at the position of the well-annealed standard (with sharp peaks), then there will be sine terms, and for small n

$$B_n = -\frac{N_n}{N_3} \left\langle \sin 2\pi \, \frac{h_0 a_3}{a_0} \, n\varepsilon_n \right\rangle \to \left(-\frac{N_n}{N_3} \frac{2\pi h_0 L}{a_0} \left\langle \varepsilon_n \right\rangle \right).$$

On the other hand, if in the analysis the center of the actual peak is used, we can write the measured strain as the value above or below the long range or mean strain.

$$\langle \varepsilon_L^2 \rangle_{\text{measured}} = \langle \varepsilon_L - \varepsilon_{\text{long range}} \rangle^2$$
$$= \langle \varepsilon_L^2 \rangle - 2\langle \varepsilon_L \varepsilon_{\text{long range}} \rangle + \langle \varepsilon_{\text{long range}}^2 \rangle,$$
$$\langle \varepsilon_L^2 \rangle_{\text{measured}} = \langle \varepsilon_L^2 \rangle - \langle \varepsilon_{\text{long range}}^2 \rangle, \qquad (8\text{–}9)$$

because
$$-2\langle \varepsilon_L \varepsilon_{\text{long range}} \rangle = -2\langle \varepsilon_{\text{long range}}^2 \rangle.$$

We are measuring the deviation from the mean or long-range strain.

Some typical data are presented in Figure 8–8. $N_n/N_3 \cong (1 - |n|/N_3)$ for small L. (Take a column of say 10 cells and evaluate N_n, the number of cells with an nth neighbor; for small n, $N_n = N_3 - n$.) Then N_n/N_3 decreases more and more rapidly with L, as N_3 is smaller—the peak will be broader the smaller the regions are, as we expect. If the values of N_n/N_3 obtained from the intersections of the curves with the ordinate in Figure 8–8(b) [see Eq. (8–8)] are plotted versus L, the initial slope is

$$\left(\frac{d(N_n/N_3)}{dn} \right)_{n \to 0} = -\frac{1}{N_3}, \quad \text{or} \quad \left(\frac{d(N_n/N_3)}{dL} \right)_{L \to 0} = -\frac{1}{N_3 a_3} = \frac{1}{D_{\text{eff}}}.$$
$$(8\text{–}10)$$

Thus if a plot of N_n/N_3 versus L is normalized so that its intercept at $L = 0$ is unity, the slope gives the average value $\langle D_{\text{eff}} \rangle$ of the length of the columns normal to the diffraction planes—a measure of the effective mosaic size in that direction. Such a plot is shown in the insert of Figure 8–8(b).

Often there is a small bend or hook in the data near $n = 0$. This occurs because with a broad peak it is difficult to estimate background; as A_0 is the area of the peak, its value will be too small. The values from

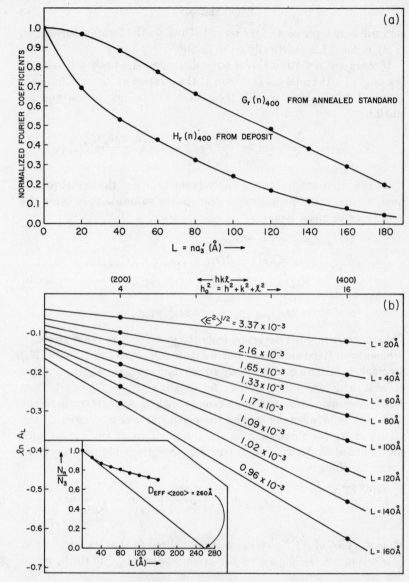

Figure 8–8. (a) Fourier cosine coefficients of 400 peaks, Hr (n), from Ag electro-deposited from KCN + AgCN solution, and from a well annealed standard, Gr (n). (b) Separation of particle size and strain and the determination of particle size, using the corrected Fourier cosine coefficients, A_L. (From R. W. Hinton, L. H. Schwartz, and J. B. Cohen, *J. Electrochem. Soc.*, **110**, 103, (1963); reprinted with permission of the Journal of the Electrochemical Society.)

beyond $n = 3 - 4$ should be extrapolated to $n = 0$ in doing this normalization.

It is a good idea to record at least four to five times the breadth of a peak on either side of it, and to compare the background of the standard and the pattern to be analyzed; the background in both should be the same and this comparison will help in any extrapolation of overlapping peaks on the broadened pattern. These precautions will minimize scatter in the coefficients. If you do not record enough of the peak's tails, "cutting it off" is equivalent to multiplying with a rectangle of unit height and width equal to the recording range. As determining a coefficient is like doing a transform, the result is the convolution of the transform of the peak and that for a square. The coefficients will show the oscillations of the transform of the square.

The peaks to be analyzed should be at least 20 per cent broader than the standard peaks, or else the analytical procedures will result in considerable scatter. (This means, e.g., that a particle size larger than about 1000 Å cannot be measured with line broadening, because of the instrumental broadening.) The errors in the particle size and in the strains are about ± 10 per cent.

With a minimum of assumptions, we are able, with this "Warren-Averbach analysis," to obtain the rms strain $\langle \varepsilon_L^2 \rangle^{1/2}$ as a function of column length in a given crystallographic direction and the mosaic size in this direction. From this information we can proceed to learn about the degree of anisotropy and the imperfections. In a deformed material, $(1/D_{\text{eff}})^2$ can be taken as a dislocation density, and from the formulae for strain around a dislocation, the data on $\langle \varepsilon_L^2 \rangle^{1/2}$ can be used to obtain a density also. These two should agree if the dislocations are randomly arranged, but if $(1/D_{\text{eff}})^2$ is smaller than the value obtained from the strains, the dislocations may be clustered. The densities so calculated in this way *are* in agreement with those observed in the electron microscope (see Reference 10); and furthermore, if the dislocations are randomly distributed, D_{eff} *is* a measure of their spacing; if there are cells it *is* a measure of the cell size. Typical values of D_{eff} run from 25 Å to 1000 Å. Thus this technique is especially useful for high concentrations of distortions and this is exactly where the electron microscope is least useful. By combining the two tools, a whole range of concentrations can be studied, with a region of overlap sufficient to allow comparison of the two.

We have already considered the result of periodic distortions when we examined "TDS." We now turn our attention to another common fault in materials, where the displacement vector is confined to a plane—a stacking disorder.

Stacking Disorder

There are many cases in materials where faults occur in the stacking of planes of atoms. As an example of how we can examine this, consider a close packed f.c.c. material, e.g., copper or silver. As we saw in Chapter 1, the stacking sequence of the (111) planes is ABCABC. That is, the atoms of each successive layer fit in the holes of the one below with the fourth layer directly over the atoms in the first. It is also possible to have close packing with the third layer over the first, ABAB...—the hexagonal stacking sequence. During the growth of an f.c.c. crystal, or as a result of deformation, one layer may be in a wrong position:

$$A \ B \ C \ A \ B \ C \ \boxed{B} \ C \ A \ B \ C....$$

There is a one-layer fault, or in effect a small hexagonal region. It will be easier in the entire discussion that follows (and for all kinds of layer faults) if we switch now to an axial system with one axis normal to the plane of the fault. Assume the fault is on the (111). Then the hexagonal axes in Figure 8–9(a) will be convenient; A_3 is normal to the (111). In Figure 8–9(b), A_1 and A_2 are shown along with the possible positions for a faulted layer. The phase angle associated with each

Table 8–1

Shift (Δx_n)	$\cdot r^* \cdot \Delta x_n$	$360°(r^* \cdot \Delta x_n) = 360° \times$ $(HB_1 + KB_2$ $+ LB_3) \cdot (\Delta x_n)$
Faulted positions		
$-\dfrac{(A_2 + 2A_1)}{3}$	$-\dfrac{(K + 2H)}{3}$	$+240° = -120°$
$-\dfrac{A_2 - A_1}{3}$	$-\dfrac{K - H}{3}$	$-120°$
$\dfrac{2A_2 + A_1}{3}$	$\dfrac{2K + H}{3}$	$-120°$
(Normal shift for the next layer) $\dfrac{A_2 - A_1}{3}$	$\dfrac{K - H}{3}$	$+120°$

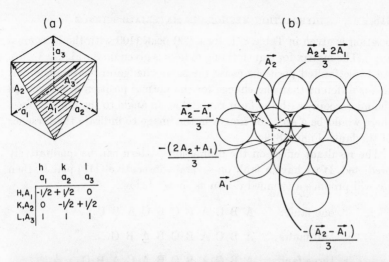

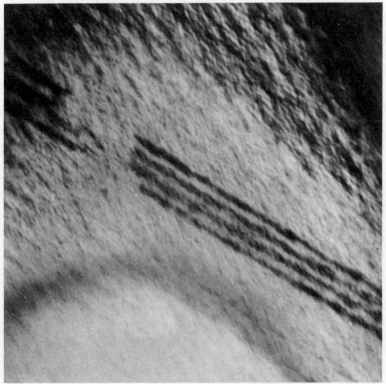

Ni-10% Ti. 150,000X, 100 Kv. Fringes at a stacking fault. (*Photo by S. Sass*)

Figure 8–9. Faulting in an f.c.c. structure.

317

position is given in Table 8–1, for a 200 peak ($\bar{1}$00 with the hexagonal axes). The matrix for transforming indices is given under Figure 8–9(a). All three faulted positions cause the same change in phase angle, but this is different than the change for the normal position of a layer. In the microscope, with the fault running at an angle to the foil's surface, there would be a series of fringes in the image to indicate the presence of the fault, Figure 8–9c.

The resultant effect on the diffraction pattern can be qualitatively predicted. If we have a fault on several consecutive (111) planes, then we will produce a twinned region as shown below:

one fault: A B C A B C $\underline{B}$ C A B C...

two faults: A B C A B C $\underline{B}$ $\underline{A}$ B C...

three faults: A B C A B C $\underline{B}$ $\underline{A}$ $\underline{C}$ A B C...
etc.

(Note that the faulted layer cannot have the same letter as the previous layer, i.e., it cannot be directly above the previous layer—nor can it have the letter for the next layer in the correct sequence.)

If we fault every other layer we will produce a hexagonal close packed region:

one fault: A B C A B C $\underline{B}$ C A B C...

hexagonal region: A B C A B C $\underline{B}$ C $\underline{B}$ C A B C...

The HOL plane of reciprocal space (with the new axial system) for the original structure, its twin, and a hexagonal structure are shown in Figure 8–10. It is clear that as more and more faults are put in an f.c.c. material the 1$\bar{1}\bar{1}$ and $\bar{1}$11 peaks will move away from the origin to the higher 2θ values of a hexagonal material, but the 200 and $\bar{2}$00 will move toward the origin; on a powder pattern the 111 and 200 peaks will be closer together than in an annealed specimen. But not all the components of a peak from a powder will be affected. The 111 is not affected in this case because the shift is normal to $\mathbf{r}^*$ and thus there is no phase change for this $\mathbf{r}^*$. All peaks but the 111 streak in a [111] direction, because the faults separate the material into "particles."

We can carry out our quantitative treatment by summing over layers, and in an identical way to the treatment for distortion and particle size. We will assume that:

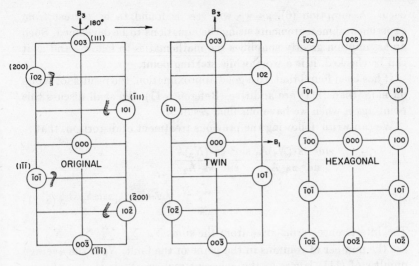

Figure 8–10. The indices in parentheses are the Miller indices of the peak with the (original) cubic axial system. On the right, note that the B_3 axis for the hexagonal cell is 3/2 that for the cubic cell because the hexagonal close-packed structure consists of two (111) layers but the cubic cell is made up of three of these. (After M. S. Patterson, *J. Appl. Phys.*, **23** (805), 1952.)

1. The faults are only on (111), not any other plane of this type.
2. The fault is as wide as the coherent domain.
3. There is no segregation to the fault if the material is an alloy, so that the scattering per layer is the same in the fault as in other layers.
4. There is no change in the interplanar spacing at the fault, which might occur due to segregation or because there are a different number of neighbors (those in the second layer below a fault are reduced from three to one, and it is at a different distance).
5. The effect of any strains has been removed by the multiple-order technique discussed above.
6. The number of faulted layers is small.

All of these assumptions have been examined in the literature (see Reference 10 for discussion, of (2, 3, 4, 6) and Reference 11 for (1)). Assumptions (2–4) can be removed and the effects included in the equations. In some cases, measurable changes in the diffraction peaks occur. Assumption (6), as we will see, is found to be correct from experimental measurements using the equations to be developed. Such an assumption greatly simplifies the mathematics to follow—and as it can be checked, it is a worthwhile starting point.

It has been found that, to a good approximation, the results for faults on more than {111} are additive (Reference 11). We shall discuss this point again when we have our final result.

We can write, following the previous treatment of distortion, that

$$I_{eu} = (\bar{f})^2 N_3 \frac{\sin^2 \pi \mathbf{s} \cdot (N_1)\mathbf{A}_1}{\sin^2 \pi \mathbf{s} \cdot \mathbf{A}_1} \frac{\sin^2 \pi \mathbf{s} \cdot (N_2)\mathbf{A}_2}{\sin^2 \pi \mathbf{s} \cdot \mathbf{A}_2}$$
$$\times \sum_n \frac{N_n}{N_3} \langle e^{2\pi i \mathbf{s} \cdot \Delta \mathbf{x}_n} \rangle e^{2\pi i (n h_3/3)} \quad (8\text{--}11)$$

The interference terms arise from the sums $\sum_{m_1} \sum_{m_2} \sum_{n_1} \sum_{n_2}$. N_1, N_2 are the number of columns in the plane of the fault, N_3 is the average number of (111) layers in the coherent regions. N_n is the number of layers with a layer n layers away. The factor $1/3$ in the last exponent arises because, in using our hexagonal axial scheme, each atom is related to the first by a vector of the form:

$$m_1 A_1 + m_2 A_2 + \frac{m_3 A_3}{3}.$$

Each layer contains only one atom, with an average scattering factor $\bar{f}$ if the material is an alloy—i.e., the axes $\mathbf{A}_1$, $\mathbf{A}_2$ define a layer with only one atom on it so that the structure factor is $\bar{f}$.

As the simplest procedure, we shall now assume that the faults are randomly distributed. The presence of one fault does not effect the stacking of the next layers. Then

$$\langle e^{2\pi i \mathbf{s} \cdot \Delta \mathbf{x}_n} \rangle = \langle e^{2\pi i \mathbf{s} \cdot \Delta \mathbf{x}_{0 \to 1}} e^{2\pi i \mathbf{s} \cdot \Delta \mathbf{x}_{1 \to 2}} \rangle \dots$$
$$= \langle e^{2\pi i \mathbf{s} \cdot \Delta \mathbf{x}_{0 \to 1}} \rangle \langle e^{2\pi i \mathbf{s} \cdot \Delta \mathbf{x}_{1 \to 2}} \rangle \dots$$
$$= \langle e^{2\pi i \mathbf{s} \cdot \Delta \mathbf{x}_{0 \to 1}} \rangle^n. \quad (8\text{--}12)$$

Let α be the probability that a (111) plane is faulted and considering Table 8–1:

$$\langle e^{2\pi i \mathbf{s} \cdot \Delta \mathbf{x}_{0-1}} \rangle^n = \langle (1 - \alpha)e^{-2\pi i (H-K)/3} + \alpha e^{+2\pi i (H-K)/3} \rangle^n.$$
$$(8\text{--}13)$$

There will be no effect due to the fault if $(H - K) = 3N$ where N is an integer. There will be an effect for $(H - K) = 3N \pm 1$, the only other possible value for the f.c.c. system.

$$\langle e^{2\pi i s \cdot \Delta x_{0-1}} \rangle = Z e^{2\pi i y} \tag{8-14}$$

$$= (1 - \alpha)e^{-2\pi i(H-K)/3} + \alpha e^{+2\pi i(H-K)/3}. \tag{8-15a}$$

$$Z e^{(2\pi i y + 2\pi i(H-K)/3)} = 1 - \alpha + \alpha \cos 4\pi[(H - K)/3]$$
$$+ i\alpha \sin 4\pi[(H - K)/3], \tag{8-15b}$$

$$Z Z^* = Z^2 = (1 - \alpha)^2 + 2(1 - \alpha)(\alpha) \cos 4\pi(H - K)/3 + \alpha^2, \tag{8-15c}$$

and, as $\cos 2x = 1 - 2 \sin^2 x$ and α is assumed small:

$$Z^2 \cong 1 - 4\alpha(1 - \alpha) \sin^2 [2\pi(H - K)/3], \tag{8-15d}$$

For small x, $\sqrt{1 - x} = 1 - x/2$ so that

$$Z \cong 1 - 2\alpha \sin^2 2\pi(H - K)/3. \tag{8-15e}$$

Also from Eq. (8-15b):

$$2\pi y + 2\pi \frac{(H - K)}{3} = \text{arc sin} \frac{\alpha \sin[4\pi(H - K)/3]}{Z},$$

and for small α, the angle is small and $Z \cong 1$ so that:

$$2\pi y \cong -2\pi \frac{(H - K)}{3} + \alpha \sin \left[\frac{4\pi(H - K)}{3} \right]. \tag{8-15f}$$

Thus recalling that

$$\frac{N_n}{N_3} = \left(1 - \frac{|n|}{N_3} \right)$$

$$I_{\text{eu}} \cong \bar{f}^2 N_1 N_2 N_3 \sum_{-\infty}^{+\infty} \left(1 - \frac{|n|}{N_3} \right) Z^{|n|} e^{2\pi i n(h_3/3 + y)}.$$

At this point we can see from the exponential term that there will indeed be a peak shift, just as we expected. The absolute values for n comes from the fact that if we look at Eq. (8-14), we can see that Z is not affected by the sign of n. As the coefficients of the series are the same for $+n$ and $-n$, the exponential form can be replaced by a cosine series.

We have two steps left to finish our equations. First we must transform our equation to a form suitable for integration and then we must obtain $P'_{2\theta}$ for a $00l$ orthorhombic reflection for one-dimensional Fourier analysis. That is, we must take any peak in the hexagonal system and change it to a $00l$ peak from an orthorhombic system, and get $P'_{2\theta}$. Second, Eq. (8–15) is for the affected components. If we are going to examine a powder pattern, we must take into account the unaffected components.

From Figure 8–11,

$$|\mathbf{b}_3|\frac{h'_3}{3} = \frac{2\sin\theta}{\lambda}, \tag{8–16a}$$

$$l|\mathbf{b}_3| = \frac{l}{d_{hkl}}, \tag{8–16b}$$

$$\left(\frac{h_3}{3} - L\right)|\mathbf{B}_3|\sin\phi = \left(\frac{h'_3}{3} - l\right)|\mathbf{b}_3|, \tag{8–16c}$$

$$\sin\phi \cong |\mathbf{B}_3|\frac{L}{1/d_{hkl}}. \tag{8–16d}$$

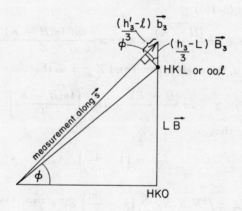

Figure 8–11.   (After B. E. Warren in *Progress in Metal Physics*, Vol. 8, Pergamon Press, New York, 1959.)

Also,

$$|\mathbf{B}_3| = \frac{1}{\sqrt{3}d_{111}},$$

and let

$$q = \frac{|\mathbf{b}_3|}{|\mathbf{B}_3|\sin\phi}. \tag{8–16e}$$

From Eq. (8–16d):

$$q = \frac{3d_{111}^2}{Ld_{hkl}^2}. \qquad (8\text{–}16f)$$

Now for a powder pattern, as shown in Chapter 6:

$$(P'_{2\theta})_{\text{eu}} = \frac{MR\lambda^3(\bar{f})^2 N_3}{8\pi V_{\text{cell}} \sin\theta \sin 2\theta} \int\int\int \frac{\sin^2 \pi N_1 h_1}{\sin^2 \pi h_1} \frac{\sin^2 \pi N_2 h_2}{\sin^2 \pi h_2}$$

$$\times \sum_n \left(1 - \frac{|n|}{N_3}\right) Z^{|n|} \cos 2\pi n \left[\left(\frac{h_3}{3} + y\right)\right] dh_1\, dh_2\, dh_3.$$

With Eq. (8–16c), Eq. (8–16a)

$$dh_3 = \frac{\cos\theta\,(d2\theta)}{\lambda|\mathbf{B}_3|\sin\phi}.$$

Therefore,

$$(P'_{2\theta})_{\text{eu}} = \frac{MN_1 N_2 N_3 R\lambda^2(\bar{f})^2}{16\pi|V_{\text{cell}}||\mathbf{B}_3|\sin\varphi \sin^2\theta}$$

$$\times \sum_n \left(1 - \frac{|n|}{N_3}\right) Z^{|n|} \cos 2\pi n \left[\frac{h_3}{3} + y\right].$$

We now rewrite this equation in the form to describe one peak around the value of $h_3 = L$:

$$(P'_{2\theta})_{\text{eu}} = \frac{K'(\theta)}{|\mathbf{B}_3|\sin\varphi} \sum_n \left(1 - \frac{|n|}{N_3}\right) Z^{|n|} \cos 2\pi n \left[\frac{h_3}{3} - L + (y + L)\right],$$

and letting $n = m/q$, with Eq. (8–16c) and (e):

$$(P'_{2\theta})_{\text{eu}} = \frac{K'(\theta)}{|\mathbf{B}_3|\sin\varphi} \sum \left(1 - \frac{|m|}{|q|N_3}\right) Z^{\left|\frac{m}{q}\right|} \cos 2\pi n q \left[\frac{h'_3}{3} - l + \frac{(y + L)}{q}\right].$$

Now,

$$\int A_n \cos 2\pi n q x\, dn = \frac{1}{q} \int A_{\frac{m}{q}} \cos 2\pi m x\, dm.$$

Therefore, using Eq. (8–16e):

$$(P'_{2\theta})_{\text{eu}} = \frac{K'(\theta)}{|\mathbf{b}_3|} \sum \left(1 - \frac{|m|}{|q|N_3}\right) Z^{|m/q|} \cos 2\pi m \left[\left(\frac{h'_3}{3} - l\right) + \left(\frac{y + L}{q}\right)\right].$$

$$(8\text{–}17)$$

We are now ready to put the equation in a form suitable for powders and to examine the terms in more detail. Let

$$\delta = \frac{1}{X} \sum_x \frac{y + L}{q},$$

where X is the number of powder components in any one peak in a powder pattern. Normally the peak occurs for $(h_3'/3) - l + \delta_0 = N$. With faults it occurs for $(h_3'/3) - l + \delta = N$ (an integer). Thus

$$\Delta h_3' = -(\delta - \delta_0) = \text{(position with faults)} - \text{(position with no faults)}.$$

As δ gets larger, the peak in the cosine series occurs at smaller values of h_3'.

Using Eq. (8–15f) in the equation for δ:

$$\delta = \frac{1}{X} \sum_X \left\{ \frac{L}{q} - \frac{(H - K)}{3q} + \frac{\alpha}{2\pi q} \sin \left[4\pi \frac{(H - K)}{3} \right] \right\}.$$

The first two terms represent δ_0, and so

$$\Delta h_3' = -\frac{1}{X} \sum_X \frac{\alpha}{2\pi q} \sin \left[4\pi \frac{(H - K)}{3} \right],$$

and with Eq. (8–16f):

$$\Delta h_3' = -\frac{1}{X} \sum_X \frac{\alpha}{2\pi} \frac{d_{(hkl)}^2 L}{3 d_{(111)}^2} \sin \left[4\pi \frac{(H - K)}{3} \right].$$

As

$$\Delta 2\theta^\circ = \frac{360}{2\pi} \frac{\Delta h_3' \lambda}{|\mathbf{a}_3| \cos \theta},$$

and

$$|\mathbf{a}_3| = d_{hkl},$$

and

$$\lambda = 2 d_{hkl} \sin \theta,$$

$$(\Delta 2\theta^\circ)_{hkl} = \frac{360}{\pi} \tan \theta \, \Delta h_3'.$$

$$(\Delta 2\theta^\circ)_{hkl} = -\frac{180}{\pi^2} \frac{d_{hkl}^2}{3 d_{111}^2} \alpha \tan \theta \left[\frac{1}{X} \sum_X L \sin \left(4\pi \frac{(H - K)}{3} \right) \right].$$

Now,

$$\frac{1}{d_{hkl}^2} = \frac{h_0^2}{a_0^2}, \qquad \frac{1}{d_{111}^2} = \frac{3}{a_0^2}.$$

Thus,

$$\Delta 2\theta^\circ = -\frac{180}{\pi^2} \frac{1}{h_0^2} \alpha \tan \theta \, G_{hkl}. \qquad (8\text{–}18a)$$

Table 8–2

(hkl)	H	K	L	$\frac{4\pi(H-K)}{3}$ in degrees	$\sin 4\pi \frac{(H-K)}{3}$
111	0	0	3	0	0
11$\bar{1}$	0	$\bar{1}$	1	$+240°$	$-\sqrt{3}/2$
$\bar{1}$11	1	0	1	$+240°$	$-\sqrt{3}/2$
1$\bar{1}$1	$\bar{1}$	1	1	$-480° = +240°$	$-\sqrt{3}/2$
200	$\bar{1}$	0	2	$-240°$	$\sqrt{3}/2$
020	1	$\bar{1}$	2	$+480° = -240°$	$\sqrt{3}/2$
002	0	1	2	$-240°$	$\sqrt{3}/2$

Some terms for G_{hkl} are given in Table 8–2 for the 111 and 200 planes of the pattern. (Terms for $\bar{h}\bar{k}\bar{l}$ give the same result as hkl so that only half the multiplicity need be considered.)

For the 111:

$$G_{111} = \frac{1}{X} \sum_X L \sin 4\pi \left(\frac{H-K}{3}\right) = -\frac{3\sqrt{3}}{8},$$

and

$$\Delta 2\theta_{111}^{\circ} = +\frac{45\sqrt{3}}{2\pi^2} \alpha \tan \theta. \qquad (8\text{–}18b)$$

For the 200:

$$G_{200} = \sqrt{3},$$

and

$$\Delta 2\theta_{200}^{\circ} = -\frac{90\sqrt{3}}{2\pi^2} \alpha \tan \theta. \qquad (8\text{–}18c)$$

These equations are simple enough when we get to them! The 200 powder peak shifts to low angles and the 111 to high angles, just as we anticipated, and from the shifts, we can measure α. We want to minimize errors due to the positioning of the standard and deformed samples. (Recall from Chapter 4 that if the specimen is slightly displaced from the center of the goniometer there will be a peak shift, which is largest for low angle peaks like the 111 and 200.) We also want to eliminate backlash in the goniometer. Suppose we record the 111 and 200 peaks continuously on the chart and take the change in the separation of these for two specimens:

$$\Delta 2\theta^\circ_{200} - \Delta 2\theta^\circ_{111} = 2\theta^{\text{deformed}}_{200} - 2\theta^{\text{annealed}}_{200} - 2\theta^{\text{deformed}}_{111} + 2\theta^{\text{annealed}}_{111}$$

$$= (2\theta^{\text{deformed}}_{200} - 2\theta^{\text{deformed}}_{111}) - (2\theta^{\text{annealed}}_{200} - 2\theta^{\text{annealed}}_{111})$$

$$= -\frac{45\sqrt{3}}{2\pi^2}\,\alpha\{2\tan\theta_{200} - \tan\theta_{111}\}. \qquad (8\text{--}18d)$$

The *difference* in the change in 111 and 200 peak positions due to any sample displacement is small, as these peaks are close together.

Next, consider the Fourier coefficients, which represent the broadening of a peak:

$$Z^{|m/q|} = 1 + |m/q|\log Z + [|m/q|\log Z]^2/2 + \cdots.$$

For small m and $Z \cong 1$ only the first two terms are important, and it is from the values for small m that, as we have seen, we get our "particle" size—in this case the spacing between faults.

$$Z^{|m/q|} = 1 + (|m/q|)\log\{1 - 2\alpha\sin^2[2\pi(H - K)/3]\}.$$

Log $(1 - x) = -x$ for small x so that for small $|m/q|$,

$$Z^{|m/q|} = 1 - |m/q|\{2\alpha\sin^2[2\pi(H - K)/3]\}.$$

Thus, from Eq. (8–17),

$$A_{\left|\frac{m}{q}\right|} = \frac{1}{X}\sum_X\left\{\left(1 - \frac{|m|}{|q|N_3}\right)\left[1 - \frac{|m|}{|q|}2\alpha\sin^2 2\pi\,\frac{(H - K)}{3}\right]\right\},$$

and, using Eqs. (8–16e and f) for q,

$$\mathbf{B}_3 = \frac{1}{\sqrt{3}d_{111}} \quad\text{and}\quad |L_0| = m\,d_{hkl} = \frac{|m|}{|\mathbf{b}_3|},$$

$$A_{\left|\frac{m}{q}\right|} \cong 1 - \frac{|m|}{|\mathbf{b}_3|}\frac{1}{X}\sum_X\left\{\frac{|\sin\varphi|}{N_3 d_{111}\sqrt{3}}\right\}$$

$$- |m|\frac{1}{X}\sum_X\frac{|L|d^2_{hkl}}{3d^2_{111}}2\alpha\sin^2 2\pi\,\frac{(H - K)}{3}$$

$$= 1 - L_0\left\{\frac{1}{X}\sum_X\frac{|\sin\varphi|}{N_3 d_{111}\sqrt{3}} + \frac{1}{X}\sum_X\frac{|L|}{a_0 h_0}(1 - Z)\right\}.$$

Call the first sum $1/D$. It is, after all, a particle size term, due to effects other than faults; i.e., consider:

$$\frac{N_3 d_{111} \sqrt{3}}{\sin \varphi}.$$

The numerator is the average thickness of a mosaic region in the [111] direction, and $1/\sin \varphi$, as can be seen in Figure 8–11, gives the size in the measuring direction s.

For the 111:

$$A_L = 1 - L_0 \left\{ \frac{1}{D} + \frac{1.5\alpha}{a_0} \left(\frac{\sqrt{3}}{4} \right) \right\}.$$

For the 200:

$$A_L = 1 - L_0 \left\{ \frac{1}{D} + \frac{1.5\alpha}{a_0} \right\}.$$

Thus from the initial slope of the Fourier coefficients[4] versus L_0 we obtain:

$$\left(\frac{1}{D_{\text{effective}}} \right)_{111} = \frac{1}{D} + \frac{1.5\alpha}{a_0} \left(\frac{\sqrt{3}}{4} \right), \qquad (8–19a)$$

or

$$\left(\frac{1}{D_{\text{effective}}} \right)_{200} = \frac{1}{D} + \frac{1.5\alpha}{a_0}. \qquad (8–19b)$$

If D is large,

$$\frac{(D_{\text{eff}})_{111}}{(D_{\text{eff}})_{200}} = \frac{4}{\sqrt{3}} = 2.3.$$

The 200 peak will be broader than the 111 because the effective particle size for the 200 is smaller. The unusual shifts and the difference in broadening of the 111 and 200 are characteristic of faults. If there were residual tensile strains, say normal to the diffracting planes, this would cause both the 111 and 200 to have larger than normal d values and hence to appear at lower angles; as $\Delta\theta = -\Delta d/d \tan \theta$ the shift would be greater for the 200 than the 111, and these would move closer together. However, so would the 222 and 400, whereas, as the reader can verify for himself by evaluating the terms for these peaks, faults on the (111) will cause these two high-angle peaks to *separate*.

Typical values of α in filings of copper and gold and their alloys are of the order of 0.01 to 0.05. (Our assumption of small α was valid!)

[4] If there is strain present, these are the cosine coefficients after extrapolating out strain in a plot of $\ln A_L$ versus l_0^2.

The corresponding changes in separation of the 111 and 200 peaks are about 0.04 degrees 2θ to 0.2 degrees 2θ with CuK_α. These values of α imply that there is one fault every 100 to every 20 (111) planes ($1/\alpha$). After severe deformation all four {111} are probably involved and the effects are additive; it is more likely that each of the {111} planes is faulted every 400 to every 80 planes ($4/\alpha$).

We have examined the mathematics in detail because exactly the same techniques can be followed for faults of different kinds on different planes—and other than random distributions can be examined. Basically we have seen how to work from a convenient reciprocal space (hexagonal in this case) to a single measuring variable (the $00h_3'$ line) and how to average our expressions for powder patterns. We have also seen that faults can cause rather specific effects on the pattern. There is a basic philosophy here to attempt to use whatever approximations are required to get the equations in a form usable with actual data— and *then* to see if the approximations were justified.

Local Ordering and Clustering

We have discussed the scattering from an alloy previously, in Chapter 5, and found that if the different types of atoms are randomly distributed, we shall have a weak continuous background—the Laue monotonic scattering. As the atoms arrange themselves in a less than random fashion, this scattering sharpens up to give broad peaks.

Let us re-examine this problem in more detail and allow for clustering of like atoms, as well as ordering. (We shall ignore the effects of displacement from lattice sites due to differing atomic size to get at the principles, but a more complete theory can be found in Reference 10.)

Considering N atoms, one per (primitive) lattice point,

$$I_{eu} = \sum_m \sum_n f_m f_n e^{2\pi i s \cdot (\mathbf{r}_m - \mathbf{r}_n)}. \qquad (8\text{-}20)$$

This can be rewritten with $\mathbf{r}_{mn} = \mathbf{r}_m - \mathbf{r}_n$

$$I_{eu} = \sum_m \sum_n \langle f_m f_n \rangle e^{2\pi i s \cdot \mathbf{r}_{mn}} + \sum_m \sum_n [f_m f_n - \langle f_m f_n \rangle] e^{2\pi i s \cdot \mathbf{r}_{mn}}.$$

The first term, $(I_{eu})_1$, represents the Bragg peaks, with "average" atoms, i.e. the averaging is over all the atoms under the beam and hence:

$$[\langle f_m f_n \rangle = (\bar{f})^2].$$

Consider a binary alloy and let p^i_{AA} = probability of an A atom next to an A in its ith neighbor shell, p^i_{AB} = probability of a B atom next to an A in its ith shell and similarly for p^i_{BB}, p^i_{BA},

$$\left.\begin{array}{r} p^i_{AA} + p^i_{AB} = 1 \\ p^i_{BB} + p^i_{BA} = 1 \\ x_A + x_B = 1 \\ x_A p^i_{AB} = x_B p^i_{BA} \end{array}\right\} \qquad (8\text{--}21)$$

$$f_m f_n{}^i = x_A f_A p^i_{AA} f_A + x_B f_B p^i_{BB} f_B + (x_A p^i_{AB} + x_B p^i_{BA}) f_A f_B.$$

Eliminating all the pair probabilities but p^i_{AB} with Eq. (8–21),

$$f_m f_n^i = x_A f_A^2 + x_B f_B^2 - x_A p^i_{AB}(f_A - f_B)^2.$$

Now

$$\langle f_m f_n \rangle = (\bar{f})^2 = (x_A f_A + x_B f_B)^2 = x_A f_A^2 + x_B f_B^2 - x_A x_B (f_A - f_B)^2.$$

Therefore the second term $(I_{\text{eu}})_2$ is

$$(I_{\text{eu}})_2 = \sum_m \sum_n x_A(x_B - p^i_{AB})(f_A - f_B)^2 \cos 2\pi \mathbf{s} \cdot \mathbf{r}_{mn}.$$

(The cosine term will be all that is necessary. We assume the structure around each atom is symmetric. If this were not true, that is if one particular lattice site was preferentially occupied by B atoms throughout the lattice, we would be altering the symmetry of the structure, causing extra reflections. What we wish to consider here is local compositional rearrangements *without* any change in symmetry.)

Introducing the Warren short-range order probability α_i:

$$\alpha_i = 1 - \frac{p^i_{AB}}{x_B} = 1 - \frac{p^i_{BA}}{x_A},$$

$$(I_{\text{eu}})_2 = \sum_m \sum_n x_A x_B (f_A - f_B)^2 \alpha_i \cos 2\pi \mathbf{s} \cdot \mathbf{r}_{mn}.$$

If there is no long-range order, α_i goes to zero ($p^i_{AB} = x_B$) beyond a small number of near neighbors from each atom. The double sum can then be replaced by N (the number of atoms in the volume diffracting)[5]

[5] For a solid flat specimen in a diffractometer, from Chapter 4, the volume irradiated for a beam of unit cross section is $\dfrac{1}{2(\mu/\rho)\rho}$. If N_0 is the number of atoms per unit volume, $N = N_0/(\mu/\rho)\rho$.

times a single sum over the neighbors of an average atom—i.e., we shall consider the measured $\alpha_i = \bar{a}_i$, an average for all starting A atoms under the beam,

$$(I_{eu})_2 = Nx_Ax_B(f_A - f_B)^2 \sum_m \bar{a}_i \cos 2\pi \mathbf{s} \cdot \mathbf{r}_{mn}. \qquad (8\text{–}22)$$

The sum over m really implies a triple sum in terms of the coordinates uvw of each shell around the average atom:

$$I_{eu} = Nx_Ax_B(f_A - f_B)^2 \sum_{u=0}^{\infty} \sum_{v=0}^{\infty} \sum_{w=0}^{\infty} \bar{a}_{uvw} \cos 2\pi(hu + kv + lm).$$

The term before the sum is the Laue monotonic for a random alloy. Whether the alloy is random or not, $\alpha_0 = 1(p_{AB}^\circ$, the probability of a B at an A atom's position, is zero). But the other α_i's are zero if the alloy is random, as $p_{AB}^i = x_B$ for all shells. Only the first term in the series, the Laue monotonic, exists. If there is local order or clustering ($\alpha_1, \alpha_2 \neq 0$) this introduces cosine terms modulating the Laue monotonic, raising and lowering it in places. The total scattering due to local order (the first term in the Fourier series proportional to α_0) remains constant regardless of the arrangement. The sharpness of the modulation will depend on the number of α's different than zero— the extent of local order around atoms.

Each α can range from $+1$ to -1. If there is local order then α_1 is negative, because $p_{AB}^1 > x_B$. (For perfectly ordered Cu_3Au, with gold at the corners and copper at the faces of a cubic unit cell, the first neighbors to a corner gold are all copper atoms and $\alpha_1 = 1 - 1/(3/4) = -1/3$, α_2, corresponding to atoms at corners of the unit cell, is zero, etc.) The first cosine term with coefficient $\alpha_{1/2,1/2,0}$ is negative at $\mathbf{s} = 0$, and peaks occur for h_1, h_2, h_3 such that $2\pi(h_1u + h_2v + h_3w) = \pi$, at the positions $100, 300,\ldots$. If there is clustering, $p_{AB}^1 < x_B$ and the intensity peaks near the origin and for $2\pi(hu + kv + lw) = 0, 2\pi, \ldots$ i.e., right at the Bragg peaks $000, 200, 400\ldots$. These two situations are sketched in Figure 8–12, along with some typical intensities for a single crystal with $x_Ax_B(f_A - f_B)^2 \cong 500$ (e.g., such as Cu_3Au). With a powder sample, the diffuse scattering is of the order of 1 per cent of the peaks. (Equation (8–22) would have to be averaged for a powder for all orientations of $\mathbf{r}$ around $\mathbf{s}$.) The diffuse scattering has a half breadth of about 10 degrees 2θ as compared to about 0.2 degrees 2θ for the Bragg peaks, and broad receiving slits can be used to make it easier to see, without affecting its shape.

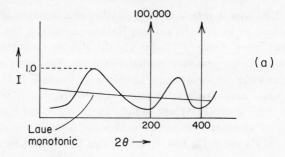

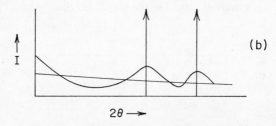

Figure 8–12. (a) Scattering due to local order; (b) Scattering due to clustering.

If the data are gathered in a volume of reciprocal space, Fourier cosine inversions will yield the α's. Before the data can be inverted, however, there are many important steps. Although the scattering can often be detected with a slow scan and chart recording, broad slits, and a pulse-height analyzer, if any accuracy at all is to be obtained it is necessary to use a monochromator and to point count. The TDS must be eliminated by calculation or by making the measurements at two temperatures; TDS is essentially linear with temperature and if two temperatures are chosen for which the local order does not change, then the two can be separated. Compton-modified must be corrected for by calculation, and this requires that the intensities be measured absolutely. Background or air scattering must be subtracted.

If instead of a binary, a ternary alloy was used, there would be two independent pair probabilities p_{AB}^i, p_{AC}^i, and both neutrons and x-ray scattering would be needed to determine these.

If the atoms have different sizes, the displacements from lattice sites will cause additional diffuse scattering (similar to TDS, but this is a "static" displacement). The scattering from this and from local order can be separated (Reference 10), and information can then be obtained about the difference in interatomic separation as a function of distance between atoms as well as the α's (see References 2, 6, 7, 10).

Note that when there is clustering, the diffuse scattering has its maxima at the Bragg peaks—including the origin. This latter region has certain interesting features which have led to a whole field of study referred to as "small-angle scattering." In this region, effects of displacement (including TDS) are small, as is the Compton-modified scattering. (There can be some trouble with multiple scattering, illustrated in Figure 8–13, but even this can be avoided by orienting the crystal so that there is no diffraction.) One of the pioneers in this field, A. Guinier (Reference 12), has demonstrated that some very interesting information can be obtained in this region. We could

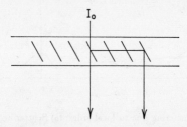

Figure 8–13. Multiple diffraction giving rise to small angle scattering.

evaluate the scattering in terms of α's, but suppose the clustering corresponds to small regions of different composition. This is the analogous situation to the case where we have small particles, such as precipitates in a solid matrix, or polymers in a solution. Suppose also that we consider the electron density in these regions constant and different than the solvent. Then, for one particle,

$$A(\mathbf{s})_{eu} = \rho \int e^{-2\pi i \mathbf{s} \cdot \mathbf{r}} \, dv_{\mathbf{r}}.$$

The transform can be evaluated for specific shapes as was done in Chapter 2 and will yield the analytical expression for the scattering pattern characteristic of the shape, rods of scattering for plates, etc. Let us take a different approach. Let $\mathbf{s} \cdot \mathbf{r} = |\mathbf{s}| r_s$ where r_s is the *magnitude* of $\mathbf{r}$ along $\mathbf{s}$. At small angles $|\mathbf{s}| \simeq 2\theta/\lambda$ and r_s is also essentially the component of $\mathbf{r}$ along a line perpendicular to $\mathbf{S_0}$, as seen in Figure 8–14. If A_{r_s} is the cross-sectional area of the particle along this line,

$$A|\mathbf{s}|_{eu} = \rho \int e^{+2\pi i |\mathbf{s}| r_s} A(r_s) \, dr_s.$$

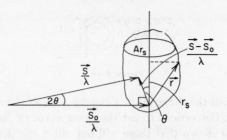

Figure 8–14.   (After A. Guinier, *X-Ray Diffraction*, W. H. Freeman & Co., 1963.)

Expanding the exponential, as $|\mathbf{s}|$ is small,

$$A|\mathbf{s}|(\text{eu}) = \rho \left[\int A_{r_s} \, dr_s + \int 2\pi i |\mathbf{s}| r_s A_{r_s} \, dr_s - \int 2\pi^2 s^2 r_s^2 A_s \, dr_s \right].$$

If we choose as our origin for the particle its center of gravity, the second term is zero. The first is the volume V. The third is the second moment of the particle—related to the radius (R_g) of gyration:

$$R_g^2 = \frac{1}{V} \int r_s^2 A(r_s) \, dr_s. \tag{8–23}$$

Thus,

$$A|\mathbf{s}|(\text{eu}) = \rho[V - V 2\pi^2 s^2 R_g^2],$$

$$= \rho V e^{-(2\pi^2 (2\theta/\lambda)^2 R_g^2)},$$

and for the intensity for n particles:

$$I(\mathbf{s})_{\text{eu}} = A|\mathbf{s}|_{\text{eu}} = n\rho^2 V^2 e^{-(2\pi^2 (2\theta/\lambda)^2 \langle R_g^2 \rangle)}. \tag{8–24}$$

By plotting $\ln I(s)$ versus $8\pi^2\theta^2/\lambda^2$ (Figure 8–15a and b), $\langle R_g^2 \rangle^{1/2}$ can be obtained, and by evaluating Eq. (8–23) (for the shape of the particle, judged say from electron microscopy or by streaking on the film), measurements of $\langle R_g^2 \rangle^{1/2}$ can be used to obtain average dimensions of the particle. As we are working at very small angles, the dimensions of

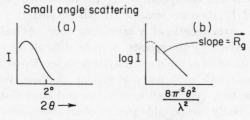

Figure 8–15.   Small-angle scattering.

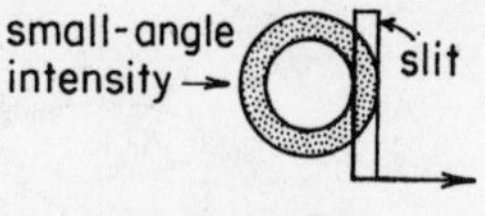

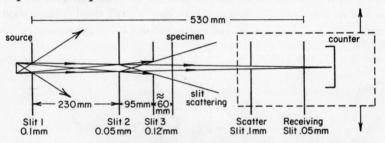

small-angle
intensity → ⬭ slit

Figure 8–16.

the slits will affect the shape of the intensity plot, as can readily be seen in Figure 8–16. Corrections to get the exact shape of $I(s)$ are difficult, but Guinier has shown that these will not affect the determination of $\langle R_g^2 \rangle^{1/2}$. Some typical equipment is given in Figure 8–17.

Note that in Figure 8–15(a) there is a "bump" in the intensity. If the particles are not randomly arranged (perhaps because the density of particles is high), there will be some interparticle interference. A range of sizes may also be present and these will be indicated by a range of slopes in the ln plot.

530 mm

source   specimen   counter

230 mm   95 mm ≈ 60 mm   slit
                                                 scattering

Slit I   Slit 2   Slit 3   Scatter   Receiving
0.1mm   0.05mm   0.12mm   Slit .1mm   Slit .05mm

Figure 8–17.   The slit system shown defines a beam about 0.05° 2θ wide and scattering from the slits is small at $2\theta \cong 0.08°\ 2\theta$, so that a d spacing of 500 Å could easily be observed with CuK$_\alpha$. (Divergence of the beam and scattering from the slits is shown.)

Liquids and Amorphous Solids

From liquids and amorphous solids, the diffraction pattern appears as in Figure 8–18; there are some details but the pattern is devoid of the sharp peaks characteristic of a crystalline solid. Actually the exact change, crystalline to amorphous, is quite difficult to specify. After extreme deformation or rapid electrolytic or vapor deposition, normally crystalline materials give patterns similar to those for amorphous material, due to a very small mosaic size and large distortions—but then, that is really one possible picture of an amorphous solid!

What can we determine from such a pattern? We recall that the

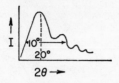

Figure 8–18.

diffracted intensity is a Fourier transform of the convolution of the atomic density, and the same density inverted through the origin—i.e.,

$$I_{(s)_{eu}} = K \int \rho(\mathbf{u})\rho(-[\mathbf{r} - \mathbf{u}])e^{2\pi i s \cdot \mathbf{r}} \, dV_{\mathbf{r}}.$$

Let $\mathbf{u} = \mathbf{r} + \mathbf{w}$

$$I(\mathbf{s})_{eu} = K \int \rho(\mathbf{r} + \mathbf{w})\rho(\mathbf{w})e^{2\pi i s \cdot \mathbf{x}} \, dV_{\mathbf{r}}.$$

The density product peaks when both values exist, when there are atoms at $\mathbf{r}$ and $\mathbf{r} + \mathbf{w}$. This led to the Patterson function in Problem 28, in Chapter 2. We assumed the densities are periodic, but if they are not, this is about as far as we can go. We can speak of radial Patterson functions, i.e., $\langle \rho | \mathbf{r} + \mathbf{w} | \rho | \mathbf{w} | \rangle$ averaged over shells around an atom and averaged over all atoms as origin. Then, referring to Figure 8–19,[6]

$$I|\mathbf{s}|_{eu} = K \int_0^{|\mathbf{r}|} \int_0^{\pi} \langle \rho | \mathbf{r} + \mathbf{w} | \rho | \mathbf{w} | \rangle e^{2\pi i |\mathbf{r}|\cos \alpha \, (2\sin\theta/\lambda)} 2\pi |\mathbf{r}| \sin \alpha \, d|\mathbf{r}| \, d\alpha$$

$$= K \int_0^{|\mathbf{r}|} \langle \rho | \mathbf{r} + \mathbf{w} | \rho | \mathbf{w} | \rangle 4\pi |\mathbf{r}|^2 \frac{\sin (4\pi \sin \theta/\lambda)|\mathbf{r}| \, d|\mathbf{r}|^*}{(4\pi \sin \theta/\lambda)|\mathbf{r}|}, \quad (8\text{–}25)$$

By gathering intensity, plotting versus $2 \sin \theta/\lambda = |\mathbf{s}|$ and inverting the radial density, $4\pi r^2 \langle \rho | \mathbf{r} + \mathbf{w} | \rho | \mathbf{w} | \rangle$ can be obtained; see

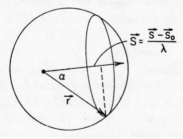

Figure 8–19.

[6] This is the averaging procedure to follow for converting Eq. (8–22) for powder pattern.

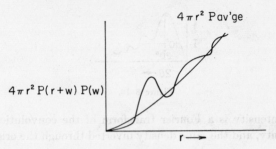

Figure 8–20.

Figure 8–20. This will exhibit oscillations around the average density, predominately for small r. The integral under any one peak over the range Δr is the average number of atoms separated by a distance $r \to r + \Delta r$. In doing this inversion, first the data are corrected for, Compton modified, and then plotted $(4\pi \sin\theta/\lambda)I|s|$ versus $|s|$ or $4\pi \sin\theta/\lambda$. This plot does not damp out even at large θ values, so that if we take only the data we can measure, once again we are in effect multiplying by a square and false peaks will appear. A damping function, $e^{-\alpha^2(4\pi\sin\theta/\lambda)^2}$ is used to cause the fluctuations of the plot to be reduced to about a third at large θ values. This slightly broadens the resulting radial density plot, but eliminates spurious effects.

At large values of 2θ, a liquid or amorphous solid scatters as if it had an average atomic density; the scattering is "structureless" as if the material were an ideal gas, and the intensity will just be the number of atoms irradiated times the sum of the square of the scattering factor per atom plus the Compton scattering per atom. For example, if we have measured the pattern from Lucite, the total scattering is the sum of f^2 and Compton for each atom in the molecule, times the number of molecules per unit volume, times the volume, times

$$\frac{I_0 e^4}{m^2 c^4 R^2} \left(\frac{1 + \cos^2 2\theta}{2} \right)$$

(for unpolarized radiation). I_0 (really I_0 times the receiving slit area) is unknown but can be obtained by matching the calculated and experimental curves at large 2θ. Knowing I_0, the entire pattern can then be corrected for Compton scattering. This technique is often used to get I_0 for other experiments.

A powder pattern from a crystalline material can be treated in this way—yielding some interesting information on binding forces, elastic constants (see Reference 13).

This ends our discussion of diffraction, and the reader (we hope) is ready to begin to read or to work in a very exciting and vital area— the description of the arrangements of atoms in materials. Good luck!

PROBLEMS

1. Consider stacking faults on (111). Draw a $(11\bar{1})$ and a (100) through the fault and show physically why the 111 powder pattern peak shifts to high angles and the 200 to low angles.

2. When Cu_3Au is fully ordered, there are gold atoms at the corners and copper atoms at the faces of a cubic unit cell. Disordered boundaries can be introduced on {100} by a $1/2 \langle 110 \rangle$ shift. The *first* neighbors to a gold atom are still all copper atoms across such a boundary, even though along the $\langle 100 \rangle$ normal to the boundary the ordering pattern has been changed from Au, Au, Au ... at corners to Cu, Cu ... Cu. As a result of the low energy, such boundaries occur during ordering of Cu_3Au, as the ordering starts at many places at once, each place "unaware" of whether the other has copper or gold at corners. Draw such a boundary. Work out the effect of such boundaries on the peak shapes and positions from (*a*) a single crystal, (*b*) a powder.

3. Anti phase domain boundaries can be produced in a CsCl structure by $\frac{1}{2}\langle 111 \rangle$ shifts on {110} planes. Work out the effects of such boundaries on the diffraction peaks, shapes and positions.

4. Calculate some typical values for the coherent and incoherent scattering from:
    (*a*) carbon
    (*b*) cobalt
    (*c*) polystyrene (C_8H_8).
    Assume you are using monochromatic CuK_α radiation ($P_0 = 10^9_{cps}$) and make the calculations at low and high values of 2θ.

5. Show that, if the incident power (P_0) is measured by comparing the calculated and measured power scattered from a plate of polystyrene in a diffractometer, the area of the receiving slit need not be measured in a subsequent experiment (using the same slits and P_0) to get the absolute power scattered. Assume you are using a diffractometer and equal angles of incidence and diffraction in both experiments (2θ is not necessarily the same, though). What are the disadvantages, if any, of this calibration method?

Suggested Readings

1. R. W. James, *The Optical Principles of the Diffraction of X-Rays* (G. Bell and Sons Ltd., London, 1950).
2. B. E. Warren and B. L. Averbach, *Modern Research Techniques in Physical Metallurgy* (ASM, Cleveland, 1953).
3. G. E. Bacon, *Neutron Diffraction* (Clarendon Press, Oxford, 1962).
4. D. R. Chipman and A. Paskin, *J. Appl. Phys.*, **30**, (1959), 1992, 1998.
5. L. Schwartz, *Acta Cryst.*, **17**, (1964), 1614.
6. B. L. Averbach, *Theory of Alloy Phases* (ASM, Cleveland, 1955).
7. A. Guinier, in *Adv. S. S. Phys.*, **9**, (Academic Press, New York, 1959).
8. A. Guinier, *X-Ray Diffraction* (Freeman and Co., San Francisco, 1960).
9. B. E. Warren, *Progress in Metal Physics*, **8** (Pergamon Press, New York, 1959).
10. *Local Atomic Arrangements Studied by Diffraction*, Edited by J. B. Cohen and J. E. Hilliard (Gordon and Breach and AIME, New York, 1965).
11. B. T. M. Willis, *Proc. Roy. Soc.* (*London*), **248A**, (1958), 183.
12. A. Guinier and G. Fournet, *Small Angle Scattering of X-Rays* (John Wiley, New York, 1959).
13. R. Kaplow, B. L. Averbach, and S. L. Strong, *J. Phys. Chem. Solids*, (1964), **25**, 1195.

Appendix A

Location of Useful Information
in International Tables for Crystallography

(*Kynoch Press, Birmingham*)

Appendix B

Chapter 1

1. Only a onefold axis. (Note that everyone does not part his hair in the middle; a vertical mirror is *not* necessarily present.)

4. Faster growing planes tend to disappear.

5. The most dense planes are those of lowest indices, and these are farthest apart. As the more dense planes will grow more slowly and hence, as shown in Problem 4, tend to predominate, a crystal's habit will generally be of planes of low indices.

9. See p. 30, International Tables for Crystallography, Vol. I.

10. The lattice points at the faces have neighbors on other faces at $\sqrt{2}$ that the corner points do not have. Thus, the former *cannot* be *lattice* points.

18. (a) *Pnma* (Space Group No. 62).
    (b) 4 molecules per cell.
    (c) Several possibilities exist; 4 Ge (Se) at $4a$, 4 Se (Ge) on $4b$; 4 Ge (Se) at $4a$, 4 Se (Ge) on $4c$; 4 molecules of GeS on $4a$, or on $4b$ or on $4c$. However, if you look up the radii of Ge, Se you will be able to show (knowing a_1, a_2, a_3) that only the case of 4 GeSe molecules on $4c$ will fit in the unit cell.

24. Look at Eq. (1–3b). What are the conditions for $u = h$, $v = k$? These conditions are: all axes equal in length, all angles of 90 degrees. Only in the cubic system does this occur. Special cases: [110] in tetragonal, hexagonal; [100], [010] [001] in orthorhombic, etc.

25. [100].

28. $\mathbf{r^* \cdot r^*} = 1/d^2$. Work this out (sketch the b's with the angles between them) and then you will find

$$\frac{1}{d^2} = \frac{4}{3}\frac{(h^2 + kh + k^2)}{a^2} + \frac{l^2}{a_3^2},$$

34. The crystal is orthorhombic as far as can be determined, and the indexing and axial ratios, of course, depend on the choice of parametric plane.

36. (a) [112], [110], [001], [110], respectively. Plot a (100) projection. The direction which is the intersection of the great circle connecting the pole of ($\bar{1}10$) and the pole of the desired plane, with the great circle representing ($\bar{1}10$), is the trace. (Analytically, solve Eq. (1–8a).)

    (b) [11$\bar{2}$]. On the ($\bar{1}10$) projection draw a line from the center through, say, the [011] (a face diagonal) and where it intersects ($\bar{1}10$) is the desired direction. Analytically you want a direction in some plane ($h'k'l'$) perpendicular to the given (hkl) which also contains [uvw], the given direction. Thus you have two equations to obtain $h'k'l'$:

$$(h\mathbf{b}_1 + k_2\mathbf{b} + l\mathbf{b}_3) \cdot (h'\mathbf{b}_1 + k'\mathbf{b}_2 + l'\mathbf{b}_3) = 0,$$
$$h'u + k'v + l'w = 0.$$

    Knowing ($h'k'l'$), the zone axis of this and (hkl), is the desired direction.

37. See H. M. Otte, *Acta Cryst.*, **14** (1961), 360.

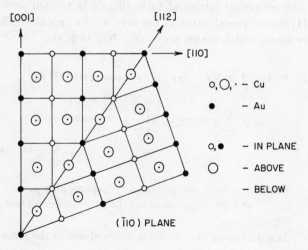

[001]   [112]

[110]

o, ◯, · — Cu

● — Au

o, ● — IN PLANE

◯ — ABOVE

— BELOW

($\bar{1}10$) PLANE

38. Keep in mind that a $\langle 112 \rangle$ shear on a close packed plane can only be in one sense—i.e., [112] but not [$\bar{1}\bar{1}\bar{2}$]. (Otherwise you have to "lift" the sheared plane to go over the plane below.) The unit cell of Cu_3Au is doubled after a $1/6 \langle 112 \rangle$ shear to make the structure a mirror image across a {111}. See the figure below. To draw the stereogram just plot a (111) projection; the twin poles can be placed by a 180 degree rotation around [111].

Chapter 2

18. $F^2 = 64f^2$ for h, k, l all even, $l = 4n$
        $= 32F^2$ for h, k, l all odd.

23. (a) The unit cell is c-centered orthorhombic.
     (b) $F_{hkl} = f_{uranium}[e^{2\pi i(ky + l/4)} + e^{2\pi i(-ky + 3l/4)}]$
$$[1 + e^{\pi i(h + k)}].$$

     (Note that, in writing F, it is possible to factor a term $(1 + e^{\pi i(h+k)})$ based on the lattice alone, as if there were atoms at the lattice points. This is very often a helpful point to remember in simplifying structure factors.)

$$F = 0 \text{ for } hkl, \ h + k = 2n + 1,$$
$$hol, \ h \text{ odd } l \text{ even or odd},$$
$$okl, \ k \text{ odd } h \text{ even or odd}.$$

25. If the reciprocal lattice of f.c.c. (b.c.c.) is rotated around the [111] the reciprocal lattice of the twin will be produced. There are new spots, which are on layers $00\frac{1}{3}$, $00\frac{2}{3}$, $00\frac{4}{3}$, etc.

26. (a) $$A(s) = \int_{-\infty}^{\infty} \sum_m \delta(x - mp)(\rho_0 + a \cos qx)e^{-2\pi isx}\, dx$$

$$= \rho_0 \sum_0^\infty e^{-2\pi ismp} + a\left[\sum_0^\infty e^{-2\pi i(s + q/2\pi)mp} + \sum_0^\infty e^{-2\pi i(s - q/2\pi)mp}\right],$$

     Therefore, there are peaks in "s" space at n/p, and "satellites" around each peak at $(n/p) \pm (q/2\pi)$. Their height depends on a.

     (b) As q decreases, the satellites move closer to the main peaks.

(c)   If the waves are finite, say of length L, the integral involving $a \cos qx$ has limits; i.e., the last two sums are not infinite:

$$A(s) = \rho_0 \sum_0^\infty e^{-2\pi i smp} + q\left[\frac{\sin \pi(L/p)(s + q/2\pi)}{\sin \pi(s + q/2\pi)}\right.$$
$$\times e^{-\pi i(s + q/L\pi)(L/p - 1)}$$
$$+ \frac{\sin \pi(L/p)(s - q/2\pi)}{\sin \pi(s - q/2\pi)}$$
$$\left.\times e^{-\pi i(s - q/2\pi)(L/p - 1)}\right].$$

Then each of the satellites has a width of $2p/L$, because a function

$$\frac{\sin \pi s N a}{\sin \pi s a}$$

has its first zero for $s = \pm 1/N$. Now:

$$q = \frac{2\pi}{\lambda} \qquad \frac{\lambda}{2} = \frac{\pi}{q},$$

The width of each satellite for $L = \lambda/2$ is $2pq/\pi$. The spacing between them is $2q/2\pi$, if $p = 1$, e.g., they can overlap.

Chapter 4

1.   (a) $3mm$,   (b) $2mm$,   (c) $3mm$,   (d) $4mm$.

2.   The marking is a twin.

4.   (a) $1/8$,   (b) 44.

8.   (a) tetragonal or orthorhombic,   (b) 3.85 Å.
     (c) orthorhombic,   (d) $mmmPna$.

9.   The extra spots are from a twin.

10.   The pattern is of an f.c.c. copper–gold alloy, with a parameter corresponding to Cu_3Au (3.74 Å).

11.   (a)   0.8 degrees 2θ for 70 degree line; 3.26 degree 2θ for 85 degree line.
      (b)   0.8 mm for 70 degree line; 3.26 mm for 85 degree line.
      (c)   1.6 mm for 70 degree line; 6.52 mm for 85 degree line.
      (d)   these lines do not appear!

$$(\sin \theta > 1).$$

13. The structure is f.c.c. and the calculated density is 8.8 gms/cm³. Thus this is not a defect structure.

15. The specimen is a zinc powder.

16. The unknown is gold.

19. To measure along an h_1oo line, set the crystal up with the [100] bisecting incident and diffracted beams and run a θ–2θ scan.

21. The orientation of the foil is $(0\bar{1}3)$. (Consider not only the ratios of the distances to spots, but also the symmetry of the diffraction pattern.) The edges of the dislocations on $(\bar{1}\bar{1}\bar{1})$ intersect the foil in a line, $[\bar{2}31]$, which is correct for the zone axis of $(1\bar{1}1)$ and $(0\bar{1}3)$. The dislocations end on both faces of the foil and hence the thickness is 1024 Å.

Chapter 5

1. With x-rays, when carbon is in the octahedral positions the intensities of peaks with h, k, l all even are raised, those with h, k, l all odd are reduced, and when it is in the tetrahedral positions there is no effect on the (111) but the (200) is reduced. The structure factor can be written, for random occupation,

$$F = F_{\text{f.c.c.}} + \frac{(F \text{ interstitial sites})(\text{at fr.C}) \times 4}{\text{number of sites}},$$

3. (a) A monochromator placed in the diffracted beam will not diffract the Compton modified scattering, once the change in θ due to the change in wavelength exceeds the divergence of the beam to the crystal and the mosaic spread of the crystal. Thus, above a certain angle we can eliminate this portion from the scattering.

   (c) $2\theta = 69$ degrees; the film is darker on the low-angle side.

10. $\dfrac{1 + \cos^2 2\theta \cos^2 2\theta \text{ monochromator}}{1 + \cos^2 2\theta \text{ monochromator}}$,

12. There is no correction.

13. One form of the equation is

$$\left(1 - \frac{(1-n)}{\sin^2 \theta}\right) 2d \sin \theta = m\lambda,$$

where θ is the measured angle, outside the specimen.

Chapter 6

2. $X_{\text{Se}} = 0.15$ $X_{\text{Ge}} = -0.12$
    $Z_{\text{Se}} = 0.50$ $Z_{\text{Se}} = -0.11$

3. (*b*) $F^2 = S^2(f_A - f_B)^2$ for $h + k + l$ odd
          $= (f_A + f_B)^2$ for $h + k + l = 2n.$

4. $\dfrac{\cos\theta}{(u/\rho)\rho}$ is the optimum thickness.

Appendix C

Crystallographic Classification of the 230 Space Groups

CRYSTAL SYSTEMS			CUBIC				HEXAGONAL								TRIGONAL				
SPACE (BRAVAIS) LATTICES			PRIMITIVE	BODY	FACE		BASE HEXAGONAL								PRIMITIVE RHOMBOHEDRAL			BASE HEXAGONAL	
INTERNATIONAL ABBREVIATIONS			P	I	F		P								R			P	
CRYSTAL CLASSES (ROGERS)			HEXOCTAHEDRAL	HEXTETRAHEDRAL	GYROIDAL	DIPLOIDAL	TETARTOIDAL	DIHEXAGONAL DIPYRAMIDAL	DITRIGONAL DIPYRAMIDAL	DIHEXAGONAL PYRAMIDAL	HEXAGONAL TRAPEZOHEDRAL	HEXAGONAL DIPYRAMIDAL	TRIGONAL DIPYRAMIDAL	HEXAGONAL PYRAMIDAL	HEXAGONAL SCALENOHEDRAL	DITRIGONAL PYRAMIDAL	TRIGONAL TRAPEZOHEDRAL	RHOMBOHEDRAL	TRIGONAL PYRAMIDAL
POINT GROUPS	INTERNATIONAL (HERMANN-MAUGUIN)		$(\frac{4}{m}\frac{3}{m}\frac{2}{m})$ m3m	$\bar{4}3m$	432	$(\frac{2}{m}\bar{3})$ m3	23	$(\frac{6}{m}\frac{2}{m}\frac{2}{m})$ $\frac{6}{m}mm$	$\bar{6}m2$	6mm	622	$\frac{6}{m}$	$\bar{6}$	6	$\bar{3}\frac{2}{m}$ $\bar{3}m$	3m	32	$\bar{3}$	3
	SCHOENFLIES		O_h	T_d	O	T_h	T	D_{6h}	D_{3h}	C_{6v}	D_6	C_{6h}	C_{3h}	C_6	D_{3d}	C_{3v}	D_3	(S_6) C_{3i}	C_3
SPACE GROUPS	POINT SPACE GROUPS		□Pm3m ■Im3m ⊞Fm3m	□P43m ■I43m ⊞F43m	□P432 ■I432 ⊞F432	△Pm3 ▲Im3 ▲Fm3	△P23 ▲I23 ▲F23	○P$\frac{6}{m}$mm	○P6m2 +P62m	○P6mm	○P622	□P$\frac{6}{m}$	□P$\bar{6}$	□P6	△P3m1 +P31m R3m	△P3m1 △P31m R3m	△P312 △P321 ▲R32	○P$\bar{3}$ ●R$\bar{3}$	○P3 ●R3
	GLIDE PLANE	P								○(6mm) ●6cc						(3m1) (31m) ▲3c1 ●31c			
		C																	
	SCREW AXIS	P			○(432) *4₁32 4₂32 *4₃32	(m3)	○(23) 2₁3				*○6₁22 ×6₂22 ○6₃22 6₄22 ×6₅22 *6₃22	□6₃/m		×6₁ *6₂ □6₃ □6₄ ×6₅			△(312) △(321) *3₁12 *3₂21		*3₁ *3₂
		I			○(432) 4₁32		▲(23) 2₁3												
		F			○(432) 4₁32		○(23)												
		C																	
		R															32	○3	○3
	GLIDE PLANE AND SCREW AXIS	P	(m3m) n3m △m3n	(43m) 43n		o3 n3		○6/mmm 6/mmm ●6₃mc ○6₂cm mc	○(62m) (6m2) ○62c ○62c2	○6₃cm 6₃2mc					(31m) (3m1) ▲3c1 ●31c			
		I	(m3m) o3d	(43m) 43d		(m3) o3													
		F	▲(m3m) m3c d3m d3c	(43m) ▲43c		(m3) d3													
		C																	
		A																	
		R														(3m) ○3c	(3m) ○3c		
TOTAL			10	6	8	7	5	4	4	4	6	2	1	6	6	6	7	2	4

	TETRAGONAL							ORTHORHOMBIC				MONOCLINIC			TRICLINIC		7
	PRIMITIVE			BODY				PRIMITIVE	ALL FACE	BODY	ONE FACE	PRIMITIVE		BASE	PRIMITIVE		14
	P			I				P	F	I	C or A	P		C	P		
	DITETRAGONAL DIPYRAMIDAL	TETRAGONAL SCALENOHEDRAL	DITETRAGONAL PYRAMIDAL	TETRAGONAL TRAPEZOHEDRAL	TETRAGONAL DIPYRAMIDAL	TETRAGONAL DISPHENOIDAL	TETRAGONAL PYRAMIDAL	RHOMBIC DIPYRAMIDAL	RHOMBIC PYRAMIDAL		RHOMBIC DISPHENOIDAL	PRISMATIC	DOMATIC	SPHENOIDAL	PINACOIDAL	PEDIAL (ASYMMETRIC)	32
	$\frac{4}{m}\frac{2}{m}\frac{2}{m}$	$\bar{4}2m$	$4mm$	422	$\frac{4}{m}$	$\bar{4}$	4	$\frac{2}{m}\frac{2}{m}\frac{2}{m}$	$mm2$		222	$\frac{2}{m}$	m	2	$\bar{1}$	1	
	D_{4h}	D_{2d} (V_d)	C_{4v}	D_4	C_{4h}	S_4	C_4	D_{2h} (V_h)	C_{2v}		D_2 (V)	C_{2h}	C_s (C_{1h})	C_2	C_i (S_2)	C_1	

(detailed space-group symbol cells)

| Counts | 20 | 12 | 12 | 10 | 6 | 2 | 6 | 28 | 22 | 9 | 6 | 4 | 3 | 1 | 1 | 230 |

Row right-hand totals (top to bottom): 7, 14, 32, 73, 23, 4, 45, 11, 4, 3, 3, 65, 27, 12, 9, 4, 4, 230

(NOTE 1)

(NOTE 2)

BUERGER GROUPS

ENANTIOMORPHIC PAIRS   ×   *

NOTE: SPACE GROUP SYMBOLS WHICH ARE CIRCLED ARE ALSO POINT SPACE GROUPS AND ARE THEREFORE LISTED TWICE.

Reproductions of this chart with color coding sized 22 x 34 inches suitable for wall mounting, may be obtained from the author, Stanley K. Dickinson, Jr., CRWE, Air Force Cambridge Research Laboratories, L. G. Hanscom Field, Bedford, Massachusetts.

Index